THE PHILOSOPHY
OF SCIENCE

THE PHILOSOPHY
OF SCIENCE

A Systematic Account

PETER CAWS

Professor of Philosophy
Hunter College
of the
City University of New York

D. VAN NOSTRAND COMPANY INC.

Princeton, New Jersey

toronto
new york
london

D. VAN NOSTRAND COMPANY, INC.
120 Alexander St., Princeton, New Jersey (*Principal office*)
24 West 40 Street, New York 18, New York

D. VAN NOSTRAND COMPANY, LTD.
358, Kensington High Street, London, W.14, England

D. VAN NOSTRAND COMPANY (Canada), LTD.
25 Hollinger Road, Toronto 16, Canada

COPYRIGHT © 1965, BY
D. VAN NOSTRAND COMPANY, INC.

Published simultaneously in Canada by
D. VAN NOSTRAND COMPANY (Canada), LTD.

First Published January 1965
Reprinted June 1966

PRINTED IN THE UNITED STATES OF AMERICA

PREFACE

The relevance of science to philosophy, and of philosophy to science, has been evident since earliest times, but the emergence of the philosophy of science as a discipline in its own right, within the general framework of philosophy, is a comparatively recent development. It has come about through the joint efforts of professors of philosophy who have realized the increasing importance of science, in intellectual as well as in practical life, and of scientists who have realized the growing necessity of clear thinking about the presuppositions of their own theories. But professors of philosophy often find scientists precipitate and naive in philosophical discussions, while scientists often find professors of philosophy ignorant of fundamental elements of the scientific attitude, and concerned about issues which seem to them simply irrelevant as far as the business of science is concerned.

The sympathies of the uncommitted observer will often be on the side of the scientists, who are at least talking about something with which they have first-hand acquaintance, whether or not they are doing it philosophically; if somebody from philosophy claims to be doing the philosophy of science it is up to him, and not up to the scientist, to show that it is really the philosophy of *science* and not merely logic or the theory of knowledge in some general sense. On the other hand, philosophy is entitled to lay down the rules of its own game, and, if the scientists' decision about the subject-matter is respected, the game, while it may be open to the charge of uselessness, will not be open to that of irrelevance. To do them justice, more and more scientists are coming to recognize the fact that it is neither useless nor irrelevant. The point is that it cannot be played properly unless both the rules, and the nature and limitations of the subject-matter, are clearly understood.

An adequate grounding in both philosophy and science is therefore required of the student of the philosophy of science. Clearly this cannot be provided by a single book. On the whole, however, it is easier to convey an adequate understanding of philosophical principles to somebody whose previous experience has been limited to science, than to provide an adequate synopsis of scientific theories for somebody whose previous experience has been limited to philosophy. The plan of this book, therefore, is such as to presuppose no training in philosophy, although it does require at least some knowledge, if not practical experience, of science. (This could, however, be provided concurrently by suitable supplementary reading, and so on.) While philosophical techniques are sometimes illustrated in scientific contexts, the illustration may be merely an allusion, or it may be left out altogether. The difficulty in providing illustrative material is that of selection. Any philosophy of science which claims generality must apply equally to the physical, biological, and social sciences, but to give an example from each of every principle would be boring. In this book the illustrations are drawn mainly from physics, but the principles can be tried on any scientific theory, according to the interest of the reader. The philosophy of science must, after all, be practiced, and not only contemplated. Some hints as to other suitable illustrations are given in the Appendix, together with suggestions for further reading.

No claim is made to novelty, or even to thoroughness, in the treatment of the various topics covered. But what there is is systematically arranged, and this will perhaps be found useful by readers who are looking for some orientation in this rather untidy discipline. The accompanying

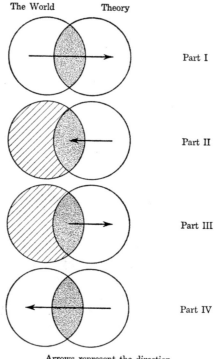

Arrows represent the direction
of the argument in each part.

diagram shows the scope of the argument in each part. It is assumed that a rough distinction can be made between the world of ordinary experience on the one hand and scientific theory on the other. These two spheres obviously overlap, however—the observations made by scientists are part of their experience as ordinary men, but at the same time form the empirical basis for theory. The relation between theory and the world can therefore be represented by an Euler diagram in which the part common to the two circles represents those observations and their description in scientific language. In Part I the transition is made from the everyday world to theory as a conceptual and linguistic structure. Parts II and III deal with questions internal to theory, so that the rest of the world is temporarily disregarded; Part II exhibits the logical structure of theory deductively, and Part III examines its inductive validation. Finally, Part IV deals with the variety among theories as they appear in the world, and with the adequacy of the account of the world which they present to our belief.

ACKNOWLEDGMENTS

This book is a by-product of ten years' study and teaching of the philosophy of science. It would be impossible to acknowledge explicitly, or even to identify, everything in the work of others which has influenced me in writing it. Most of what it contains is or has been current in the philosophical community of the English-speaking world. My own entry into that community came about through the generous interest of Henry Margenau, and it gives me great pleasure to record here my debt to him and to my other teachers at Yale—especially C. G. Hempel and F. S. C. Northrop—to whom anything of value in what follows is indirectly due. The form of the book was worked out during the course of my teaching at the University of Kansas, and I am grateful to my students and colleagues there for many challenges and suggestions. I am grateful also to the administrative officers of the University for a series of grants for secretarial expenses. I have had the help of a succession of typists, in Lawrence and in New York; the list is too long to be reproduced here, but my thanks are due to each of them, especially to Mrs. Joan Wicks, who read most of the proof and constructed the index. President John Gardner of Carnegie Corporation of New York allowed me to suspend my regular duties with the Corporation during two crucial periods near the completion of this work, and I am glad to express my appreciation of this kindness.

Parts of Chapters 31 and 34 have appeared previously in *Philosophy of Science* and *Philosophy and Phenomenological Research*, respectively; I am grateful to the editors of those journals for permission to reprint this material here.

This book has been read in manuscript by Henry Margenau, Sidney Morgenbesser, and Ernest Nagel; an earlier, incomplete draft was read by Ernest Nagel and Edward S. Robinson. Their comments have been of incalculable value to me. Finally, I owe special thanks to my wife, whose encouragement and critical perception have helped me at many points. The numerous faults of style and content which remain in spite of all this are my responsibility alone.

PETER CAWS

New York, October 1964

TABLE OF CONTENTS

PART I

THE DISCOVERY OF THEORY

PROLOGUE

The first part begins with the ordinary man in an everyday world. He possesses sense organs and a brain, has a memory and speaks a language, and is, as an individual, a center of consciousness confronting the world and knowing it, subject to limitations imposed by the range and discrimination of his sense organs and the capacity and versatility of his brain. The world presents itself to him as a spread of sensory awareness, intermittent in time but more or less continuous in the limited space he perceives directly, within which objects stand out having detectable patterns of behavior. The task of this part is the location of theory in the system defined by the individual and his world.

CHAPTER 1

PHILOSOPHICAL ANALYSIS

The philosophy of science is a part of philosophy, which attempts to do for science what philosophy in general does for the whole of human experience. Philosophy does two sorts of thing: on the one hand, it constructs theories about man and the universe, and offers them as grounds for belief and action; on the other, it examines critically everything that may be offered as a ground for belief or action, including its own theories, with a view to the elimination of inconsistency and error. But science also constructs theories about man and the universe, offering them as grounds for belief and action, and in its own way brings critical methods to bear on them in experimental tests. It must therefore be a kind of philosophy too, and this view has historical support; in their origins science and philosophy were indistinguishable, while in the titles of some journals and university professorships science is still referred to as 'natural philosophy'. The definition of 'science' is one of the perpetual problems of the philosophy of science, and the separation of science from philosophy has been a long process which is by no means complete. As a first rough distinction it may be said that science aims at explanation, philosophy at understanding; this distinction will be sharpened and clarified later.

The two kinds of philosophical activity referred to above have been called respectively 'speculative' and 'critical' by C. D. Broad,[1] but more usual labels for them at the moment would be 'metaphysical' and 'analytic'. The first requires breadth of experience and imagination, while the second requires patience, insight, and concentrated attention to detail. In the history of philosophy there have been fashions of metaphysical speculation and fashions of logical analysis, but very seldom have imagination and analytic patience, or breadth of experience and narrowness of concentration, been possessed by the same person. There have been a few exceptions, but to name them would be to name the very greatest philosophers. In fact most philosophers who are engaged in speculative construction employ standards of criticism too loose to detect gross flaws in their own systems, while most philosophers who are engaged in critical analysis do not have the ingenuity to construct any system at all which their own criticism cannot immediately destroy. Neither kind of philosophy has the right to call the other unphilosophical, and neither can stand alone: construction without analysis is irresponsible, analysis without construction is trivial. But although there could never be a sound defense for a policy of doing only metaphysics, there may sometimes be such a defense for a policy of doing only analysis, namely at times when a great deal of unanalyzed and conflicting metaphysics has been inherited, some of which must be wrong and may be harmful. It is generally true that there is more analytic work to be done than metaphysical, since novelists, poets, politicians, and religious men are amateur metaphysicians who do not hesitate to inundate the world with their theories. This has been especially true in the twentieth century, the nineteenth having produced some glaring examples of bad *professional* metaphysics. Analysis is therefore the dominant mode in philosophy today, and this influence is felt strongly in the philosophy of science.

There are three main ways of going about analysis, which may be called the method of *redefinition,* the method of *explication,* and the method of *illustration in use.* The first is the method associated with the name of G. E. Moore; it consists in replacing the terms or statements to be analyzed by other terms or statements which have the same meaning and are couched in the same sort of language, but which are more carefully formulated and more clearly understood. (It has also at times been called 'interpretation'.) A typical example of Moore's use of this method occurs in a famous paper[2] where he examines the contention of the idealists that *"esse* is *percipi,"* or "to be is to be perceived." This is the kind of thing that philosophers say, Moore held, without being aware of how absurd it really is; and the function of analysis is to rephrase such absurd statements so as to make their absurdity quite obvious. Accordingly he offered the following statement as an analysis of *"esse is percipi"*: "What is experienced is identical with the experience of it." Nobody in his right mind, he thought, could seriously uphold *that*. This is not as irrelevant to science as it might sound, since some scientists have shown an inclination to go back to idealism on the basis of recent discoveries in quantum physics. The principal difficulty with the method lies in determining when terms or statements have the same meaning; if one's favorite philosophical belief is in danger of being analyzed away, one can always take refuge in the claim that it is being distorted in the process.

The other two methods of analysis represent attempts to get away from this difficulty. The method of explication was so called by Carnap,[3] whose work in the philosophy of science has consisted largely in the construction of symbolic language systems for specialized purposes. These language systems parallel the functions of ordinary language, but because of the vagueness of the latter they cannot use the same concepts; instead, precisely specified concepts are introduced to serve the purposes served in ordinary languages by familiar, but fuzzy, concepts. The new and precise concept is spoken of as an *explicatum* of the old and vague concept (the *explicandum*). Such artificial languages are free of a great deal of the ambiguity and uncertainty of ordinary languages, and in particular they are free of all emotive overtones, nuances, suggestions of hidden meaning, and the like, which may obscure important philosophical issues. The critics of this method have suggested that in purging themselves of all these unwanted elements, constructed languages are in danger of rendering themselves sterile; certainly some unexpected difficulties have appeared in the construction of languages complex enough to handle philosophically interesting problems. But even if it could be shown that a completely formalized language of the required complexity was unattainable, it might still be useful to provide explications for as many concepts as possible in ordinary language by *beginning* the construction of such a language. Sometimes the only satisfactory way of clearing up the meaning of a term is to *stipulate* a meaning and use the term consistently thenceforward in that sense. In doing so, one runs the risk of leaving some important elements of the meaning behind, and if one made very many bad mistakes of this kind one might end up speaking a language which contained many familiar, or almost familiar, terms, but which was talking about nothing, or hardly anything, that the original language was talking about. The advocates of this method would maintain that they have not made very many, or very bad, mistakes, and that they prefer to run this risk rather than flounder in the swamps of ordinary language.

The third method of analysis takes the opposite point of view, holding, in effect, that it is only by keeping close to the multiple uses of terms, and the continuous shift of meaning on passing from one use to the next, that it is possible to get any idea of what is really going on when men communicate with one another, whether it be about science, or philosophy, or anything else. This is the method practiced by Wittgenstein[4] in his later period, and still practiced by many of his followers. The meaning of terms, according to this view, is to be found in their *use*, and the task of analysis is to exhibit their various uses, not in order to decide that one is better than another, but rather the reverse—to show that any attempt at fixing a unique meaning is bound to end in failure. Philosophy, carried on in this way, becomes above all a technique for the clarification rather than the solution of problems, a technique for rendering oneself sensitive to exactly what is intended by *this* use of *this* term in *this* context. Clarification is often tantamount to solution, however, since what looks like a contradiction may be only the result of confusing this use in this context with that use in that context. Actually, this kind of success is called 'dissolving' rather than 'solving' the problem, and it is sometimes held that metaphysical problems which might appear to demand solution in the traditional sense are not really problems at all, just odd ways of talking among themselves which have been developed by philosophers.

It would not be profitable to enter here into disputes about analytic method, but the method of explication has some features which make it especially useful in dealing with the formal structure of scientific theory, and a few more remarks about this aspect of it are in order. Explication might not seem at first sight to be a method of *analysis* at all, since what it does is to build up systems, not take them apart. But one of the clearest ways of gaining an understanding of the function of the parts in a piece of complicated machinery, for instance, is to watch somebody putting it together, and one would not have to ask at the end of the process that it be taken apart again in order for a proper 'analysis' to be made. The method might be called a 'constructivist' method, or, if one wished to sound paradoxical, 'analytic synthesis'. It is certainly not a new method; Plato, in the *Republic,* when he wishes to examine the nature of justice in the State, proposes to "imagine the State in process of creation" so that the parts played in it by justice and injustice may be clearly seen, and Socrates, the narrator, indicates that he does not consider the method an easy one: " 'But ought we to attempt to construct [a State]?' I said; 'for to do so, as I am inclined to think, will be a very serious task.' " [5] Nevertheless he is encouraged by Adeimantus to proceed, in spite of the implied risk that what he ends up with may not be much like the real State. It is in fact usually called "Plato's Ideal State," and yet the *Republic* has always been regarded as a masterly analysis of political and social organization. Of course, Plato's system is not fully formalized; in fact, it is constructed in a standard language, namely classical Greek. But his method is such that the system could be formalized, or at least a beginning could be made in that direction.

The comparison of what Plato does with what Carnap does would be grotesque if a close analogy were insisted upon; its usefulness lies in drawing attention to the difference between what they have in common, namely a technique of construction, and the techniques of the other kinds of analysis. Plato's method in the *Republic* might seem to be merely a modification of the method of redefinition in a standard language were it not for the fact that instead of starting from some common definition (a device he uses frequently in other dialogues) he puts a new one together element by element. The terms used in this process need not be specially invented for the purpose, although for added rigor Carnap chooses to do that; they may be familiar terms which occur both in ordinary language and in the natural language. The only condition (which in Plato is not always fulfilled) is that they should be defined stipulatively and, as far as possible, precisely and unambiguously.

This method appears in fact to be a combination of speculation and analysis, and in this it shares the principal characteristic of science itself: it is *hypothetical.* Scientists often construct theories and only later look to see whether they fit the facts; in the same way it may sometimes be desirable to construct a philosophical system and then determine whether it gives a satisfactory account of the problem in hand. If it does not, a new system will have to be devised, but the effort of developing the first will not have been wasted, since it is possible to learn by experience even in the construction of philosophical systems. Certainly, if philosophers were to be judged solely according to their success or failure in solving the problems they set themselves, the history of philosophy would make depressing reading. This now makes philosophy look like a kind of science, and some people, like Reichenbach,[6] have tried to say that that is what it is; but such an amalgamation of the two overlooks a fundamental distinction. Science is about things in the world, but it is also one of the things that philosophy finds in the world. The philosophy of science, while it is about something in the world, namely science, does not refer to the things that science refers to, except in the incidental sense that it incorporates some general truths of philosophy about the world in general. We might say that science is a first-order activity and the philosophy of science a second-order activity; Bunge, for example, calls it "metascience."[7] The speculative part of this work, then, will construct a philosophical theory about scientific theory, and the analytic part of it will examine a number of such theories of theory, including its own, for inconsistency and error. The end in view is an understanding of science.

Science being, as was said above, one of the things that philosophy finds in the world, speculating about it might be thought unnecessary. The task of the philosopher of science might be regarded as one of description and classification merely, which could, from an examination of the various sciences as finished products of a historical process, arrive at easy generalizations about their method and structure. But it is not as simple as that. Science has, it is true, grown historically in a way which it is the business of historians of science to investigate. But this historical order of development, determined by curiosity, accident, or the pressure of necessity, tends to conceal the structure of science rather than otherwise. On the whole the sequence of events has been fortuitous, and has led to a great variety of scientific activities without anything obviously in common. The question which first arises, in fact, is one of logical reconstruction and identification. Philosophy finds science in the world, but as fragments embedded in contemporary culture and mixed up with other things. The first part of this book is therefore called "The Discovery of Theory," in an archaeological sense, to indicate that although we know science to exist, and to affect our lives, locating it in a world which contains such a diversity of objects requires a certain amount of exploration. As a means to that end we shall imagine science in process of creation, starting, as Aristotle insisted, from what is known to all.

It will be useful to draw together from the preceding discussion the elements of a definition, so that what is being sought will be clearly in mind. Science, it was said, explains, while philosophy tries to understand. These are very closely related objectives, but it is not always true that having an explanation leads to understanding, or that understanding means the ability to give an explanation. For centuries the will of God was given as the explanation of almost everything, but the people who advanced this explanation would have thought it blasphemous to claim understanding. Such an explanation would not of course count as scientific; not only is it very hard to find evidence for or against it, but also the idea of God seems obviously brought in from outside the realm of science. Science grew out of *natural* philosophy, and deals with nature; it declines to become involved with the supernatural, if there is any such thing. (The scientific explanation of what seems to be supernatural shows it to be natural after all.) But although there is not an invariable relation between explanation and understanding it is clear that scientific explanation is a most important way of arriving at philosophical understanding of one aspect of the world; explanation and understanding lie on the same continuum, and the boundary between them—and therefore, according to what was said above, between philosophy and science—cannot be made hard and fast. Explanation, however, makes the more modest claim, and the scientist does not ordinarily demand more. Finally, it must be pointed out that science is not merely explanation, but also something done concretely, such as the curing of diseases or the exploding of bombs.

From all this we can extract a preliminary definition: Science is the explanation of nature in its own terms, together with all that follows from doing that successfully, such as the ability to predict how things will behave and hence to control them. This book is a commentary on that definition.

REFERENCES

1. C. D. Broad, *Scientific Thought* (London, 1923), pp. 18, 20.
2. G. E. Moore, "The Refutation of Idealism," in *Philosophical Studies* (London, 1922), pp. 1-30.
3. Rudolf Carnap, *Logical Foundations of Probability* (Chicago, 1950), p. 3.
4. Ludwig Wittgenstein (tr. Anscombe), *Philosophical Investigations* (Oxford, 1958), *passim*.
5. Plato (tr. Jowett), *Republic*, 369a.
6. Hans Reichenbach, *The Rise of Scientific Philosophy* (Berkeley and Los Angeles, 1931).
7. Mario Bunge, *Metascientific Queries* (Springfield, Ill., 1959), ch. 1.

CHAPTER 2

KNOWLEDGE

The argument of this part of the book is to end with scientific
theory, but it must begin from something agreed upon by scientist
and layman alike. There are few, if any, philosophical assumptions
which all men can be trusted to hold in common, but there are four
matters of fact, and one judgment of value, which would probably
be conceded by all except the insane and the totally indifferent to
underlie philosophical activity. The four matters of fact are (1)
that something exists; (2) that something can be known; (3)
that there is something which matters; and (4) that something
(including the foregoing statements) makes sense and can be reflected upon. The judgment of value is that philosophy is one of
the things that matter. Note that the existence, or knowledge, or
value, or intelligibility of any particular thing is always open to
challenge; all that is insisted on here as indispensable is the truth
of the general claim.

The four matters of fact correspond to four branches of philosophy: ontology, or the theory of being, deals with what exists;
epistemology, or the theory of knowledge, deals with what can be
known, and how it can be known; the theory of value, sometimes
called axiology, but more familiar by the names of its principal subdivisions, ethics and aesthetics, deals with what matters; and logic,
or the theory of inference, deals with the way in which statements
make sense. The bald assertion of all this may appear dogmatic,
and I do not wish to suggest that it cannot be challenged. But if it
were true that nothing existed, or that nothing could be known,
or that nothing mattered, or that nothing made sense, then either
the opportunity for doing philosophy or the motivation for it would

13

be missing. And the latter would be missing even if all the facts were true, if philosophy were not one of the things that mattered.

The philosophy of science has traditionally concentrated its attention on epistemology and logic, that is on questions of scientific knowledge and scientific inference. Logic will occupy most of the second part of the book, and can for the moment be left aside, but before any progress can be made toward scientific theory the nature of knowledge must be looked into. 'Science' after all *means* 'knowledge', from the Latin *'scire'*, 'to know'; although etymologies are not to be taken too seriously, since 'philosophy' means 'the love of wisdom', from the Greek *'philein'*, 'to love', and *'sophia'*, 'wisdom', which is altogether too sentimental for twentieth-century taste. But at any rate science has something to do with knowledge—acceptable explanations cannot be based on mere conjecture—and it has been defined as 'organized knowledge', which when suitably qualified (to exclude telephone directories, for example) is not too misleading. Bertrand Russell once claimed that it was all the knowledge we had: "What science cannot discover, mankind cannot know."[1] And a similar point is put more plausibly by Karl Jaspers: "It is only when using the methodologically clarified sciences that I know what I know and what I do not know."[2]

Whatever may be the subjective state of mind of a man who is said to have knowledge, the only way of finding out whether he has it is to put him into a situation where it would make a difference. This is not to equate knowledge with a practical skill of some kind, which has from time to time been a temptation in philosophy. It is merely to assert that whenever one man has some knowledge which another man does not have, the first is able to do something which the second is not able to do. The obvious cases of this occur in what one might call the practical or applied sciences; the engineer knows how to get the maximum thrust from a rocket engine, how to prospect for oil, how to transmit many messages on the same cable, and so on; ordinary men do not. The very use of the phrase 'knows *how*' emphasizes the idea that knowledge is an ability rather than a possession. This view seems to encounter some difficulty, however, when the theoretical or 'pure' sciences are under discussion. The theoretical scientist knows *that* the boiling point of copper is 2310°C., *that* thorium decays with the emission of an alpha particle, *that* a conflict between desires and rules may lead to psychoneurosis. Ordinary men do not know these things; but what is the scientist able to do with them that the ordinary man cannot do?

The answer to this question is suggested by the above examples; the scientist is able to make the true statements, 'The boiling point of copper is 2310°C.', 'Thorium decays with the emission of an alpha particle', and so on. But 'the ability to make true statements' is not yet satisfactory as a definition of 'knowledge', because it is conceivable that one might make a true statement without knowing that it was true (that is, without being able to make the further statement, 'That is a true statement'). One might have guessed at it, or even just *said* it without intending to assert anything—and the idea of assertion is part of the definition of 'statement'. In order to exclude such accidental cases, it is necessary to modify the definition of 'knowledge', which then becomes: the ability to make true statements and defend them as true. One does not actually have to make the statements; one might wish to lie, and the morality of the knower does not, at least in science, affect his knowledge. But once made they will not be accepted as evidence of knowledge unless they can be backed up.

This definition of 'knowledge', while it clarifies the notion to some extent, only shifts the philosophical problem, which is now focused on 'truth' instead. In order to make and defend a statement as true, one has to have criteria for the application of the term. The most straightforward way of defending the truth of a statement about the world of experience is to point to the state of affairs it describes; if the state of affairs corresponds to what has been asserted, everybody will agree that the statement is a true one. This kind of truth may be called 'empirical' truth, since it depends on experience of the world; and the view that truth consists in a correspondence with the facts is called the 'correspondence theory'. One may also, however, point out in defense of a claim to truth that the statement in question follows from some other statement already admitted as true—not challenging the latter statement or inquiring why it was originally accepted, but saying merely 'If that statement is true (and everybody admits that it is) then this new statement, which follows from it, must also be true'. This kind of truth may be called 'systematic' truth, since it depends on the place of statements within a system; and the view that truth con-

sists in a fitting in with other truths is called the 'coherence theory'.
There is much more to the correspondence and coherence theories
of truth, of course, than is indicated here, but for the present it is
enough if the main outline of the distinction between the two is
clearly understood.

A little reflection will show that, as a matter of fact, most of what
we know to be true we know systematically, and not because of
direct experience. Our acquaintance with the world is extremely
limited, so that when a new statement is presented to us for acceptance or rejection our only recourse, as a rule, is to fall back
upon previous knowledge, to see whether the adoption of the new
statement would involve the rejection of anything already known.
If no such consequences would ensue, the statement might be accepted provisionally; it would be shown to be an integral part of
the system only if it could be seen to follow from some statements
already known. The term 'system' is, of course, hardly warranted in
speaking of everyday knowledge, which is an odd mixture of empirical and systematic truths, together with beliefs, rumors, preju-
dices, inclinations, memories, and all sorts of other things. One of
the good features of the definition of science as 'organized knowledge' is the implicit suggestion that it tries to bring some kind of
order out of all that confusion. Obviously there can be systematic
truth only if there is already a system of some sort. The details of
the origin of this system in the individual case pose problems whose
answers are lost in the remote period of our mental development
before memory began. By the time we reach any awareness of our
own knowledge, it is already organized to some extent.

But at the same time it is fairly clear that the *origin* of most of
this knowledge is empirical, either springing from our own experience of the world or having been communicated to us by others on
the basis of their experience. One of the classic disputes in philosophy concerns the question whether all knowledge whatever can be
traced back in principle to an origin in experience, or whether there
are other sources of knowledge, such as revelation or intuition or
reason. The view which maintains that there are no other sources
is known as *empiricism,* and the alternatives to it are the various
forms of *rationalism.* This controversy will be encountered again,
but for the moment we do not have to settle it; it is enough to say
here first that nobody has ever succeeded in showing that any other

source of knowledge is *necessary* for science, and second that even if there were other sources of knowledge science would insist on checking them against experience.

A much more puzzling question, and one which does demand attention, is why experience should lead to knowledge at all, and in particular why it should lead to knowledge of a world. Experience, in this sense, is individual and unique—the kind of thing that happens when *I* see that a pointer is moving on a scale—whereas the world of science is a world in common, from which in introspection or sleep, as Heraclitus puts it, "each turns aside into a world of his own." [3] There are then three problematic steps to be examined: first the step from any experience at all to experience of a world of one's own, then the step from experience of that world to knowledge of it, and finally the step from knowledge of that world to knowledge of a world in common. It is the character of part of this latter knowledge which gives rise to scientific theory.

REFERENCES

1. Bertrand Russell, *Religion and Science* (New York, Galaxy ed., 1961), p. 243.
2. Karl Jaspers (tr. Godman), *Reason and Anti-Reason in Our Time* (London, 1952), p. 30.
3. Heraclitus, fragment 95.

CHAPTER 3

PERCEPTION

In order to understand the transition from experience to knowledge, it is necessary to put oneself, imaginatively, in a position of experiencing but *not* knowing. The German philosopher Edmund Husserl recommended for this purpose a process which he called 'bracketing'; this means forgetting, for the time being, all that one has learned, in order to take an unprejudiced look at what is presented. Of course it is impossible to attain complete philosophical amnesia, and what is thus put in brackets "remains there," said Husserl, "as the bracketed in the bracket." [1] This study of appearance for its own sake, without interpretation, is known as *phenomenology,* a phenomenon being just something which appears.

Bracketing, or reduction, properly carried out, has the effect of putting the individual in the position of a newly born child, to whom things are appearing for the first time, and who has no past experience on the basis of which to interpret these sensations. We have all learned that certain shapes and sounds are indicators of other things: the world of appearance, for us, is a complex network of suggestion from which it is hard to free ourselves, although that is what the phenomenological reduction calls for. The child, on the other hand, has acquired as yet nothing that calls for reduction. In a visual sense the same is true of people who have been cured of congenital blindness by operations, but in this case the phenomenological purity of the situation is soon corrupted by the fact that the world is already known by means of other senses. (What has been learned by touch can soon be learned again by sight, just as someone who knows how to write with the right hand can soon, if necessary, learn to do so with the left.) But the reports of such people are the nearest thing we have to a record of what it is like to encounter sensation for the first time, and this initial experience is reported as a very disturbing shock, which must be quite as startling to the newborn child as to the newly seeing man, if not more so. Thrown into a totally incoherent and chaotic world, it is immediately assailed by lights, noises, pressures, and smells, which crowd in from all sides; and it is never again free, except in sleep, anaesthesia, and the like, from this perpetual bombardment. The child, fortunately, does not know what is going on, having nothing to compare it with; the idea of disorder is meaningless if there is no previous idea of order. The whole subsequent history of the child, and of the man it grows into, in so far as it is more than the history of an animal, might be regarded as a struggle to achieve such an idea of order: a struggle to make a cosmos out of the chaos, an ordered system out of primordial confusion.

We have already used the word 'sensation' in this discussion; the lights and noises of the previous paragraph correspond to the senses of sight and hearing, and so on. They were said to "crowd in," and one might add "uninvited"—the child does not ask for them. The common name for an element of sensation is 'sense-datum', which contains the idea of something *given;* and philosophers sometimes call the whole of our experience of the world 'the given'. Initially the child is a passive recipient of these gifts, and is not even aware that he is getting them; but as time goes on he begins to *respond* to certain sensations. (There are of course some reflex activities that begin as soon as birth has taken place, but although these are responses to stimuli there is no reason to suppose that they have anything to do with *sensation* as we ordinarily understand the word.) The same sets of sense-data recur, and take on individuality; things begin to stand out from the confused background of experience. In other words, the child finds himself in a world of *objects* which behave in a more or less reliable fashion. He accepts them for what they are—elements of his experience—and does not raise philosophical questions as to their *real* existence. Before long, however, he has somehow got hold of the very common idea that these objects exist when he is not looking at them; and at this point he has already left the purely phenomenological realm, thereby ceasing to be useful to us.

We wish to dwell on the pure phenomenological object—some-

times called an *intentional object,* one regarded from the point of
view of the subject, without considering whether it forms part of
an external world. What kinds of thing can be detected in the world
of phenomena alongside these objects—chairs, tables, coffee cups,
and so on? First there are aspects of these, their *properties,* among
which are colors and shapes; then arrangements of entities or
properties, *configurations;* then sets or *collections* of any of these.
So far the point of view has been static, but part of our immediate
experience is that things are happening, not just standing still—
they are not simply objects, but events; and, having said this, we
must add to the contents of the phenomenal world *processes,* events
in continuous change. Finally, to provide for the regular recurrence
of certain configurations or processes, we introduce patterns or
sequences, the elements of which may all be present at once or may
succeed one another at intervals of time. All these things, I think,
can be recognized without breaking the rule of bracketing. Phenomenologically speaking, objects are no more than the sum of
their properties; all six categories listed above are abstracted out
of the confused expanse which confronts us, but there is some evidence that objects are abstracted first, as wholes or *Gestalten* which
have an irreducible unity and individuality. (The term *'Gestalt',*
which means 'shape', has been used by some psychologists, such as
Koffka and Köhler, to indicate the unitary character of objects of
awareness.) Not all these things are exclusively visual, of course;
we may come to know explosions or changes in temperature by
hearing or feeling, and so on.

Some philosophers have felt that it is never necessary to leave the
world of phenomena, and have maintained that nothing else exists.
These *phenomenalists* would say that when we speak of objects
which we cannot see we do not mean that they really exist but are
invisible to us; we mean only that we *could* see them *if* the conditions were different. If I say, for example, "There is an owl in the
attic," what I really mean is that if the phenomena associated with
the attic were present to me, they would be accompanied by phenomena associated with owls. This view is quite consistent, because
it is true that we can know nothing about the existence of objects
apart from what is conveyed to us through the senses, which therefore constitute a barrier which we cannot penetrate, but it is not
generally accepted. Instead, most of us agree with the child in

giving independent existence to the objects we see; it makes sense to us to suppose that, corresponding to the thing that disappears and reappears in the world of phenomena, there is a real thing that continues to exist somewhere in the intervals between its appearances. Thus we form the idea of an 'external' world, in which we exist along with other things. Instead of being pure appearance, the thing takes on substantial existence; if before it was an intentional object, now it becomes a *perceptual* object, for perception means a grasping of something through the senses—we reach through appearance, as it were, to take hold of something below the surface of experience. We are not content with sensation merely, but must interpret the incoming data; one might write an equation:

$$\text{perception} = \text{sensation} + \text{interpretation.}$$

It is an excellent intellectual exercise to try to see the world as sensation *without* interpretation—people and things as complex patches of color, forming a fluid pattern whose parts have more or less consistent, although quite unintelligible, spatial and temporal relationships to one another.

The reason why the postulation of a real, substantial thing makes so much sense is that without some such explanation this regularity of the world of appearance seems preposterous; miracles must constantly be performed if objects cease to exist while my attention is directed elsewhere, only to spring back into being when I look in that direction again. And without some substantial carrier how can the properties which make up an entity hang together in the way they do? The English philosopher Locke appealed to the notion of 'material substance' to perform this function, although he had to confess that apart from its doing so he could only describe it as "a something he knew not what." [2] His countryman Berkeley criticized him severely for using a meaningless concept, and adopted a phenomenalist view, but he did not substitute any better explanation for the regularity of events, for he had recourse to God, who is always too powerful for scientific purposes. [3] A later philosopher in the same general tradition, John Stuart Mill, declined to entertain the notion of substance at all except as a "permanent possibility of sensation," [4] but again this view failed to satisfy the common-sense requirements of ordinary people with a taste for good solid matter. Nobody, it is true, has ever succeeded in showing that there is anything more to this solidity than a sensation of resistance to touch. But at the stage we are now discussing the mind seems incorrigibly disposed to think in terms of real, independent, material objects. The reason for this almost universal view, and the philosophical dangers inherent in it, will be discussed in the last part of the book; at any rate it is a convenient hypothesis, and this will be borne out when we come to deal with things for which there is no room at all in the world of appearance.

Accepting without proof, for the time being, an external world which makes itself known to us in perception, we leave phenomenological analysis behind. Not all intentional objects, it is true, correspond to perceptual ones; in dreams, for example, we live in a world of appearance to which we suppose that no real world corresponds, and we may invent intentional objects, by rearranging phenomena (as in the case of unicorns), or by overinterpreting sensation (as in the case of mermaids). But these are exactly the objects which do *not* exhibit the regularity of behavior which led us to introduce the external world, and consequently we do not grant them a place in it. We shall call those elements of the world of appearance, which are taken to indicate features of an external world, *percepts*. The six intentional categories spoken of above therefore become perceptual categories when attention is turned to the external world.

As soon as this transition has taken place, we realize that there must be far more in the external world than we can detect in appearance at any moment; the number of objects we encounter even in a single day, some of them for a few seconds only, is very large. In fact the remarkable thing about perceptual experience is its *incompleteness*. An examination of the perceptions one is now having makes this very clear; how much of the world is being perceived? Vaguely, one's immediate surroundings; clearly, only part of a line of print. We touch the world intermittently at one point, the focus of our attention, yet what occurs there has to be the foundation of all our knowledge.

This state of affairs, however, does not as a rule disturb us greatly. We have no difficulty in thinking of the world as a whole, or in believing that objects existed and events occurred before we were born, and exist and occur now in other places. We resist very strongly the suggestion that there might be gaps in the world, preferring to defend the view that objects and events form a continuous interrelated pattern, a *plenum,* as earlier philosophers might have said. This deep-seated conviction of spatial and temporal continuity is, considering the flimsy evidence at our disposal, quite remarkable, and we must now inquire how it arises.

REFERENCES

1. Edmund Husserl (tr. Boyce Gibson), *Ideas* (London, 1931), p. 108.
2. John Locke, *An Essay Concerning Human Understanding* (Oxford, 1894), pp. 230, 392.
3. George Berkeley, *Three Dialogues Between Hylas and Philonous* (New York, Liberal Arts Press ed., 1954), p. 55.
4. John Stuart Mill, *A System of Logic* (New York, 8th ed.), p. 54.

CHAPTER 4

THOUGHT

The world as experienced is fragmentary, brief, and discontinu-
ous, extended in two dimensions with a hint of a third. The world
as commonly known is whole, enduring, and continuous, extended
fully in three dimensions. This knowledge, according to the definition given above, is betrayed by the making of statements; in the
case of other people at least, the second sentence of this paragraph
might be a reasonable response to a question about the world.
Other people could therefore be regarded as machines whose input
consists of miscellaneous and apparently unrelated data and whose
output is a coherent account of a world. But in one's own case there
seems clearly to be something interposed between the experience
and the report, which in the case of other people is not open to
inspection, and this we call thought. We introduce it here as a
mechanism for the synthesis of a full world out of the bits and
pieces of experience.

The discussion of this topic is full of philosophical dangers. Introspection has rightly been considered suspect as a basis for
theories of knowledge, and mental entities (including the mind itself) are elusive and unstable, and hence unpopular. Thought will
therefore be regarded as a second convenient hypothesis (the external world was the first) whose introduction will have to be justified by its success in throwing light on disputed questions. Into this
hypothetical realm we now bring a set of hypothetical entities,
called *concepts,* which correspond initially to the percepts of the
previous section, and whose relation to those percepts requires
clarification.

Percepts appear and disappear, and yet the child gets hold of the idea that objects exist when he is not looking at them. He would hardly do so unless the same object appeared again after a period of absence. But how does he know, when it reappears, that it is the same object? The obvious answer is that he remembers its previous appearance and thus recognizes it as the same. But memory is only a name for the process, whatever its nature, which links the two occasions, and in our hypothetical model we shall say that the *recognition* of the object as the same object is one of the functions of the concept of that object. The concept has an even more basic function than recognition, however; we shall say that it is responsible for the constitution of the object as a self-identical unit in experience—its *identification* as the object it is. Corresponding to the percept which endures through some time, however brief, is a conceptual response which also endures, and which continues in existence after the departure of the percept. The third function of the concept comes a little later, when the child begins to think of absent objects (to desire or fear them, for example). In this case, we say that the concept serves as a *representation* of the object. (The term 'object' is used here to mean indifferently any sort of percept which is identified, recognized, or represented in this way, as the concept fulfills its respective functions.) Representation may look backward, as in memory, or forward, as in anticipation or prediction; it may also be inventive, as in the case of centaurs and winged horses.

To each of the six kinds of percept given in the previous section corresponds a kind of concept, as follows:

Percepts	*Concepts*
Objects	Substantive
Properties	Adjectival
Configurations	Spatial
Collections	Numerical
Processes	Temporal
Sequences	Periodic

It may be thought that we have now peopled a real world with objects, and duplicated this world by peopling the mind with concepts, as though there were things of one kind moving about inside our heads, representing and recognizing things of another kind which were to be found outside them. But it is a mistake to suppose that concepts have the kind of existence that heads have. Heads, and the configurations which we describe by 'inside' and 'outside', belong in the perceptual world, but concepts cannot belong there, since they were introduced to account for our ability to conceive of that world as complete when perceptually it is so fragmentary. At first, it is true, the full world as we conceive it is just like a perceptual world, except that it seems to be 'perceived' all at once (as God might be thought to perceive it) instead of one aspect at a time; concepts might then seem to be just like percepts which happened at the moment not to be actually perceived. But this is a very elementary stage which is soon passed. Apart from the logical difficulty that the meaning of 'percept' is just something perceived, so that an unperceived one would be a contradiction, there would always be the perplexing question of choosing under which of its many perceptual disguises to conceive an absent object. And further it is possible, and often useful, to conceive of things that never have been and perhaps never could be perceived.

What kind of existence, then, do concepts have? For the benefit of those who are uncomfortable about admitting strange entities of this kind, it must be conceded that there *are* things inside our heads that bear just the kind of relationship to external objects which we have claimed for concepts. There are circuits of neurons in the brain which, on receiving certain stimuli, reverberate; impulses travel round the circuit indefinitely, because the time taken for one complete cycle is greater than the time taken for any neuron in the circuit to recover from one activation and prepare itself for the next. (McCullough[1] likens such a circuit to a ring of dominoes stood on end; if one is pushed, all of them fall down one after the other, but if the one which fell first is stood up again before the last one [that is, the one behind it] falls, and so on round the ring, the process will continue cyclically.) This cyclic activity is the response to perception which serves as identification, and as recognition after short-term memory. The reverberations, if they last long enough, also leave a permanent imprint in the brain,[2] in the form of lowered resistance along that particular path, so that the circuit can easily be activated again, either by a fresh perceptual stimulus (which corresponds to recognition after a long-term memory) or even by an internal stimulus in the absence of perception (which corresponds to representation). Various well-known facts, like the inability of old people to remember what happened a few moments ago even though their memories of childhood are vivid, are thus explained. In this case, the imprinted circuits are intact, but the energy to activate new reverberating circuits, or the free neurons to constitute them, are lacking. Machines can be built which react in a similar way to patterns of light and sound, and they may then be said to be able to 'form concepts'.

The trouble with all this is that it assumes just what we are setting out to investigate, namely the existence of ways of dealing with natural events conceptually. If a concept is a kind of circuit, what serves as the concept *of* a circuit, which was repeatedly used in the previous paragraph? Nothing perceptual was involved, except black marks on white paper. Of course the significance of those marks had been learned, and the metaphor of the dominoes was an attempt to put the point in perceptual terms, by visualizing an actual ring. But the use of a metaphor also means that what is being said cannot be exhausted by any image—the brain is not full of dominoes. Discomfort at the vague ontological status of concepts has led to other theories, for instance that concepts are really habits of expectation associated with various perceptual experiences, and our conception of a full world a disposition to be surprised if we were to find any gaps in it (other than the ones we are used to, such as the gap between falling asleep and waking). And this may be true. The point is that a habit of expectation is different from what is expected,[3] so that the distinction between experience and thought is still necessary.

The concept, then, is a functional entity; we know what it *does* (identification, recognition, and representation) even though we do not know what it *is*, or where it is, if anywhere. We cannot know these things, because all possible answers to the questions "What is X?" or "Where is X?" involve relating the concept of X to other concepts, adjectival, spatial, and so on. In particular, we cannot expect to know concepts as visual, or as having the characteristics of any other sense. The psychologist Titchener used to report what came into his head when he was using certain ideas; he had a very strong visual sense, and was therefore led to support what was called an "image theory" of thought.[4] Unfortunately, many other people did not get images—at least, not the same ones —and his theory, although it enjoyed a certain vogue, was not acceptable to them. But whatever they *did* have in mind when those ideas were appealed to, it fulfilled the same function as Titchener's image, namely the conceptual function of providing a focus of mental attention. It is the functional interrelation of concepts which is important and which can be communicated—how they serve the processes of thought, not what they are in thought. It may be said, again, that this is too elusive to make any contribution to philosophy, or that it does nothing that language cannot do—in other words, that the concept is really nothing but a *word*. But this misses the whole point. Words are public, as will be seen in the next chapter, and what is public cannot account for our private ability to conceive of the world as extending beyond the spatial and temporal limitations of immediate experience.

As to the elusiveness of concepts, it is true that they cannot be captured in introspection, but that is only because introspection, as a kind of thought, itself makes use of them. Hume, when he tried by introspecting to discover what the self looked like, could find nothing but "bundles of perceptions," [5] but the fact that he was able to recognize them as such shows, according to the theory we are developing, that he was using concepts. Thinking about the world does not require the conscious apprehension of concepts, but simply their use. The admission that they are there for use allows us to make them part of the structure of science, and explains, as we shall see, a good deal about science that is otherwise mystifying. But to ask a question about the concept 'electron' as a *scientific* question is to make what Ryle has called a "category mistake";[6] science is about electrons, not concepts. This does not mean, of course, that scientists are not interested in the concepts they use; on the contrary, the clarification and refinement of concepts are important parts of their activity. But this is a metascientific activity, having much the same relation to science proper as a piece of scaffolding has to a building which is under construction, so that the interest in concepts is an intermittent one.

We have now a world of experience containing percepts and a world of thought containing concepts, neither of which is the 'real' world, if such a thing exists. The treatment of concepts and percepts as if they were things in these worlds, enduring and unchanging, is of course a serious oversimplification and distortion. Conceptualization freezes a world which is in constant flux, as Bergson pointed out,[7] and Heraclitus long before; and the objects which we recognize in perception are more or less arbitrarily carved out of the continuous stuff which fills the universe, according to accidents of heredity which allow us to see light and hear sound in limited ranges of wave lengths. If this were not the case, however, the attempt to make sense of experience would be doomed to failure from the start, being lost in a series of nonrecurring complexities. There is a sense in which no object endures and no experience is repeated. Man, however, has survived, and science developed, because of an ability to seize on simple and recurring aspects of this complex process, and to manipulate such simple aspects in thought even when they are absent in experience.

REFERENCES

1. Warren McCullough, *Finality and Form* (Springfield, Ill., 1952), p. 21.
2. J. Z. Young, *Doubt and Certainty in Science* (Oxford, 1951), p. 82.
3. Compare Moore's analysis of experience and the experienced, ch. 1.
4. Edward B. Titchener, *A Text-Book of Psychology* (New York, 1924), p. 367.
5. David Hume, *A Treatise of Human Nature* (London, 1739), p. 252.
6. Gilbert Ryle, *The Concept of Mind* (London, 1949), p. 16.
7. Henri Bergson (tr. Hulme), *Introduction to Metaphysics* (New York, 1912).

Chapter 5

LANGUAGE

Among the percepts with which, during the course of our up-
bringing and education, we become acquainted, are some with a
special function. They are interesting, not principally for themselves, but for the relation they bear to other percepts; they direct
attention to other percepts, or indicate when to expect them. These
are *signs*. In the simplest case they may be natural signs, blood for
example being a sign of injury, or clouds of rain, and here there is
a natural relation between the sign and what it signifies; in other
cases this relation may be merely conventional, as between red
lights and danger or names and the people who are called by them.
In all cases, however, discussion of signs and what they signify is
incomplete without reference to the person or persons who interpret
the sign as meaning what it does. The essential ingredients of the
situation are therefore three: the sign, the thing of which it is the
sign, and the person to whom it is a sign of that thing, or in other
words sign, object, and interpreter (Fig. 5.1).[1]

Nothing in this situation suggests that any other person besides
the interpreter is involved, and of course it is quite possible to have
signs whose significance is private, such as bookmarks, or at least
impersonal, as in the case of natural signs. The latter might, however, be taken as a message from nature about events not actually
observed at the moment (just as the former might be taken as a
message from somebody to himself). And this suggests that one of
the functions of signs is communication. If more than one interpreter is assumed, and if every interpreter interprets the sign in the
same way, then one may draw another's attention to it in the expectation that both will then share whatever meaning it is that the

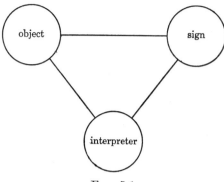

FIG. 5.1

sign conveys. Of course, nobody can ever be sure that anybody else does in fact interpret any sign in the same way, so that a more accurate way of representing the situation might be given by Fig. 5.2; but such agreement (like the existence of the external world) is incorporated as another hypothesis which is indispensable for further development. It might be the case that no two people had ever understood the same thing by any sign, but this could not be known to anybody who depended on signs for information about other people, as we all do. Other people, and for that matter signs too, belong to the class of percepts, that is, of appearances which are taken to indicate features of an external world. Those features, we assume, are indicated to others by similar percepts, although we have no way of confirming this. At any rate, we have the impression that meaning is being conveyed and received, and while this impression might conceivably be misleading, and solip-

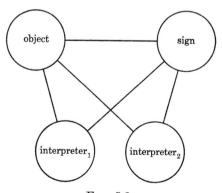

FIG. 5.2.

sism (the view that there is only one consciousness, namely my own) be true, it is difficult to take this prospect seriously without ceasing from all activity whatever which involves any genuine attempt to communicate with other people.

Signs, in other words, are public. A set of signs having understood meanings constitutes a *language,* and the most common kind of language is of course one in which the signs are words, that is, written marks or spoken sounds. We therefore introduce, not this time hypothetically, a realm of language in addition to the realms of thought and experience, the elements in which will be called *terms.* For the special case of terms, the sign situation is a modification of that given above (Fig. 5.3); since it is unenlightening to

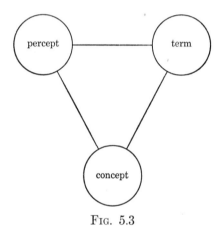

Fɪɢ. 5.3

add the same interpreter for every new case in which a term signifies some percept, we use only the relevant aspect of the interpreter, namely the concept which that situation calls into play.

In the languages with which we are familiar all terms do not have perceptual meanings. Those which do not have such meanings fall mainly into two classes: on the one hand, there are logical and grammatical terms, and, on the other, abstract and theoretical terms. If however we follow in the case of language the genetic method already applied to perception and thought, it will be clear that while there might once have been languages without grammatical or abstract terms (languages consisting merely of names of objects, such as the one suggested at the beginning of Wittgenstein's *Philosophical Investigations,*[2] or languages consisting merely

of expressions of feeling—a type that will be left out of consideration in this book as unsuitable for scientific purposes) there could
hardly have been languages containing *only* such terms. The primitive situation can therefore be imagined as one in which each term
has its perceptual reference. This need not of course be an object
or property, although that is the most natural assumption for
Western languages; it may be a process, and Whorf, among others,
has brought evidence to show that this probably is the dominant
type of perceptual reference in some American Indian languages,
for example.[3] It cannot be too strongly stressed that percepts do
not belong in the postulated external world, even though they are
tacitly taken to indicate various features of it, but in experience.
And if different ways of experiencing the world give rise to different
patterns of language, the reverse influence is also possible: learning a particular language may induce a characteristic way of dividing up or 'segmenting' what presents itself in perception.

The original appearance of language in the world, and the way
in which terms became attached to their referents, are outside the
scope of this book. Part of this attachment was no doubt conscious
and deliberate, particularly in the later stages—it has seemed to
many people, as is made clear in the story of Adam's naming of the
animals, that it could hardly have come about by chance. But there
is no difficulty, given an animal species with the vocal mechanism
to produce a variety of sounds and the brain mechanism to remember and associate them, in regarding the emergence of language as
completely natural. One might approach this question by a study
of the *relations* (onomatopoeic, and so on) between terms and what
they stand for. Our concern here, however, is with the *meaning* of
terms, not their origin.

What a term means—on this elementary level, what it correctly
refers to in perception, which has been called its "sense meaning"
by C. I. Lewis[4]—can only be determined, in the first instance, by
a study of its use or its effect, that is, of the circumstances in which
people employ it or react to it more or less consistently. Its utility
in communication obviously depends on such consistency, not only
between uses on different occasions by the same person, but also
between uses by different people on the same occasion. Once a term
has such a consistent use, even among a small number of individuals, we will say that it forms part of the *ordinary language*

of those individuals. An outsider wishing to know with any accuracy what the term meant would have to be sensitive to nuances
of context and intention, and after listening and reading enough
he might sum up what he had discovered in an especially clear example of ordinary use among the individuals in question which
could be presented as a *paradigm case.* Apart from the use summed
up in such a paradigm, the term could not strictly be said to have
any meaning—the meaning from this point of view *is* the use. But
it would be improper in ordinary language to speak of correct or
incorrect uses of terms, only of customary or unusual ones.

All languages begin as ordinary languages, under the pressure of
the immediate necessity of communication. Gradually, however—
but not, of course, in all cases—customary usage hardens and
spreads; grammatical terms, declensions, case endings, tenses, and
so on, are introduced; fixed sentence forms are adopted; and what
was merely a widespread ordinary language establishes itself as a
standard language, in which it becomes possible to speak of correct
and incorrect usage. The emergence of a standard language means
that some ordinary language has won a racial or regional hegemony,
and this process is often assisted or reinforced by the influence of a
great writer, such as Cervantes or Luther, whose work dominates
a crucial period and sets an example to subsequent generations.

By the time this metamorphosis into a standard language has
taken place, the state of affairs in which every term had its perceptual reference has of course been left far behind. Even terms
which still have such reference may have become infected with one
or other of two very common shortcomings—*vagueness,* an uncertainty in borderline cases as to whether or not the term correctly applies to an object or situation, and *ambiguity,* the uncertainty of reference which arises from a term's being correctly
applicable to more than one class of objects or situations. These
troubles are mitigated, however, by the fact that in most standard
languages it is possible, by virtue of their enriched vocabularies or
through the use of circumlocutions, to say the same thing in more
than one way and to distinguish precisely expressions whose meanings differ only slightly. Instead of having sense meaning merely,
terms now acquire 'linguistic meaning', one or more equivalent expressions which can be used in their place whenever they occur
without altering the truth of what is being said. Just as it was seen

earlier that most of the truths known to us are known systematically rather than empirically, so it now appears on reflection
that the terms used to express these truths are understood, for the
most part, through their linguistic associations rather than in a
directly empirical sense. But again it is sometimes maintained that
the chain of such associations always leads back eventually to a
term or terms having perceptual reference.

There has been some controversy, hinted at in Chapter 1, over
the question whether philosophical puzzles are to be solved mainly
or exclusively at the level of ordinary language, by analyses of
meaning-in-use which might show that they arose out of simple
misunderstandings, or by traditional discursive methods, or even
by the more drastic method of reconstructing language as a formal
system, without the obscurities which may lie at the root of our
confusions—with no waste, no duplication, no vagueness, no ambiguity, no literature, but merely a kind of mathematical and logical
precision. On the side of ordinary language analysis is the argument
that any language which is adequate as a transmitter of the nuances
and shades of meaning on which everyday conversation depends so
heavily must be fluid, living, and changing, and that the assumption of standard meanings covers over profound discrepancies due
to period and context. It is the mark of an educated man that his
ordinary language approaches a standard language; but if it approaches too closely he is called a pedant. This is a powerful argument in philosophy generally, but it lacks force in the philosophy of
science, because in science we are all pedants, the success of science
largely depending, as is obvious, on an exactness of use over considerable expanses of space and time. As far as that is concerned,
it would certainly be convenient if the language of science were a
formalized language. Many scientists have this as an end in view,
and some of them are perhaps approaching it, parts of mathematics and even parts of physics having become highly formalized.
It will be argued in Part II that in principle all sciences can be
brought to that stage, but for the moment it must be admitted
that the language of science is a standard language. It has its own
special vocabulary, referring to particular kinds of object and
process, but it does not as yet have the precisely specified, unam-
biguous, clean, economical grammar and syntax that a formalized
language would have. The parallel holds also in another respect,

since the forms of this standard language in the various sciences bear the mark of such men as Newton, Darwin, and Freud, whose eminence was as great in their own fields as Luther's and Cervantes' in theirs.

If the use of language to describe the world is mediated, for the individual, by concepts, it is equally true that the exchange of concepts between individuals has to be mediated by language. But the use of *philosophical* language to talk about *scientific* language introduces a complication; scientific *terms* become *objects* rather than signs of objects. A distinction has to be made between languages which are used to talk about things, and languages which are *talked about* in other languages. A language which is being used to talk about the world is called an *object language*. There are two senses in which this is appropriate: one is that it is a language about objects, and the other is that it is to be the object of a second language. Of these senses the second is the more important. The language which we use to discuss this first language is then called a *metalanguage*. In talking metalinguistically, one *uses* the terms of the metalanguage but *mentions* the terms of the object language, while in talking simply 'linguistically' one uses the terms of the object language but mentions objects in the world. We shall adopt the usual convention of enclosing things that are mentioned in single quotation marks. For instance, the sentence "The sentence 'copper sulphate is soluble' is true" is a metalinguistic philosophical remark, mentioning a scientific sentence (belonging to the object language) which actually says something about copper sulphate.

REFERENCES

1. This three-termed arrangement is due to C. S. Peirce.
2. Ludwig Wittgenstein, *Philosophical Investigations* (London, 1953).
3. B. L. Whorf, "An American Indian Model of the Universe," in *Language, Thought and Reality* (New York, 1956).
4. C. I. Lewis, *An Analysis of Knowledge and Valuation* (La Salle, Ill., 1947), ch. VI.

CHAPTER 6

CLASSIFICATION

The relation between the term and the object to which it refers in perception (where there is such a reference) may be thought of as a one-to-one relation, but this is obviously a gross oversimplification. To begin with, words do not exist as single entities but as collections of utterances and inscriptions, each one a particular use of the word on a particular occasion. A distinction has been made between the word *type* which is embodied on each such occasion and the word *token* which is its concrete physical embodiment as an individual sound or mark.[1] The token is a sign in the original sense; the type belongs to language on a more abstract level.

Not only is the term a complex entity capable of analysis in this and other ways, but the object to which it refers is if anything more complicated still. We have seen how the process of conceptualization identifies regularities of appearance which we then come to accept as indicative of enduring entities; the object even on this level is seen to be a class of appearances, no two identical, which brings under one head our various experiences of it. But we do not have a distinct term for each such class of appearances. The usefulness of language, since we are capable of learning only a limited vocabulary, obviously depends on our ability to reduce the multiplicity of events, even in our own experience, to a few kinds of event, and the multiplicity of objects to a few kinds of object. Objects bear likenesses to one another, and history repeats itself.

But on further reflection it is quite clear that no event is ever exactly repeated, and no two objects are ever exactly alike. Leibniz went as far as to claim that if ever there were two objects which were so alike that they could not be told apart they would be the same object, an assertion known as his principle of the *identity of indiscernibles*.[2] We might conceive of a pair of apparently identical objects side by side as a challenge to this claim, but according to Leibniz there would be, quite apart from an obvious *material* difference between them, an essential dissimilarity in their properties, since one would be situated in a slightly different spatial relation from the other with respect to all the remaining objects in the universe. Space, on this view, is a property of the objects in the world, rather than a property of the world in which objects may exist indifferently.

Every two occurrences in the world can be distinguished from one another in some way, and yet there is only a small number of terms to cover all these occurrences. A small number of terms, it is true, is enough to generate a very large number of descriptive phrases by suitable combinations. One term gives only one possibility, and two terms only two; but three terms give six, and four terms twenty-four. In fact, n terms can make $n!$ descriptive phrases distinguished from one another simply by altering the order of the constituent terms. Each of these phrases, however, would be long and cumbersome; in general, we do not use such complicated expressions to describe experience, but a rather small number of single terms, or phrases made up of very few terms, which we apply to large classes of occurrences. The term 'day', the term 'green', the term 'square', and so on are all simple terms which we apply to great numbers of cases. The problem is therefore to account for the usefulness of *such* terms in describing the complexity of the world of experience. Quite clearly what is involved here is the ancient distinction between the particular and the universal. By 'particular' is meant an individual thing, event, occurrence, or the like, while by 'universal' is meant something which is found in many things, events, or occurrences. The relation between word type and word token is a special case of the relation between universal and particular.

The problem is simply that of finding out what it is that objects have in common when we say they are like one another, when we call them by the same name, when we classify them together. Plato's theory of *universalia ante rem,* the universals *before* the things, maintained that the link between members of the same class was that they were all imitations of an archetypal 'form' or 'idea' which existed before the world as we know it was made; a variant of the theory said that the archetype participated in every example of the class. The imitation theory ran up against the difficulty that one would not know that something was an imitation unless one already knew that it was like the thing it imitated, and both theories were accused of explaining this world by inventing another which was just as hard, if not harder, to understand. Aristotle therefore developed a theory of *universalia in re,* or the universals *in* the things; according to this theory everything was a combination of two elements, form and matter, the matter accounting for the thing's being a real thing in the real world, and the form accounting for its being the *kind* of thing it was, and thus playing the part of the universal. The forms were arranged in a hierarchy of definition by *genus* and *species,* as is still done for the animal and plant worlds, everything having its place in a logical order— an order not only of definition but also of generation, so that if one knew what a thing was one knew also the chain of causes which had produced it and which maintained it in being. This scheme, which was taken over by St. Thomas Aquinas and turned into one of the greatest articulated systems of philosophy ever built—one which has been compared to the other great product of the medieval period, the Gothic cathedral—did not prove very illuminating when applied to actual cases, although it worked very well in connection with spiritual beings which could not be observed.

The 'nominalist' or 'conceptualist' movement (the name depending on whether names or concepts were considered more important) arose in the late Middle Ages as a reaction, on the part of William of Ockham and others, to the Aristotelian and Thomistic systems. According to those systems, a thing could come into being *only* because of a chain of causes moving down through the hierarchy, and only those things which had a place in the scheme could come into being at all. Even God was unable to break the authority of the system. This state of affairs seemed blasphemous to Ockham, who considered God's power superior to the philosophy of St. Thomas; he therefore maintained that each thing was what it was not because it belonged to a class deductively related to a larger class, but because God wished it to be what it was. The way to find out about things was not to learn the system, but to investigate the world. This provided, in an unexpected way, an impetus to scientific inquiry, but that was not Ockham's purpose, which was simply to safeguard the omnipotence of God. What was implied by his position would have been completely destructive of science, for any genuine likeness between cases was denied, along with any objective order in the natural world. Everything depended contingently upon God, and if he wished to suspend the operation of the laws of nature he was perfectly free to do so. The only common property (if it could be called a property) of members of a class was that they were called by the same name or represented by the same concept, which could not in itself guarantee anything. Even apart from theological considerations Ockham would have said that universals were only names, since any statement in general terms (All men suffer the wrath of God) is only a summary of many statements in singular terms (Adam suffered the wrath of God and Job suffered the wrath of God and . . .). Nothing general exists, only individuals; the theory is one of *universalia post rem*, the universals *after* the things.

With part of the foregoing we are bound to agree. Everything that exists is individual, it is true, so that in a sense universals can only be individual concepts—in so far, that is, as they can be said to 'exist'. On the other hand, this conclusion is useless if all it does is to deny objective order in nature. What science aims at is the development of concepts which will stand for *any* individual in a particular class, on the assumption that there is a similarity between the members of the class which entails a similarity in their behavior under similar circumstances. *Why* objects and events should resemble one another is a difficult question, to which we shall return. *That* they do so is obvious from daily experience.

Reference has already been made to Aristotle's scheme of definition by genus and species, which is at the same time a scheme of classification. This formed in the hands of Linnaeus the basis for the first serious attempt at systematizing the nomenclature of plants and animals. The reason for its success in this field was of course that there is a very obvious basis for the similarity of members of a class of living things—they have a common ancestor, and each is the offspring of another more or less exactly like itself. Individuals differ less from one another within the species, with respect to the characteristics which define the species, than any one of them differs from a member of another species. Even in this case, the borderlines between species have at times been very difficult to draw, and some rather artificial criteria (such as the ability to produce offspring together) have been used for judging whether or not a pair of individuals belongs to the same species. It used to be thought, nevertheless, that there were such borderlines, and that they could not under any circumstances be crossed; every living thing belonged to its fixed species, every inanimate object to its fixed class, and every man to his station in life. This doctrine was undermined by the theory of evolution, which envisaged species as developing out of earlier species and themselves subject to further change. The new viewpoint opened up whole areas to scientific investigation which had previously been dogmatically closed, and in so doing made clear the adverse effect which rigid schemes of classification may have on the development of science. Some sort of classification is of course indispensable, since without it we would not have a vocabulary of universal terms and could not enter into any discussion at all. But the fact that classes have blurred edges and merge into one another is to be regarded less as a hindrance than as an invitation to further work. If boundaries have to be drawn sharply, they have to be drawn arbitrarily. Objects and events which are not close to these boundaries fall into *natural kinds* which are clearly distinct from one another. It is from such obvious differences that science begins, but the scheme of classification must be kept flexible.

The hint as to classification in general which can be gathered from a study of the biological case is that, wherever possible, objects and events should be looked at from the point of view of their origins rather than from the point of view of their apparent qualities, since this enables the question of similarity to be pushed back one generation, as it were. We may distinguish in fact four different senses of similarity, in descending order of usefulness for purposes of classification. The first may be called *genetic* similarity, that is, between objects having similar origins (produced by similar forces under similar conditions, and so on); the second *structural* similarity, between objects having similar constituent parts, or similar relations between their parts; the third *functional* similarity, between objects having similar behavior; and the last the merely *apparent* similarity from which we began. All classification is bound to begin from, and ultimately to rest on, apparent similarity, but science attempts wherever possible to arrange its categories on the basis of the other kinds of similarity. This has led to the isolation of a very small (although at the moment increasing) number of ultimate constituents of the universe, and to the recognition of a small number of fundamental principles according to which nature operates.

It has often been the hope of philosophy to reduce the number of ultimate constituents and the number of fundamental principles to one. There is of course an obvious sense in which the universe is one, but such radical *monism* has not so far met with great success. Science is as usual more modest, giving at every point the explanation of observed similarity in terms of the smallest possible number of primitive concepts but not demanding an impossible reduction of this smallest number. Like all explanatory schemes in science this reduction to ultimate constituents and fundamental principles is hypothetical. The observation of similarity remains a matter for immediate judgment and is not itself explained in terms of anything else.

The relation between term and object is now seen to be a many-many relation, and if this fact is kept clearly in mind it will help to guard against naive mistakes about language and its applicability to the world. The multiplicity on the side of language can be safely overlooked if what is under discussion is the understanding of the world by an individual scientist—*his* concept and the corresponding term *he* uses are likely to be highly consistent, and this may be true also for a group of scientists working in the same field. The multiplicity on the side of objects is, as we have seen, just the condition for the usefulness of language.

REFERENCES

1. C. S. Peirce, "Prolegomena to an Apology for Pragmaticism," *The Monist*, 16 (1906).
2. G. W. Leibniz (ed. H. G. Alexander), *The Leibniz-Clarke Correspondence* (Manchester, 1956), p. 37.

CHAPTER 7

DEFINITION[1]

The class of actual objects or events to the members of which a term applies correctly is called the *denotation* of that term; and while the term denotes the objects in question, the objects constitute a *definition* of the term. On the most primitive level a term may be defined by pointing out something to which it applies, that is, by *showing* its meaning, and this procedure is known as *ostensive* definition.

But direct observation, when rendered in language, is not as free of ambiguity as we might like: ostensive definition leaves plenty of room for misunderstanding. Pointing to a zebra and saying 'zebra' might lead somebody to believe that 'zebra' meant 'animal' or 'striped' or 'four-legged' or any one of a number of things. Of course, it would become clear after a sufficient number of examples of the process that only that particular combination of properties deserved the title 'zebra'; one could remove the possibility of taking the word to mean 'striped', for example, by pointing again to a different striped animal and saying 'skunk'. (Even then an intelligent stranger might think that 'zebra' meant 'transversely striped' and 'skunk' 'longitudinally striped'.) In a sense, it is impossible to be mistaken at this level, since as long as the report is invariant between observers—that is, as long as they use the same term—*what* term they use does not matter. But what does invariance itself guarantee? Two observers might both report 'skunk' correctly in the presence of a skunk, and we would believe that they were agreeing, but then one of them might say 'skunk' again on seeing a zebra, and the other might say it again on smelling the fumes from a chemical experiment. There is no ultimate escape

43

from traps of this sort, but the dangers become minimal after long
sequences of observations by people of similar training. As a matter
of fact, where scientific language is concerned, it is never necessary
to give aboriginal ostensive definitions by merely pointing and
uttering a word. Such definitions are always embedded in a context
of ordinary language which makes it clear what feature of the
world is being drawn attention to.

The denotations of terms in ordinary language, and for that
matter in standard languages, are vague at the edges, as can clearly
be seen by considering simple terms like 'animal' and 'vegetable'.
Ostensive definition is clearly not enough. Moreover, a set of isolated statements about isolated phenomena is not yet science; only
when the terms in the statements are related to one another does
scientific theory emerge. There must of course be *some* ostensively
defined terms before any such relationship can be established. One
might say that ostensive definition is the lowest form of definition
in science, or that it is prescientific. At this level, all the term does
is to name some element or elements of experience; responding to
an experience with the appropriate name is part of learned be·
havior and does not necessarily involve much conceptual activity.
It does of course involve the concept which completes the triangle
percept, term, and concept; the concept, however, may be isolated,
not forming part of any conceptual scheme, but merely providing
a criterion for the application of the term on confrontation with
that particular percept. At a later stage, a more explicit criterion
for the application of the term to some object or event may be
demanded, and this will amount to the specification of certain requirements which must be met by the object or event before it can
be classified as part of the denotation of that term. A list of these
requirements will amount to an alternative, but longer, name for
the object or event. Instead of referring to the object by its usual
name, one might instead say 'an object which satisfies the following requirements . . .' . This is equivalent to saying that wherever
the original name occurs in a statement, the circumlocution just
given may be substituted for it without altering the truth or falsity
of the statement, so that in fact the original name is dispensable.
Terms can thus be defined away by means of other terms, but there
will always be at least some terms left for which no such definitions

are available without making the process circular, and these will have to have ostensive definitions if they are defined at all.

A list of the properties which an object *must* possess if it is to be included in the denotation of some term specifies the *intension* of the term. There is clearly a simple relation between denotation and intension: the more restricted the denotation, the more detailed the intension. This does not necessarily work in the other direction, since a further specification added to an intension might not in fact eliminate any objects from the denotation. It would necessarily eliminate some *possible* objects, but these could hardly have belonged to the denotation in the first place, in view of the fact that it is a class of actual objects. There appears therefore to be an asymmetry between intension, every element of which is necessarily entailed by the meaning of the term, and denotation, the elements of which are contingent in the sense that there need not actually be anything to which a given term applies. This imbalance may be corrected by introducing two further notions—*extension,* the necessary analogue of denotation, and *connotation,* the contingent analogue of intension. The extension of a term is the class of all possible objects, past or future, known or unknown, which if they existed would belong to its denotation; the connotation of a term is specified by a list of the properties which the members of its denotation happen to have in common, including those essential properties which constitute its intension. The denotation of a term is a subclass of its extension. An anomaly appears in the case of proper names, which have denotation without extension—there is a class of men properly called 'John', but it makes no sense to speak of a class of possible men who *might* properly be called 'John' —but the difficulty may be put aside here by pointing out that there are no proper names in the language of science.

Although definition gets started in contingent situations, where actual objects are referred to, it is clear that the more useful notions for its purposes are extension and intension. But from the point of view of definition most of the intension may even be superfluous. The intension of 'equilateral triangle' includes having equal sides, having equal angles, having angles of 60°, and being symmetrical about the bisector of every vertex, since any such triangle must have these properties, but any one of them will serve as a complete definition of the term 'equilateral' for triangles. It is this possibility of alternative expressions of the same concept which allows the construction of chains of definitions.

Definitions of terms by reference to other terms belonging to the same language system (for example, the language of physics) are *internal* definitions, and one might, by using this kind of definition alone, build a whole ingrown language whose terms referred to each other but to nothing else. Definitions which go outside the language system to something else—perception, for instance—are *external* definitions, and they are required if the whole system is to mean anything. Ostensive definitions are of course external, while definitions which depend on the intension of terms are internal. One useful but dangerous property of intensional definitions—and of internal definitions in general—is that names for nonexistent objects may be created by means of them. When it was found that the behavior of light could best be explained by saying that it was a form of electromagnetic wave-motion, the question was raised of the nature of the medium in which light-waves were propagated. The speed of other kinds of waves was known to depend on the rigidity of the medium through which they traveled (the greater the rigidity, the greater the speed), and, as the speed of light-waves was extremely high, the medium would have to be extremely rigid; on the other hand, light was known to be propagated through interstellar space (where there was practically no matter), and from this it was obvious that the density of the medium had to be extremely small. Using these two properties, it was possible to define a new concept, *ether,* as a substance of very low density but very high rigidity through which electromagnetic waves were propagated. The most careful search for this substance failed to discover any trace of it. Its internal definition was apparently quite in order, but there was no way of defining it externally—of relating it to anything outside the language system appropriate to the discussion of electromagnetic waves. This deficiency was enough to make physicists abandon it as a tool of explanation. There are cases in which concepts having only internal definitions are admitted, when there are obvious reasons why they should not be detectable directly, but at least some concepts in any system must have external definitions to tie the system down to observation or to some other system itself linked with observation. *Observation* is just a special form of perception, concentrating on particular phenomena with a view to describing them by means of carefully defined class terms so that they can form the starting points of theoretical work.

The two functions of definition so far discussed are (1) the grounding of concepts in actual observation, and (2) the descriptive interrelation of concepts. Both of these take place in a standard language, the language of science. There are three other functions which will be touched upon here but discussed in more detail later. The introduction of a formalized language demands a formal counterpart for the second of these kinds of definition, which will now however not be in terms of properties, relations, and so on, as they apply to the objects named, but will be concerned exclusively with formal relationships between terms—what terms or expressions can be substituted for what other terms or expressions. In the case of the first two kinds of definition, it was possible to speak sometimes of terms, sometimes of concepts, bearing in mind the three-cornered relationship of Fig. 5.3, but in this case we are concerned exclusively with language as an *empty* device (or calculus) for the manipulation of signs. These definitions are of the internal type. The introduction of metrical considerations demands a new kind of external definition which links the calculus containing names of concepts to a calculus containing variables which represent the names of numbers. This kind of definition is crucial to the operation of measurement (and incorporates what is important in so-called *operational* definition). Finally a fifth kind of definition, once more internal, provides links between concepts, but links borrowed this time from the *mathematical* calculus.

It was said earlier that where a term is defined by means of other terms the original term (the *definiendum*, 'that which is to be defined') is dispensable, that is, eliminable in favor of the term or terms used to define it (the *definiens*). This is not strictly accurate. Where such elimination is possible, we say that the definition is *explicit*, and we may exhibit the form of such a definition by the equation

$$x =_{df} \ldots$$

where 'x' is the definiendum and the dotted line represents the definiens. The sign of equality is not the mathematical sign of equality, but the analogy is clear; the algebraic equation

$$x = 3y + 2,$$

for example, allows us to eliminate 'x' wherever it occurs by writing instead '$3y + 2$'. It sometimes happens, however, that the definiendum has significance only in certain contexts; and where this is the case, the entire context has to stand on the left of the defining expression:

$$(\ldots x \ldots) =_{df} \ldots.$$

Such *contextual* definition is often necessary, for example, where adjectival concepts are in question, or terms like '$+$' or '5' or expressions like 'gravity' (which occurs only in phrases like 'gravity field' or 'acceleration of gravity'). In some such cases, the necessity of a contextual definition is a hint that the term has no meaning by itself and can be dropped from the scientific vocabulary. But the distinction between explicit and contextual definitions is not as radical as might appear. A contextual definition is in fact an explicit definition of a context or class of contexts in which the term defined occurs.

The importance of precise definitions can hardly be stressed too strongly. There may, however, be several correct definitions of the same term or concept. A definition is correct if it characterizes the concept unambiguously by means of other concepts in the same system (internal), or percepts, or concepts in another system (external), in such a way that no statement which was previously false becomes true by virtue of the definition alone, and no statement which was previously true becomes false. It may be that before the introduction of the definition there were no true or false statements incorporating the term in question, that is, no statements in which substitution *could* lead to a change in truth value; in such a case, the definition is said to be *stipulative*—it merely introduces the defined term, and accepting it constitutes an agreement as to the way in which the term is to be used. For example, the decision to call the element of atomic number 100 'fermium' was a stipulative definition both in the internal and external senses—internally because it enabled scientists to replace circumlocutions such as the one above (or 'the next element after einsteinium') by the term 'fermium', and externally because there is an actual substance (at present only in very small quantities, very occasionally) which is named by 'fermium'. Once a term defined stipulatively is accepted into a standard language, it becomes possible to insert it—along with all the other terms already accepted—into the dictionary of that language, and the definition given there is sometimes known as its *lexical* definition.

Scientific theories may be put together in various ways, and this too may determine what kinds of definition terms or concepts are given. Historically, theories were put together rather unsystematically, depending on accidents of discovery. This led to a *historical* order of definition, starting from terms having a meaning in ordinary language, and then in standard languages, which were not defined especially for scientific purposes, and gradually incorporating more characteristically scientific terms by reference alternately to new observations and discussions involving the old terms. The establishment of science is marked by such a constant oscillation back and forth between the empirical and the systematic (or the 'rational', since reason is the all-inclusive system into which man tries to fit everything he finds out about the universe). This way of going about the construction of theory is wasteful, in spite of being the original way, and when one learns a scientific theory one rarely does so in the historical order. There is a sense in which every student of science recapitulates the history of science, since he brings to his study of the subject exactly the kind of equipment with which the human race approached the scientific investigation of nature, that is, his sensory apparatus, ordinary language habits, and some more or less accurate knowledge of a standard language or two. But teachers of science are able to rearrange things into what might be called a *heuristic* order of definition, introducing new concepts in the most appropriate place, given the preparation of the student, rather than in the order in which they were discovered. Finally, the introduction of formalized languages brings about a third order of definition, the *logical* order, in which, starting from a smallest possible number of *primitive,* that is, undefined, terms, others are introduced stipulatively to serve as abbreviations for very complex expressions made up out of the primitives.

REFERENCE

1. For a fuller treatment of the material of this chapter, see Peter Caws, "The Functions of Definition in Science," *Philosophy of Science*, **26** (1959), pp. 201-228.

Chapter 8

DISPOSITIONS AND THEORETICAL CONSTRUCTS

Most of the remarks about definition in the previous chapter could be applied, not only to science, but also to any other discipline requiring clarity and precise distinctions of meaning. In every such discipline a technical terminology is developed—a departure from common usage involving the refinement and redefinition of familiar concepts for unfamiliar tasks. On this level the difference between science and other fields of intellectual inquiry is simply that it begins from a different set of everyday concepts. It would be convenient to distinguish between the concepts on which the refining operations of the special disciplines are carried out and those which emerge from the process, and the term *construct*[1] has sometimes been used in the philosophy of science to stand for the latter: something deliberately devised for specific ends, purged of ambiguity and vagueness, and suited for the precise expression of the behavior of and relations between precisely specified perceptual objects and events. It is, after all, the possession of such trained concepts which marks science off from mere common knowledge and common sense. This use has not been widely accepted, and there is, it is true, some danger that speaking of 'constructs' might be interpreted as subscription to the philosophical view that the objects referred to by scientific theories are logical constructions out of sense-data. Nevertheless, as long as this danger is remembered, the introduction of the term is worthwhile, since it serves as a reminder that science is to be distinguished from everyday concerns by the quality of clarity and distinctness (to borrow a phrase from Descartes) which it insists upon in its concepts.

The concepts which science borrows from the knowledge and

51

experience of ordinary men—their possession of which in fact makes it possible for them to become scientists—yield principally substantive and adjectival constructs directly linked to perception. Constructs having this direct link will be called *observables,* and the terms which refer to them will be called *observation terms.* One of the ways in which the stock of such constructs is enriched, and one which the layman associates very strongly with scientific activity, is by the use of instruments which extend the range of perception, such as telescopes, microscopes, and spectrometers. Such instruments are auxiliary perceptual mechanisms which may be regarded as forming part of the scientist's sensory apparatus while they are being used, and they pose no problems of a philosophical nature which are not posed by that apparatus in its normal form. Once this detail has been mentioned, all the kinds of observation necessary to science have been dealt with. The scientist *sees* nothing in the world which the ordinary man may not see.

The point is important because it is often said that science could not have developed its characteristic method without privileged means of observation, depending on special instruments such as those mentioned above. This is not true; while certain specific theories—such as the germ theory of disease, for example—require the microscope for their serious evaluation, there would be nothing to prevent a science developing which used no such instruments and yet illustrated every principle of the philosophy of science. As a matter of fact, by far the greater proportion of scientific observations is still made with the naked eye. In another sense the dependence of modern science on instrumentation is much more acute, namely when the instrument is used to *produce* the phenomenon to be observed, rather than to observe it. Photographic plates, bubble chambers, pH meters, and the like are indispensable tools without which science could not have advanced to its present state. These are tools of experiment, but an experiment is only an artificial device for putting the observer in a favorable position with respect to nature—a contrivance to have things happen where they can be seen. The happenings are just what they would have been if the circumstances had arisen naturally rather than having been contrived, and the observation similarly is not different in principle from the observation of natural events like lightning or the feeding habits of sea anemones.

The stock of scientific constructs is by no means exhausted, however, when those having counterparts in perception, with or without the help of instruments, have been taken into account. There are two kinds of construct which are indispensable to science but which do not correspond to any permanent features of the world of experience, and they require special treatment. The first kind does have an intermittent perceptual referent; the second, none at all. It will be convenient to start with the easier of the two cases, and with an illustration from ordinary language. It may be said of a man that he is bad-tempered. Now bad temper is not a permanent feature of such a man, open to observation at all times, like being bald or having blue eyes; it is a *disposition* which only becomes apparent under special circumstances, but we feel justified in calling him bad-tempered, even when he is perfectly calm, if the slightest irritation always produces a bad-tempered reaction. On the scientific level, terms like 'soluble', 'conducting', and 'recessive' stand for dispositions, and such terms are called *disposition terms*. Copper sulphate is soluble even in its dry crystalline form, copper is a conductor even when it is not part of an electrical circuit, and the gene for albinism is recessive even when the phenotype is albino.

The definition of constructs in this case presents certain problems. The function of definition is to link the definiendum unambiguously with constructs already established, and in this case enjoying a more stable relation to perception. We might try a definition of 'conducting' as follows:

x is conducting $=_{df}$ if x is attached to one terminal of an ammeter and an e.m.f. applied to the system, the ammeter shows a deflection.

The conditional form reflects the fact that this effect is only to be obtained when the appropriate circumstances are realized. The difficulty arises when we consider the case in which x never is, or perhaps never could be, attached to the terminal of an ammeter. Is the iron in a meteorite which has traveled past the earth and on into space conducting or not, according to this definition? Things are made worse by the fact that, according to the usual interpretation of conditional statements, the whole statement is taken to be true if the antecedent is false; this is why somebody who is not

Dutch can say truly, for example, "If Bruges is in France then I'm a Dutchman." This being the case, it would have to be conceded that according to the definition the best insulator in the world was conducting as long as it was *not* connected to the terminal of an ammeter, and so on.

The solution to this problem requires two steps, the first of which is due to Carnap.[2] In his famous paper "Testability and Meaning" he restricts the applicability of disposition terms to cases which can in principle be brought under the test conditions envisaged in the definition; and he closes the loophole in the definition by rewriting it as a *reduction sentence:*

> If x is attached to one terminal of an ammeter and an e.m.f. applied to the system, then x is conducting if and only if the ammeter shows a deflection.

This is a *bilateral* reduction sentence of the form

> if a then c if and only if b;

it might be necessary to use instead a *reduction pair*

> if a then if b then c
> if d then if e then not c,

if testing for the absence of the disposition required different conditions from testing for its presence. Here a and d are the test conditions, b the sign that c is present and e the sign that it is absent. The pair reduces to a bilateral reduction sentence if a and d are identical and e is the negation of b. This rewriting of the definition destroys it as a definition, since the definiendum is no longer eliminable in cases where the test condition is not met. It might be thought that the main interest of the scientist lay with the cases in which the condition is in fact met, and in part this is true. But the practical application of science often requires that the condition be withheld until the moment when it is needed; if all matches were tested at the factory by being struck on the side of the box, the match industry would soon collapse.

The other step in the solution of the problem takes us back to the chapter on classification and forward to the third part of the book. It is generally assumed that samples are representative of whole populations, and while this assumption cannot be justified here it may be said that if there seems to be good reason, on the grounds of similarity of origin, structure, function or appearance, for classifying objects together, then the dispositions of one of them as revealed when it is brought to test are likely to be shared by the other even though it is not brought to test. The reasonableness of this assumption is testified to by our confidence in matches which have never previously been struck—a confidence which is almost never shaken as long as the matches are dry, and so on. It would be absurd to doubt seriously the reliability of matches as a matter of practice, although, as will be seen later, philosophical reservations are necessary even here.

The other problematic case is that of *theoretical constructs,* that is, constructs which have no direct links to perception at all. These arise normally in the fairly advanced stages of science, although in a purely speculative way they were introduced very early. The atoms of Democritus, for example, had no direct manifestations in experience, but combinations of them, according to his theory, *produced* appearances which men had agreed to call by familiar descriptive names: "For by convention colour exists, by convention bitter, by convention sweet, but in reality atoms and void." [3] This notion that the world might really be constituted by objects quite other than those which appear became rooted in philosophy as the distinction between *appearance* and *reality,* or between two aspects of nature known respectively as *natura naturata* and *natura naturans. Natura naturata* is the finished product—it might be translated 'natured nature', that is, nature clothed in the qualities whose appearance constitutes the surface of things. *Natura naturans,* on the other hand—'naturing nature'—is nature at work behind the scenes *producing* those qualities; and it was the secret of these workings which was so much coveted by the alchemists. Bacon points out that we recognize things for what they are only through their surface properties, so that, if we only knew what secret agency (*naturans*) produced the yellowness, hardness, and so on of gold (*naturata*), we could superinduce these qualities on other materials, and achieve the dream of transmutation. [4] The all-pervading Aristotelian belief in the separability of *matter* and *form* is evident here, as also for example in the theory of transubstantiation (but in the opposite sense) which from this point of view is perfectly plausible. So much may go on beneath the surface; even Hume speaks of "secret powers." [5]

The trouble with these early attempts at guessing what theoretical constructs might account for the complexities of observation was that they provided no link between the two realms, theory and observation, *natura naturans* and *natura naturata*. They were brilliant conjectures, but nothing more. (The same may be said for much more recent theoretical constructs in younger sciences, for example, Freud's id, ego, and superego.) But as scientific investigation penetrated further into the world presented in observation, certain regularities began to suggest possible mechanisms for these secret workings; theories of light, of electricity, of atomic structure, of heredity, began to appeal to waves, particles, fields of force, genes, and so forth which never appeared themselves *but which enabled predictions to be made about what did appear*. So real did these theoretical entities become that Sir Arthur Eddington, in a famous passage, put them on a level with the familiar features of the observed world by speaking of his "two tables"—one a hard, brown, wooden object which could be leaned against and written on, the other a collection of fundamental particles in furious motion which supported the papers on it (also collections of fundamental particles) only by millions of tiny bombardments from beneath.[6] Susan Stebbing made great fun of him for this, although not quite fairly,[7] for there is no reason why the *simple* object, itself an inference from many momentary perspectives, should take precedence over the complex one which is an inference from more minute and technical observations. But there is a difference in the conditions under which we can get to know the two tables. Only the most ordinary sense organs, lighting, and so on are called for in the observation of the hard, wooden table, and such an observation counts as a direct contact with the table. The theoretical table, on the other hand, comes to be known only by analogy with other things—samples of gas, metal, and so forth—which have been induced to yield clicks, flashes, scale-readings, and the like on complicated instruments by suitable manipulations. (Tables or pieces of table are rarely used in these experiments.)

The introduction of theoretical constructs can, I think, be handled by an extension of the device used for dispositions. Suppose Eddington had drawn up his chair to a *collapsible* table; he would hardly have found it necessary to distinguish this from the firm table on which he proceeded to write, and yet collapsing was not a characteristic of that table. If challenged on the point he might have replied that he could make it collapse if he wished, but that for the moment he was using it to write on. And similarly we might say that we could obtain the clicks and flashes indicative of atomic structure if we wished, but that for ordinary purposes the world is best left as it is. The world is disposed to reveal itself as having this structure if certain conditions are imposed upon it. We might thus introduce the theoretical term 'electron' into the language of science by a reduction sentence of the form

> If x passes with a given suitably high velocity through a bubble chamber in a transverse magnetic field of a given strength, then x is an electron if and only if it leaves a track of a given curvature.

Why should such sentences be called *reduction sentences?* They do not, as we have seen, play the part of definitions which enable terms to be *eliminated*—one simply cannot replace theoretical terms with observation terms in cases when test conditions do not hold. But any empirical question which arises about a theoretical construct can be answered (if it can be answered at all) by reference to the observation terms used in the reduction sentence by means of which the theoretical term was introduced. A question about a theoretical construct can be *reduced* to a question about observables. They are not exactly the same question, but whatever is contained in the first question that cannot be answered by an answer to the second, cannot be answered at all from an empirical point of view. It is of course possible that some other connection might be discovered which would relate the construct to other observables not mentioned in its reduction sentence, but that is a different matter. In the case of a disposition term, it might be defined by means of theoretical terms not linked to observation at all but belonging to a set of primitive terms used as the starting point of a deductive theory. For example, given a vocabulary containing 'electron', 'binding energy', and so on, 'conducting' might be defined in terms of the energy necessary to displace electrons inside an atomic lattice. The distinction between theoretical and empirical significance becomes crucial here. Only that part of the theoretical structure, questions about which can be reduced to questions about observables, can be known to be empirically meaningful. The rest —sometimes spoken of as the 'surplus meaning' of the theory— might therefore appear to be dispensable. What science has actually achieved would be unchanged, it might be argued, even if such theoretical superfluities were removed.

This question goes much deeper than at first sight it appears to. To begin with, there is a sense in which all terms are disposition terms; there is always an implicit condition standing as an antecedent to every definition, or even to every attribution of a property, namely the condition that there should be an observer and that he should be equipped with the necessary sensory apparatus, intelligence, and so on to make observation possible. Strictly speaking, only what is actually observed by some actual observer qualifies for description by means of observation terms, and this of course rules out all universal concepts whatever, leaving only particulars bound as to time and place. The very introduction of universals already brings with it a great quantity of 'surplus meaning', namely everything having to do with the world when and where it is not under scientific observation, that is, at most times and in most places. The distinction between observation terms and the others is therefore not quite as radical as it seems to be. Every empirically meaningful question about the world can be reduced to a question about the particular experiences of a particular individual, but most of us do not for that reason suppose that there is no more to the world than our experience of it. In one sense, it would not matter if we did; what we have experienced, or what science has achieved, does not go beyond what we have experienced, or what science has achieved—a fairly trite point. But our attitude toward what we are yet to experience, and the attitude of science toward what it is yet to achieve, will depend very considerably on whether or not we are prepared to think of the world as wider than the content of our experience, and on whether science is prepared to regard as meaningful statements which go beyond what has already been observed. The 'surplus meaning' referred to above contains all the potentiality for scientific development in the future, and is an indispensable part of theory for those who are concerned with the progress of scientific knowledge. None of it, of course, can be taken as final; what is observed in the future may cause us to abandon our theory, to introduce different terms by means of modified reduction sentences. But unless we are simply to sit open-mouthed, waiting for an unintelligible future, we are bound to create theories which go beyond the evidence. And these theories, in fact, not only help to prepare us for what is yet to be discovered, but also put into perspective what is already known.

The principal contrast which emerges from this chapter is in the end that between observables and theoretical constructs, or on the level of language between observation terms and theoretical terms. Dispositions and disposition terms form the bridge between them. These categories are not immutable; not only is it sometimes difficult to decide whether a property is theoretical or dispositional, but also theoretical entities are sometimes found in observation, when for example a planet previously known only as a hypothetical influence on the orbits of other planets is seen through a telescope. But the fact that boundaries are hard to draw does not remove the difference between things separated by them. Objects which behave in special ways under special circumstances may have properties, not ordinarily observable, which account for this behavior. Science will not leave the matter in terms of dispositions if this can be avoided, but will rather try to explain the disposition to react in these ways by reference to theoretical properties which are permanently present. This reflects a conviction that objects, properties, and so on do not come and go, but on the most fundamental level endure unchangingly, or at least that whatever changes may occur do not do so capriciously, but in some orderly and intelligible way. Such a conviction cannot finally be justified; it is, in Whitehead's phrase, the "widespread instinctive conviction in the existence of an *Order of Things*" [8] without which science, or any rational approach to the world, seems to many people inconceivable.

REFERENCES

1. See H. Margenau, *The Nature of Physical Reality* (New York, 1950), p. 69.
2. Rudolf Carnap, "Testability and Meaning," *Philosophy of Science*, 3 (1936) and 4 (1937).
3. Democritus, fragment 125.

4. Francis Bacon, *Novum Organum,* Book II, Aphorism V.
5. David Hume, *Enquiry Concerning Human Understanding,* Section II, Part IV.
6. A. S. Eddington, *The Nature of the Physical World* (London, 1928), introduction.
7. Susan Stebbing, *Philosophy and the Physicists* (London, 1937), p. 54.
8. A. N. Whitehead, *Science and the Modern World* (New York, Mentor ed., 1948), p. 4.

CHAPTER 9

SENTENCES AND PROPOSITIONS

Constructs are only the elements out of which theory is put together, just as terms are only the elements out of which language is put together. We have seen how definition provides links between constructs and between terms, but obviously there is a sense in which, once a definition has been carried out successfully, it does not need to be done again. Any true statement referring to a construct, or containing a term, *could* be made the basis for a definition, but ordinarily such statements are not treated in this way. Most scientific activity consists in using constructs and terms, not in defining them. We must now ask how use is made of them, and into what relations they characteristically enter.

Definitions themselves are obviously special cases of these characteristic relationships. In the case of terms, it is very easy to see what is going on; the definition is a *sentence* of a certain structure, obeying grammatical rules of a particular sort:

fermium $=_{df}$ the element of atomic number 100.

Ordinarily, terms do go in sentences, and when the sentences are not definitions they may be descriptions, or reports of observation, or laws, and so on. On the other hand as *sentences* they are only noises (when spoken) or marks on paper (when written). What enables them to convey information is the fact that the terms in them correspond to concepts (or, in the scientific case, to constructs), so that when heard or read they set off the appropriate reactions in thought. Clearly there is not a one-to-one correspondence between sentences and reactions, even when the sentences are correctly understood: a sentence in English may set off the same reaction in an Englishman as a different sentence in French sets off in a Frenchman—'No smoking' and *'Défense de fumer'*, for example. Even the grammatical structure of the sentences may be different, as that example shows. This has suggested to some people that it may be necessary, in studying language, to pay attention to whole sentences rather than simply to the terms that occur in them. And yet the sentences themselves are somehow unsatisfactory for this purpose. To begin with, the same sentence said on two different occasions is not really the same sentence, any more than two different elephants are the same elephant. This difficulty can be averted by distinguishing between the sentence *type* (corresponding to the species) and the sentence *token* (corresponding to the individual) and saying that when we speak of sentences we really mean the type, not the token. (The same device was used earlier to get over the ambiguity of the term 'word'.) But then the sentence 'Pressure and volume are inversely proportional to one another' cannot even by this distinction be said to be the same as 'The product of pressure and volume is constant', yet they certainly convey the same idea, as does '$p.v. =$ const.' and equivalent statements in French, Russian, and so on. What seems to be needed is a way of talking about *what the sentence is saying* rather than about the sentence itself. If asked what a *term* means, we are ready with an answer—we appeal to its definition, and say that it means either that perceptual object, or that construct, or that other term or expression. But what does a sentence mean? If it is a true sentence, it presumably means a state of affairs—it *designates* a state of affairs, as a term designates an individual object. But one cannot appeal to a state of affairs always, any more than in the case of the term it was possible always to appeal to the object. In that case, recourse was had to the notion of the concept (or later the construct) in its dual function of representative in the absence of the object, and criterion of application in the presence of the object. What is called for here is the conceptual counterpart of the sentence, and whatever it turns out to be it will obviously, because of the parallel between language and thought, display the relationship between constructs which was in question at the beginning of this chapter.

The obvious candidate for this post is the *proposition*, which is ordinarily defined as the meaning of a declarative sentence. (Declarative sentences are those used for assertion, as interrogative sentences are used for questioning, imperative sentences for commanding, and so on.) 'Meaning' here cannot be the state of affairs referred to by the sentence, although that is undoubtedly part of what the sentence means, so that the definition of 'proposition' is ambiguous as it stands. This meaning must in fact be the third element of a three-cornered relationship like that in Fig. 5.3; in this case we would have, instead of 'percept', 'term', and 'concept', the three elements 'state of affairs', 'sentence', and 'proposition'. The proposition is therefore located in thought rather than in language, which is reasonable enough. The consequences of this view have, however, caused some difficulty. The main trouble is that the triangular diagram represents a private individual, and while there is some excuse for supposing that language may be shared with others, at least as far as spoken and written language is concerned, and a rather slimmer excuse for conjecturing that perceptual experience may also be shared, at least as far as its structure is concerned, there is almost no excuse for saying that the region of thought is anything but a private domain inaccessible to anybody except the subject who occupies it. (Some philosophers have tried to make individuals participants in a supra-individual Mind, but they have not had much success, at least in the West.) But if this is the case then there is no transcendent proposition, which sentences (in the public realm of language) express, and, if the matter is carried to its conclusion, no scientific theory either in an objective sense, only a large number of private schemes of constructs, as many as there are scientists. I believe this is to be a true account of the matter, but it is not as bad as it sounds.

First of all, the public nature of language makes it possible for all these schemes of constructs to have, at least up to a point, the same structure—to be *isomorphic* with one another. It might seem a very attractive idea to let language carry the burden of theory, especially as theories, once they are established, are preserved in books. The French philosopher Bachelard has even suggested that there ought to be a special name for the mode of being which ideas may have in books, and has proposed that something existing in this way should be called a 'bibliomenon', as what exists in appearance is called a 'phenomenon'.[1] But books, like the terms and sentences they contain, need interpretation. When one reads and understands a theory, one does not merely repeat the symbols to oneself—one endows them with conceptual content. This content, as has been pointed out before, is an individual matter, but it is essential to the process; the theory cannot be anything but an empty formalism without it. We may say, then, that theories are made up of propositions, which are made up of constructs, and that all this is private, but that language is made up of sentences, which are made up of terms, and that this is to a certain extent public. Secondly, it is still possible to talk about scientific theory in general, or about a particular theory (for example, the quantum theory), but what must be meant in this case is a set of partially isomorphic conceptual schemes held by scientists, or in the latter case by quantum physicists. The better the isomorphism, the stronger the agreement between different workers in the field. Not every conceptual scheme, nor every such set of conceptual schemes, deserves the title 'scientific theory'; later on we shall place some restrictions on what kind of observations, for example, will be allowed to generate theories, and in general (there have to be exceptions in the case of genius) a conceptual scheme which has no parts in common with the schemes of other scientists will not be admitted as a theory. Science is after all a cooperative activity. But none of this militates against the view that science exists nowhere except in scientists' heads, and that in the end it exists there privately.

The term which has most frequently been used up to this point when speaking of sentences or propositions is *statement*. A statement is, strictly speaking, the *assertion* of a proposition, and the vehicle for this assertion is of course the corresponding sentence. Empirical and systematic truth, which were said in Chapter 2 to be properties of statements, are now seen to be so only because they are also properties of propositions. The passage from some perceptual experience to a true statement about it proceeds via the formation of a proposition out of the appropriate concepts, stimulated by observation of the corresponding percepts in association with one another; the assent to the proposition as true constitutes a *judgment* which is irreducible to anything else. The proposition having been formulated and assented to as true may then be stated by uttering the sentence. Of course, we frequently come to know propositions not by observation of percepts in the usual sense at all, but by hearing or reading sentences—that is, by the perception of certain special kinds of object, namely the sentences. In this case the sentences belong to perception as well as to language, which is in keeping with the origin of language itself in signs, which, as was remarked in Chapter 5, are percepts with a special function.

A proposition then consists of concepts in relation, just as a state of affairs consists of percepts in relation and a sentence of terms in relation. The rules of grammar, however, prevent the phrase 'blue cat', for example, from being regarded as a sentence, and yet it undoubtedly stands for concepts in relation. The view taken here is that 'blue cat' is in fact a genuine proposition, but that it is what might be called a static proposition; nothing happens to the concepts, whereas in the usual way of things thought is active, and the relations between concepts dynamic. One could make a sentence for the proposition 'blue cat' by saying 'There is a blue cat' or something of that sort. But most propositions are time-colored—'the blue cat jumps'. In perception, as in thought, there are no totally time-free entities. This is best seen, of course, in the case of processes and sequences; but even objects and their properties are experienced as embedded in a passage of time. An instantaneous experience would be no experience at all, and the present, as has often been pointed out, has a certain thickness—it is always a 'specious present' of longer or shorter duration, depending on the tempo of events. In restrospect, we can break down this stretch of time as finely as we please, but while it is going on it is, to use another expression of Whitehead's,[2] "divisible but not divided." In language, however, this kind of temporal quality is almost entirely lacking, and has to be expressed by tensed verbs and participles which, as terms, are no more colored with time than nouns and adjectives. It takes no longer to say 'aeon' than to say 'instant'.

There is another sense in which the reflection of perception and thought in language runs into difficulty. Language of course *has* its own brand of temporality; it is in fact a one-dimensional process in time, term following term—what Suzanne Langer calls a 'discursive form'.[3] But perception and thought may involve complex many-dimensional relationships. Perception is limited to three dimensions in space and one in time, within which Mrs. Langer's 'presentational forms' occur; thought can probably be even more complex. It may take hours for a scientist to report, discursively, an event which occupied a few seconds, and scientists often have to store up, on photographic plates, tapes, drums, and so on, all the data from such an event, so that they can be scanned at leisure. *Propositions* do not have to be discursive, *sentences* do; *terms* cannot simply reflect temporality, *concepts* or *constructs* can. This is the point at which thought differs most strikingly from language, and it is the point at which philosophy most often comes to grief. The view that language bears a simple relation to fact (held, for example, by Wittgenstein in his early days, although he later repudiated it)[4] forces upon the world all the logical and grammatical exigencies of language, which do not properly belong to the world at all but only to our attempts at communicating our knowledge of it.

REFERENCES

1. Gaston Bachelard, *L'Activité Rationaliste de la Physique Contemporaine* (Paris, 1951), p. 6.
2. A. N. Whitehead, *Process and Reality* (London, 1929), p. 96.
3. Suzanne Langer, *Philosophy in a New Key* (New York, Mentor ed., 1948), pp. 75 ff.
4. Ludwig Wittgenstein, *Tractatus Logico-Philosophicus* (London, 1933), p. 64 (4.014).

CHAPTER 10

THE CORRELATION OF PERCEPTION, THOUGHT, AND LANGUAGE

In spite of the reflections of the last chapter, there must be, nevertheless, some sense in which language mirrors the world not entirely alien to the sense in which thought mirrors it, since language is used to convey thought, and does so (as far as we can tell) more or less faithfully. The relations between thought, language,

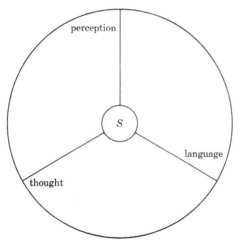

FIG. 10.1.

and perception may be clarified by the accompanying diagram (Fig. 10.1), in which they are represented by three segments of a circle. The small central circle represents the subjective pole of experience; from this vantage point we may conduct an examination of the world of perception, or of language, or of concepts, but it does not belong to any of them. What lies outside the large circle is everything unperceived, unheard of, and unthought of—in other words, most of what there is. One might want to call it 'natural reality', although to some extent what is perceived, spoken of, and thought of is also natural and real; the difference is that what falls within the circle is submitted to human reason and takes on its characteristic structure. Inside the small circle and outside the large one is what the German philosopher Jaspers has called *das Umgreifende*, "the Encompassing," [1] which is always beyond whatever we have been able to grasp with reason (in our case by means of science). It cannot be subjected to scientific scrutiny—if it were, it would fall within the circle. Earle illustrates this point by imagining people with flashlights, and somebody directing their attention to the darkness which surrounds them; they say, "Where is it?" and point their flashlights in all directions, looking for the darkness.[2] Of course they do not find it, just as with the tools of science one can find neither the subjectivity of the individual nor the ultimate being of the world. The circumference of the large circle corresponds to what the American historian of science Gillispie has called the "edge of objectivity";[3] as science advances it takes in more and more of natural reality, but there is always a good deal left. Nearly every scientist has felt the smallness of that circle; Newton spoke for all of them in confessing that he felt like "a boy, playing on the seashore, and diverting myself in now and then finding a smoother pebble or a prettier shell than ordinary, while the great ocean of truth lay all undiscovered before me." [4] That is not to be interpreted, however, as meaning that there is any better way than the scientific way of exploring truth. Science ought to be aware of its limitations, but it remains the only equipment so far invented for discovering empirically true statements about the natural world. Restrictions on the scope of science are not to be made an excuse for superstitious nonsense.

The main virtue of such a *symmetrical* diagram is its suggestion that the ground covered by perception, by language, and by concepts is in some way the same ground. The three-cornered diagram of meaning on page 32 can obviously be superimposed upon the circle (see Fig. 10.2), and relationships (such as causality, for example) may be illuminated by reference to the diagram, where it can be seen how the causal relation among percepts, the category of causality in concepts, and the logical relation between cause statements and effect statements, are to be distinguished from one another and yet refer to the same relationship in natural reality. There are three segments to the circle, but only one world; each segment represents one way of grasping the world. In concepts and in language there will sometimes be elements not found in per-

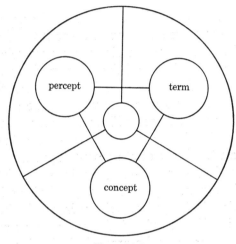

FIG. 10.2.

ception (theoretical constructs and terms) which are nevertheless taken to refer to real objects and events. The internal structures of the three segments will exhibit at least a partial isomorphism or similarity of form, and it is the hope of science that all three show some isomorphism with natural reality, although as has been pointed out this can never be known directly. If there is any objection to this talk of natural reality, it can be dropped without affecting the main argument of this book, although in fact most scientists are realists and have good reasons for being so.

Starting from perception, which is regarded as a gross smoothing over of the surface of reality (owing to the crudity of our sense organs), science proceeds to the construction of conceptual schemes whose order reflects the order of perception, and links these with specialized languages for the purpose of making predictions, and so on. In the course of this, it becomes necessary to say that events are taking place which are too fast or too small to be detected, and if one is not a realist it is difficult to see how this can be the case except in a sort of fictitious way. The real objects corresponding to fully theoretical constructs and terms are taken here to lie as it were in the interstices of perception, or to be in some other way systematically concealed from observation, for example, by lying outside the range of sense. No new assumption is involved here beyond the original hypothesis of the existence of an external world in Chapter 3.

In what sense can these three realms really be said to be isomorphic with one another? The notion was introduced in the last chapter as holding between the linguistic expressions of what is known to different scientists, and there it is perhaps too tentative a term—to the extent that language is public and the knowledge genuinely shared, different scientists will use the *same* expressions, not merely *similar* ones. There will be differences in detail and in scope—some scientists know more than others, or know it better—but a common central body of statements for each of the sciences. And these themselves overlap—physics into chemistry, chemistry into biology, biology into psychology, psychology into sociology. What in fact exists in language, written in all the books and journals in all the scientific libraries, is far more than could possibly be taken in by any one man, and a great deal of it is actively taken in by none. The latter therefore remains as a collection of signs no more significant, for the time being, than the voice crying in the wilderness—less so, in fact, since presumably the crier knew what he was up to.

This at least establishes one point about the circular diagram, namely that language can exist without thought or perception, and therefore deserves a segment of its own. Clearly thought does too; it is involved in the appropriation of what is spoken or written, but this evokes nothing apparent in the hearer or reader, or at least it need not. Examples of thought without perception or language cannot of course be offered here—the reader will have to supply his own. And perception also can stand alone, without thought or language, although this is harder to show. Perception after all was defined as sensation with something added, and it might look as if this was already thought. But in the condition known as *awareness*, in the course of many forms of *activity*, and in aesthetic experience, we are able to concentrate on perception to the exclusion of language and conceptual thought; the contents of perception are grasped in a form which makes them suitable for thought, without in fact leading to it, the experience being immediate and complete in itself. Each of the three segments, therefore, can stand without the other two. But this independence never lasts long, and in particular the dependence of thought and the use of language on perception has been dramatically exhibited in sensory deprivation experiments, so that there is some plausibility too in their fitting tightly together.

But the question of isomorphism *between* the three (whatever this may mean) has been put off and must now be taken up again. In logic two systems are said to be isomorphic if every element of one system can be matched with a unique element of the other, and vice versa, according to some rule, and if furthermore every relation linking elements of one is matched by a relation linking the corresponding elements of the other. The elements and relations need bear no resemblance to one another, but the internal arrangements of the systems must have a formal likeness. The question then is, Does there exist a rule for matching elements of perception with elements of thought, elements of thought with elements of language, elements of language with elements of perception, and vice versa in each case? And are relations in each realm matched by relations in each of the others? Reflection on the development in the foregoing chapters shows, in fact, that this is the case; the system has been put together in just this way. A rule linking language with thought and perception can be found in definition—it is the rule which governs the use of language for the expression of thought and the description of perception, and it provides, in the ideal case of a formalized language, exactly the one-to-one correspondences called for. And a rule linking thought and perception can be found in concept formation—it is the rule by which perception stimulates thought and thought recognizes and represents objects of perception. ('Rule' here is of course a shorthand for a set of rules.) These relationships were not, it is true, set up *as* rules, and it might be impossible to carry through, except for the simplest of systems, the notion of a *strict* isomorphism. But the definition of isomorphism was borrowed from logic only to show that the use of the term here is not altogether inappropriate, and this will be achieved if the second condition, namely, the matching of relations, can be met in the same way. Clearly it can; we have logical and grammatical relations in language, spatial and temporal relations in perception, and whatever psychological theory calls for in thought. These various elements are given diagrammatically in Fig. 10.3.

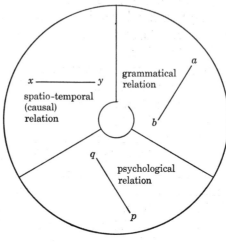

spatio-temporal (causal) relation — x ———— y

grammatical relation — a — b

psychological relation — q — p

FIG. 10.3.

This isomorphism is only partial, of course. We have already discussed elements of thought and language not corresponding to anything in perception, we saw earlier that any attempt at rendering perception in language or thought is bound to leave something out, and there are thoughts which cannot be expressed in language, and linguistic expressions which correspond to nothing in thought. This autonomy of the realms is not unexpected in the light of the earlier discussion, but it does not in any way spoil the account. Science simplifies, and it also elaborates; and there are other things besides science.

REFERENCES

1. Karl Jaspers (tr. William Earle), *Reason and Existenz* (New York, Noonday ed.), 1955, pp. 51 ff.
2. *Ibid.*, p. 14.
3. C. G. Gillispie, *The Edge of Objectivity* (Princeton, 1960).
4. Brewster's *Memoirs of Newton*, vol. II, ch. XXVII.

CHAPTER 11

PROTOCOL SENTENCES, GENERALIZATIONS, AND HYPOTHESES

It was remarked in an earlier chapter that in principle the scientist enjoys no advantage over the ordinary man in matters of observation, since both of them have the same sensory apparatus, and the ordinary man could, if he wanted, look into the eyepiece of a spectrometer or watch the screen of an oscilloscope. They *see* the same thing. This is true, of course, but in a sense it is misleading. The newborn child of Chapter 3 sees the same thing too, as far as that goes, but just as it does not take in what it sees, being unable to distinguish the recurring and stable features of the world from the evanescent and insignificant ones, so the ordinary man is lost in the laboratory. The advantage of the man over the child is an advantage of experience (in the sense of practice) and of education, and the scientist enjoys a similar advantage over the ordinary man. He has had practice in recognition and discrimination, and he has learned to classify and define. He is thus able to do what the ordinary man is quite incapable of doing in similar circumstances, namely to write down what he sees explicitly and unambiguously.

The sentence in which he records his observation will contain no terms except observation terms and grammatical or logical connectives, and it will be *singular,* referring to some perceptual object or state of affairs located in space and time. Such a sentence, used to assert that something is in fact the case, will be called a *protocol sentence.* Not all grammatically correct singular sentences made up of observation terms will be accepted, of course, as protocol sentences; in particular, we insist on two conditions. A protocol sentence must be such that a decision as to its empirical truth or falsity can be reached after a finite number of observations, and it must be invariant between different observers, that is, it must be *intersubjectively corroborated*. A whole set of philosophical problems, some of which we have already encountered, is posed by these requirements. For example, it is assumed that an object under examination endures, and that an event can be repeated, so that successive observations can be made of it, and that there is such a thing as empirical truth which is common to different observers. Sometimes protocol sentences have to be accepted even though it has actually not been possible to get the corroboration of another observer; in such cases the scientist would beware of sentences of a totally new *kind,* but be ready to accept at least tentatively protocol sentences of a sort that had been made frequently and were familiar. These sentences do not have to be subject-predicate sentences. They can also be class-inclusion sentences, used to assert, for example, that some object is a member of a class of objects all of which have a certain property; or relation-sentences, used to assert that some relationship holds between two or more objects or events. And they may even be simple existential sentences, used to assert merely that some object is present in the field of perception.

A set of protocol sentences—perhaps drawn from an interview or an experiment—constitutes a *protocol.* The use of the term 'protocol' to mean any empirical record, and of the expression 'protocol sentence' to mean any sentence in observation language which by virtue of being corroborated has been admitted to the empirical record, is a widely accepted but somewhat looser version of their original use among members of the Vienna Circle.[1] For them, *'Protokollsatz'* meant a bare phenomenalistic assertion about sense-data —'blue here at time *t*', for example. This kind of minimum assertion was in keeping with the view, held by some workers in this group, that the only way to guarantee that science did not fly off into speculation but dealt only with what was positively assured (thus fulfilling the positivistic program to which the group adhered) was to found it on unvarnished sense-datum statements. Here, on the other hand, we draw the vocabulary of observation from a stock of terms whose meanings are conventionally agreed upon by scientists—a refined version of what Carnap calls the "thing-language." [2] And this is not so dangerous a proceeding by comparison; there may be closer agreement among scientists about the meaning of 'crystalline' than among ordinary men about the meaning of 'blue'.

The conventions involved in formulating protocol sentences go a little further than those involved in straightforward definition. In particular, problems of consistency arise in borderline cases which for the sake of getting the empirical record down are settled arbitrarily. A familiar example occurs in the reading of meters where there is doubt as to the exact position of the needle, or when it is midway between two markings; the convention is 'unless the needle is obviously below the center read the next higher figure'. Such conventions, which may be called 'techniques of protocol', are familiar to all experimental scientists.[3] Also there are techniques for collapsing many observations into a single protocol sentence, for example, by taking the mean of a series of readings and computing the standard error. This yields a statement of decidable truth-value and invariant between observers, as long as all the observers use the same convention. In some sciences the establishment of such conventions is itself a matter for theoretical controversy; and it must be realized, of course, that since the point of making observations in the first place (at least in scientific research as opposed to the routine use of science) is to suggest or establish or refute some theory, the observational vocabulary itself is likely to be colored by the theory. This does not matter as long as the invariance between observers, insisted upon above, extends in principle to at least the majority of workers in the field. Every observer's observation is private and subjective, but the corroboration of others provides an *intersubjectivity* which is the nearest science gets to the 'objectivity' so often claimed for it. Of course we might all be deceived about what is really the case. But even if there were *really* no such things as galvanometers, the corroborated galvanometer readings of a sufficiently large population of scientists would form an acceptable basis for certain parts of electromagnetic theory. We would all believe in ghosts if we could all see them.

There is a sense in which all protocol sentences are existential—they reflect the existence of some object, event, or state of affairs, while at the same time characterizing it in a determinate way. And all existential sentences are bound in space and time (with the possible exception of those referring to the universe as a whole, which could hardly serve as protocol sentences for the ordinary scientist), so that even if there were not practical limitations on the extent of individual observations this kind of sentence by itself could not attain the universality required for science. Observation is indispensable to science, but the most elegant protocol is not yet science; it awaits connection to the general statements through which its relation to other protocols can be seen. The general statement, however, must have the kind of affinity with the protocol which makes this connection possible.

Suppose a series of observations of some class of object, say A, to have been made, with a view to determining whether or not the members of this class have some property, say B. The result of these observations will be a series of protocol sentences, 'This A is B', 'This A is B', and so on. In order to avoid confusion, the observer is likely to try to identify the A's in some way so as to keep them distinct from one another, so that the sentences will read 'A_1 is B', 'A_2 is B'. . . . 'A_n is B'. Suppose further that, among a large number of such observations, no A has been found which is not B, and also that no A-like objects are known which exhibit great variety in B-like properties. Men have a tendency, in such situations, to jump from the collection of singular statements about A_1, A_2, . . . to a universal statement about the class of A's: All A's are B. Such a jump is called a *generalization,* and the sentence which results from it will be called an *empirical generalization.*

The justification for such a jump will not occupy us here—it will be dealt with in Part III. We now wish to know what relationship holds between an empirical generalization and the protocol sentences from which it arises. It is quite clear that one protocol sentence of the form 'A_i is not B' (called a *contrary instance*) is enough to ruin the empirical generalization 'All A's are B', while no additional number of sentences of the form 'A_j is B' (called *confirming instances*) will be sufficient to remove the possibility of an adverse case (unless all the A's are examined, in which case 'All A's are B' ceases to be an empirical generalization and becomes merely a shorthand way of writing a rather long protocol sentence). As a matter of fact we rarely require large numbers of instances before generalizing, as long as the second of the conditions mentioned above is fulfilled. A famous case in which it was not fulfilled was that of the generalization 'All swans are white', which was widely accepted until the discovery of Australia, which turned out to have many black swans. But swan-like objects (birds) were certainly known which exhibited great variety in white-like properties (colors), so that it would have been wise not to place too much reliance on the generalization. Probably no one did—it is not a very important or interesting generalization. At any rate, the first black swan discredited it for ever. Now the sentence 'A$_i$ is not B', which, as we have seen, is singular, is a special case of another sentence, 'Some A's are not B', which is known as a *particular* sentence ('some' in this case means 'at least one'), and in traditional logic particular sentences have the property of being the *contradictories* of universal sentences when one is affirmative and the other negative. This suggests that an empirical generalization might be defined as 'any sentence whose contradictory has the form of a protocol sentence'. (We say 'has the form of' rather than 'is' since, in the case of a true generalization, a contradictory protocol sentence could arise only by mistake.) But there are other cases of empirical generalizations on which this must be tested before it is accepted.

It may often be the case that the relationship between events which is directly observed and about which a protocol sentence is formulated is a relation of temporal succession. Such a protocol sentence might read 'A, and B following after'. The empirical generalization which will arise out of a series of sentences of this sort will be 'whenever A, then B following after'. This is equivalent to saying 'If A, then B', since what it does is to assert a constant relationship between A and B, which in this case happens to be a temporal one. (The same kind of relationship might of course hold between contemporary events.) Appealing again to traditional logic, in which this sentence is known as a conditional sentence or *implication,* one finds that the contradictory of 'If A, then B' is 'A, but not B', and this clearly has the form of a protocol sentence, being in fact just that protocol sentence which would be obtained if for some reason B failed to follow or accompany A. The definition therefore works for conditionals too. Neither of these extremely simple examples, however, constitutes a very severe test, because although both kinds of sentence are of fundamental importance, in practice there are generally complications. In particular, there are many cases in which association between A and B is not invariable but only frequent. Suppose, for example, that in a series of α A's β are found to be B, or to be followed by B, what kind of generaliza-

tion can be expected to emerge? Fortunately, it can be shown that
such cases reduce to the previous ones, in the following way: Instead of writing a protocol sentence for every observation, suppose
one to be written (according to one of the conventions mentioned
above) only after a *fixed* number α of observations—'This series of
α A's contains β which are B'. As these protocols accumulate, suppose the mean of all the B's to be calculated, and suppose further
that no value of B differs from this mean by a number greater than
some number ϵ. As before, an empirical generalization suggests itself: 'All series of α A's contain $[\beta \pm \epsilon]$ which are B'. This can be
contradicted by the protocol sentence 'This series of α A's contains
a number lying outside the interval $[\beta - \epsilon, \beta + \epsilon]$ which are B'.
Of course, if ϵ is large—especially if it is comparable to β—this
would not be a very significant generalization. At this stage, however, we are concerned merely to study the form of the statement,
not its content.

All the sentences so far dealt with are formulated in observation
language, and contain only terms which name percepts (objects
with their properties and relations, and so on) besides grammatical
terms, such as 'this', 'all', 'is', 'if . . . then' ('this' might be considered to name a perceptual relation, but that is not important
here). Terms which name percepts we have agreed to call observation terms, since they refer to what is directly observed. It is not
very hard, however, to find in scientific sentences terms which are
neither observation terms nor grammatical terms (in which class,
for the time being, we include logical and mathematical terms),
but which nevertheless *seem* to refer to objects and events. Consider, for example, the sentence 'The mass of the electron is
9.107×10^{-28} grams'. Obviously the truth of this sentence rests in
some way on observation, but the term 'electron' names nothing that
is available for inspection by an observer. If we assume that there are
electrons and that they have such a mass, calculations about various experiments in physics come out right, and explanations are
provided for some otherwise unaccountable elements of observation
like tracks in cloud chambers and on photographic plates, but the
relationship between sentences about electrons and protocol sentences about photographic plates is clearly not the same as that
between empirical generalizations and protocol sentences. Sentences

about electrons are interesting because of what follows from them, not because of particular cases of them.

Unlike empirical generalizations, sentences about such unobservable objects are invulnerable in the face of contrary instances. 'The mass of the electron is 9.107×10^{-28} grams', which, formulated to look like the other universal sentences we have considered, would read 'All electrons have a mass of 9.107×10^{-28} grams', is clearly in no danger of being confronted by a protocol sentence saying 'This electron does not have a mass of 9.107×10^{-28} grams'. But from that universal sentence, together with some other universal sentences about the charge on the electron and the behavior of moving charged bodies in magnetic fields, another universal sentence can be inferred which *is* vulnerable to contrary instances, namely a sentence about electron tracks obtained under certain conditions in magnetic fields. The second sentence is an empirical generalization, since electron tracks are perceptual objects. The first sentence we will call a *hypothesis,* defined as 'any sentence which has as a consequence at least one empirical generalization, but whose contradictory does not have the form of a protocol sentence', or, since (as is evident in the case just given) the hypothesis may need some supplementary sentences before an empirical generalization can be inferred from it, 'any sentence which, together with any set S of other sentences, has as a consequence at least one empirical generalization which is not a consequence of S alone, but whose contradictory does not have the form of a protocol sentence'. The original formulation follows from this if S is the empty set. Hypotheses of course always contain theoretical terms, since any universal sentence containing only observation terms would necessarily have a protocol-type sentence for its contradictory.

Not all sentences containing theoretical terms, or propositions about theoretical constructs, are hypotheses—only those from which empirical generalizations follow. There might, it is true, be some sentence whose consequences were empirical generalizations of such a kind that we lacked the intelligence or ingenuity to discover them, but in this case the sentence could not be distinguished from one which had no such consequences; for us it would not be a genuine hypothesis. Such sentences cannot, strictly speaking, belong to science at all. If later on they prove to have testable consequences, they become scientific; and in the same way, if a scientific sentence whose consequences we can now test turns out not really to lead to them, we would have to reject it. It is evident therefore that what is called scientific is relative to the state of knowledge at the time. This must be so, because many theories which used to be regarded as scientifically reputable have been discarded—the phlogiston theory, for example, or the theory of spontaneous generation, or the theory of the luminiferous ether. It is to be noticed that scientific status is denied to sentences not on grounds of *falsity* (since empirical generalizations can be false, and therefore derivable from false hypotheses) but on grounds of *irrelevance*. The truth or falsity of a sentence does not affect its logical classification, and tests of truth or falsity on empirical grounds do not belong to logic. Here we are interested in what kind of structure a theory has, not whether the theory is correct, which is a problem for Part III.

In this connection, it must be pointed out that the meaning of 'hypothesis' given here differs slightly from its traditional meaning. Generalizations may be put forward 'hypothetically', in the sense that their truth is not certain but tentative, and sometimes any generalization which is not yet strongly confirmed is called a 'hypothesis'. But all generalizations are *confirmable* in exactly the same way, and this differs from the way in which hypotheses, in our sense, may be confirmed. The difference in the *method* of confirmation seems to warrant a difference in terminology, but I do not think the difference in *degree* of confirmation warrants one. Logically speaking, a generalization is a generalization whether it is true, false, probable, or improbable; in any case it is tied down to actual or possible observations, the reports of which, even for statistical generalizations, will be particular cases of the universal expressed in the generalization. Hypotheses, on the other hand, have no particular cases, and are therefore tentative in a quite different way from weakly confirmed generalizations. Of course, a hypothesis may become a generalization through the refinement of techniques of observation. Sometimes other kinds of sentence—even singular sentences—are called 'hypotheses' when they are put forward as tentative accounts (for example, the hypothesis that a particular murder was committed with a carving knife). It is pointless to try to be rigorous about terminology in such cases, but if the expression 'working hypothesis' is used no confusion need arise. The distinction made here between 'hypothesis' and 'empirical generalization' is reinforced if one considers how they are arrived at. Generalizations emerge naturally after a large enough number of particular observations, while hypotheses have to be invented. Anybody can make the jump from 'many' to 'all', but it takes genius to jump, as J.J. Thomson did, from the discharge of electricity in gases to the electron.

Every sentence of science falls into one or another of these categories: protocol sentences, empirical generalizations, or hypotheses. In some highly developed sciences, however, the stage of generalization has been almost completely eliminated, at least with respect to new discoveries. The systematic outlines are so clear that observations—sometimes very few observations—may be immediately referred to the network of hypotheses for explanation. A generalization is implicitly present; one could always repeat the experiment a few more times, and draw attention more directly to the observable regularity. But once or twice is enough, and instead of stating the result in terms of observables the physicist, for example, accounts for it at once as an interaction between theoretical entities. This shows a confidence in the *repeatability* of observations which is little short of astounding; what grounds there are for such confidence will be discussed in Part III.

REFERENCES

1. The original use is discussed in two articles by O. Neurath and R. Carnap in *Erkenntnis* III (1932-1933), pp. 204-228. Since that time the expression occurs frequently in the literature of the philosophy of science.
2. R. Carnap, "Testability and Meaning."
3. See B. Schultzer (tr. Fausbøll), *Observation and Protocol Statement* (Copenhagen, 1938).

CHAPTER 12

LAWS, PRINCIPLES, AND THEORY

An examination of the grammatical construction and vocabulary of any sentence of science should be enough to place it in the appropriate category according to the criteria laid down in the last chapter, but that will not give any hint as to the truth or falsity of the sentence. That problem will be taken up in Part III, where it will be seen that no universal sentence which actually says anything about the world can be certainly known to be true. Yet all the sentences of scientific theory must be universal sentences; protocol sentences, as we saw earlier, are only the anchors of theory in observation, and cannot be included in theory except as instances of empirical generalizations. It has sometimes been said that such existential sentences as 'There exists an upper limit to all velocities, namely the velocity of light' are exceptions to this rule of universality. The logical questions involved cannot be gone into here, but clearly a sentence of this sort is not singular, as can be seen by contrasting it with 'There exists a mouse which is in the cupboard'. The velocity of light is a universal limit of velocity in the same way as the law of gravitation is a universal relation between massive bodies.

A true empirical generalization, either affirmative (All A's are B) or conditional (If A then B), is called a *law*. But from what was said above it follows that by this definition there are no such things as scientific laws, or at least that there cannot be known to be such things. We therefore change the definition of law very slightly to avoid this difficulty, and say that a scientific law is an empirical generalization which is *accepted* as true. The logical status of the scientific law depends on its being a generalization and nothing else, but its historical status depends on what scientists of the period believe, and this I think reflects what we mean by 'scientific law'. We would not want to say that there were no such things as scientific laws, but we would want to admit that sometimes some apparently true generalizations (as we now believe) have not been accepted as laws, while others which later turned out to be false were accepted.

The problem posed by the narrow interpretation of 'law' as 'true generalization' has sometimes been solved in another way, namely by asserting that laws are not to be taken as universal statements at all but rather as 'inference-licenses'. According to this view, 'All A's are B' says nothing about the class of A's but expresses merely a kind of official approval of the inference, for any given A, that it is also a B. This certainly avoids the difficulty that no general statement can be conclusively verified, but it seriously weakens the meaning that scientists themselves have usually wished to attach to the laws they have enunciated. It embodies in fact a logical caution quite foreign to science. Events may prove him wrong, but for what it is worth the scientist *does* wish to say something about the class of A's. Of course, his assertion carries with it implicit approval of any future inference from A to B, and to that extent the inference-license view is correct. But it is trivially correct, because the law is prepared, subject to empirical rectification, to make all such future inferences here and now.

If the definition of 'law' as 'accepted generalization' is agreed upon, it will be seen that to talk about 'the immutable laws of nature' is meaningless, and this may cause some temporary discomfort—are not *such* laws just what science is seeking? The answer to this question is, in a sense, that science is seeking immutable laws, and may even have found some, but that no law, however firmly established, can ever be *known* to be immutable. The lesson of history is quite plain. On a number of occasions, it has seemed that some science was on the point of final completion, nature having all but yielded up its ultimate secret. The last such occasion was at the end of the nineteenth century in physics, when Kelvin announced the imminent end of fundamental research. Hardly anything remained to be done. There were just a few oddities which were either accidental or were sure to yield to minor investigation—a fogged photographic plate or two in the laboratories of Röntgen and Becquerel, a slight difficulty in the theory of energy-distribution in the spectrum, an anomalous result in an experiment designed by Michelson to measure the earth's velocity relative to the ether. But physics does not seem to learn its lesson; the same hints at finality have quite recently been heard from some of the Copenhagen quantum physicists.

This conception of the laws of nature, which nature must obey, probably springs from the belief that the world is the creation of a rational mind, a Supreme Lawgiver, or the like. This is an innocent but useless belief. Unless such a lawgiver chose to reveal his laws by divine grace, or something of that sort, they would be just as inaccessible to us as any other universal truth. And if we reflect on the fact that accurate observation of the world is by the most generous estimate only a few thousand years old, and the fragment of the universe open to our detailed examination by the most generous estimate only a few light-years across, any claim to universal knowledge seems preposterous. Nevertheless, some laws seem so inherently plausible and have become so firmly embedded in the historical structure of science that they *seem* certainly true—Newton's laws, for instance, which Pope celebrated in his familiar couplet:

> Nature and Nature's laws lay hid in Night
> God said, "Let Newton be!" and all was light.

In particular, the second law, expressed in the equation

$$f = ma$$

—that is, acceleration takes place in the direction of the impressed force, and is proportional to that force and inversely proportional to the mass of the body accelerated—lies at the root of all physics. But if this is taken as an expression of empirical relations, for example, between the thrust of a rocket engine and the mass and acceleration of the rocket as quantities known independently, it is subject to the same limitations as any other empirical generalization. It may, of course, be taken as a definition of force in Newton's system, and thus *stipulated* as true, but if this is the case then it cannot be said with certainty to apply to the world. The whole system may contain a flaw; and, as we know, it does, when stretched to its limits in the direction of the very fast or the very large—a

fact which prompted Sir John Squire to write his equally familiar
sequel to Pope:

> It did not last; the Devil, howling "Ho!
> Let Einstein be!" restored the status quo.

The distinction between hypotheses and empirical generalizations
suggests a distinction between two different kinds of scientific law,
one corresponding to empirical generalizations which are accepted
as true and the other to hypotheses which are accepted as true. In
the latter category would fall, for instance, the law of conservation
of energy; energy is not observed, but rather the penetration of
bullets or the compression of springs, so that any statement about
it must be hypothetical. But it is more usual to speak of the *principle* of the conservation of energy, and this usage may be taken to
embody the distinction in question. Principles are hypotheses accepted as suitable starting points for theoretical work. Ordinary
language, it is true, restricts the term 'principle' to a few important
and widely used hypotheses, but as far as that goes it similarly restricts the term 'law' to a few important and widely used generalizations. All generalizations accepted as true have the status of
laws, and all hypotheses accepted as true have the status of principles, but only those which have won general and historic acceptance
are commonly referred to as such. But the distinction cannot be
pushed too far in ordinary language, since although Kepler's laws
according to this account would remain laws, Newton's laws, because of their introduction of the theoretical term 'force', would
have to be called principles—not that Newton would have objected
to that.

The problem of distinguishing between law and definition acquires an added complexity when hypothetical principles are introduced: if the constructs are invented and theoretical in the first
place, surely their interrelation must have been *stipulated* in the
hypothesis, which as we have seen is invulnerable to direct contradiction. The ambiguity of lawlike or *nomological* statements
(among which, of course, are hypotheses) involved here has caused
some confusion, but it is not difficult to clear it up. The same statement can at different times and under different circumstances be
a principle, a definition, or a law. If its truth is *asserted* and not
considered liable to empirical challenge, it is a definition; if not—

that is, if it is taken to be empirically significant—then it is a principle if it contains theoretical terms, otherwise a law. A principle turns into a law if what before could not be observed becomes observable by virtue of some advance in experimental technique.

There would be no point in insisting on a hard and fast distinction between 'law' and 'principle', and the latter may be objected to as inappropriate in the empirical sciences, suggesting as it does something known *a priori,* reminiscent of Aristotelian 'first principles', and so forth. As a matter of fact, of course, principles do play the role of the *a priori* with respect to the scientific system in which they occur, since *within* that system they cannot be challenged—the system itself depends on them, and a change in principles leads to a new system. For this reason, they have sometimes been called 'functionally *a priori*'. There may perhaps be a tendency to forget that this certainty is only relative, and to conclude that principles embody final truths about the world. But in fact it is only in physics and physical chemistry, which reached an advanced stage of development comparatively early, that this problem arises acutely. In most other cases—for example, the principles of heredity or of economics—the empirical and hence fallible nature of the statement is obvious.

If a world were to be built which was, as it were, legally compelled to behave according to the laws and principles of science as we have come to accept them, it would, as far as we can tell, behave as our world behaves. Descartes, after following a procedure not unlike this to account for the present state of the world, was compelled to add: "I was not, however, disposed, from these circumstances, to conclude that this world had been created in the manner I described; for it is much more likely that God made it at the first such as it was to be." [1] But then Galileo had just been tried before the Inquisition. We do not need to make such gestures of conformity, and we claim, in fact, that theory is as nearly as we can make it so *a replica, in constructs and language, of the real world.* It is not, of course, an exact replica, which would be just as hard to understand as the world is, besides not being able to be grasped by any finite mind or finite set of minds; it is not even completely faithful to such observations as are actually available. Scientists commonly make *scientific* observations only during working hours, and even then a great deal of their time is spent turning stopcocks, testing for vacuum leaks, adjusting microscopes, feeding experimental animals and computers, or traveling from interview to interview. And often their conception of the world as a whole is quite as naive as that of ordinary men. Any particular law rests, therefore, on partial and intermittent observations, and even those are rarely related *exactly* as the law requires. A certain inexactitude, however, is the price which must be paid if the law is to cover a large number of cases, and can be regarded, paradoxically, as a condition of its usefulness.[2] Also, laws are limited in the scope of their application, and a specification of these limitations—of the conditions under which the law can reasonably be expected to hold—is an indispensable accompaniment to any law statement. But, poised between the extremes of a complex and exacting duplication of the world on one hand, and a simple but shallow rough outline of it on the other, science aspires to be as close to the former as possible.

Theory, then, is a set of universal propositions asserted by means of a corresponding set of universal sentences. More strictly, it is a set of such sets of propositions, one for every scientist. These sets are isomorphic with one another, within limits already discussed, so that we might speak of the union of all the sets as theory in an all-inclusive sense; the only trouble with this is that, unless we could be sure that every scientist was thoroughly consistent and agreed with every other, such an inclusive set might turn out to be inconsistent. Since scientists form a changing population and are, like the rest of us, comparatively short-lived beings, theory is constantly changing: new laws are discovered, old ones discarded or forgotten, old mistakes corrected and new ones committed. The education of scientists consists in their being provided with a set of propositions, or scheme of constructs, partially isomorphic (and ideally wholly so) with those of their teachers, and science thereby acquires a certain historical momentum and continuity. The teachers' task is made easier by the fact that a kind of *skeleton* of theory exists in books, ready to be brought to life when the student reads them intelligently. But as we have said before, books by themselves will not do. It is quite clear that, if all the scientists were to die, science itself would die with them, all the libraries in the world notwithstanding. The student needs acquaintance with the elements of perception referred to by the propositions before he can appropriate them *as* propositions; otherwise, he will take them in as sentences merely, remembered as any other perceptual experience is remembered. This quite often happens in any case. When a sentence is uttered, nobody except the speaker knows whether or not it springs from a corresponding proposition. As a matter of fact, the most efficient scientist, from one point of view, might be one who had trained his memory for work with sentences to the exclusion of conceptual content. This would be a positive virtue in some branches of mathematics, but elsewhere it would hamper new discovery very seriously.

Scientific theory, finally, constitutes a particular outlook on the world. The term comes, after all, from the Greek 'theorein', 'to look at'; and a fair translation of 'scientific theory' would be 'knowledgeable outlook'. There is a sense, it is true, in which everyone has a world outlook, and thus in which "the meanest of men has his theory, and to think at all is to theorize." [3] 'Theory' in ordinary speech does not often mean this, however (more usually it means roughly what we have called a working hypothesis—the theory that the butler committed the crime, for instance), but for scientific theory it is important. For science provides the only systematic and corrigible world outlook not requiring any special suppositions beyond those readily made by ordinary men in the daily course of their affairs,[4] and it thus makes possible agreement and collaboration among people who in other respects would be in severe disagreement. This is not to say that science ought to be adopted as *the* world outlook, to the exclusion of everything else; there are other ways of looking at the world, and we may not always want to look at it in the scientific way. But as *a* world outlook open in principle (and I believe in fact) to everybody, it has potentialities which ought not to be overlooked.

REFERENCES

1. René Descartes, *Discourse on Method* (Paris, 1637), p. 45.
2. Michael Scriven, "The Key Property of Physical Laws—Inaccuracy," in Feigl and Maxwell (eds.), *Current Issues in the Philosophy of Science* (New York, 1961), pp. 91 ff.
3. Samuel T. Coleridge, *The Friend* (1865).
4. It will be remembered that the argument of this part has rested on a number of hypotheses introduced in the early chapters. The first, at the end of Chapter 3, admitted an external world populated with real

objects; the second, at the beginning of Chapter 4, added an internal world of thought populated with concepts; and the third, at the beginning of Chapter 5, introduced a similarity of apprehension of the world, and a common use of language, among different people.

CHAPTER 13

SCIENTIFIC EXPLANATION AND
PSEUDO-SCIENCE

Archaeological discovery sometimes turns up forgeries, as was the case at Piltdown, and there is therefore required what Popper calls a "criterion of demarcation"[1] to distinguish between the genuine and the false—in this case science and pseudo-science, true theory and the pretense to theory. Everybody would agree that physics ought to be included among the sciences while astrology ought not, and that the contemporary pharmacist works according to scientific principles while the primitive witch doctor does not. But there are borderline cases in which the decision is much more difficult, and in which acrimonious disputes spring up between those who wish to see their own activities dignified by the name of science and those who think that the name would be cheapened by the inclusion of such activities under it. Such controversies are hardly in the spirit of the contemporary scientist, but even so it is desirable to have some means of resolving them.

The most popular conception of the uniqueness of science has to do with what is called the 'scientific method', but this is not particularly useful in distinguishing scientific from a number of other kinds of activity. That science has a characteristic method is undoubtedly true—it is the method of hypothesis, deduction, and test; but science does not always use it, and it can be applied to all sorts of other inquiries, even philosophical ones. It is this fact that has led some people into confusing the philosophy of science with 'scientific philosophy'—that is, a program for putting the whole of philosophy on a scientific basis, and rejecting as useless those parts of it which do not lend themselves to this adaptation. But there is a great difference between using a method because it usually gives good results in the pursuit of some objective, and having the method identified with the pursuit of the objective. Suppose there were a swimmer named Jones who had invented a new and very rapid stroke; it might be called 'Jones's stroke', but that would not mean that whenever Jones used some other stroke he was not really swimming. Nor would it mean that if somebody else managed to adapt the principle of Jones's stroke to another intricate bodily movement, like getting over the bar in the high jump, high jumping would turn into swimming too. The objectives in the two cases are different, and, in order to understand what is distinctive about science, it is necessary to look at its objectives.

In the writings of scientists we find three well-marked positions adopted with respect to the nature of the objectives of science. All three can be summed up by saying that science is seeking for knowledge, but knowledge means different things to different people. Some speak of discovering the reasons for things; others remember the old proverb, "Knowledge is power"; still others concentrate on the mere accumulation of facts. The work of collecting and classifying facts is the scientific activity of description, and in some sciences it is almost the only objective at the moment, not because the workers in those fields would not like to do other things but because they are still laying an observational foundation. Parts of biology and archaeology are cases in point. The search for reasons goes behind the facts to relationships between facts and the general laws which can be derived from those relationships, and the discovery of these things constitutes scientific *explanation,* which can be defined briefly as accounting for particular events by reference to general laws, together with the actual conditions under which those laws act, or accounting for laws by reference to principles still more general. For instance, in classical mechanics the falling of heavy bodies might be explained by reference to the law of terrestrial gravitation, and this law in turn might be explained by reference to Newton's more general principle of universal gravitation. Finally, the attempt to anticipate, and therefore control, events relies on the ability of science to *predict,* that is, to obtain knowledge of future events. We may therefore summarize three aspects of scientific activity as leading to three objectives: classification which leads to description, explanation which leads to understanding, and prediction which leads to control.

There is a sense in which all these three may be reduced to one, namely, explanation. It is easily seen how classification functions very often as explanation (consider the question, "Why does that animal have stripes?" and the answer, "It's a zebra, and zebras always have stripes"). Every classification involves such an attribution to a singular event of some universal characteristics—exactly those which mark off the members of that class from those of other classes. We would not always be satisfied, of course, with an answer of that sort, and to explain why zebras have stripes would require reference to the genetic basis of pigmentation or perhaps the evolutionary environment in which zebras developed or both. In a way, the principles ultimately appealed to are themselves glorified classification statements—when an event has been classed as a case of some universal law, explanation can go no further. But to demand more would be unreasonable. Events are explained by showing how they fit into the universe, but the universe is not explained. Prediction is of course the application of an explanatory scheme to future events, arguing that if the principles hold and the conditions are fulfilled which are called upon to explain some event, the event will follow.

We say of explanations, in ordinary language, that they are 'satisfactory' or 'unsatisfactory'. It is one of the marks of an educated man that he is not satisfied with explanations which satisfy children and primitives. Persons who are too easily satisfied are looked down upon as credulous, while those who are harder to convince are said to be healthily skeptical. Skepticism is not, it is true, an altogether comfortable state, and it has been pointed out that primitive men, who have a consistent explanation for everything (in terms of demons, gods, and the like), live in a much more secure world than we do. But the dissatisfied mind is one of the strongest motivations for research. It is said that when somebody met Pauli, whose brow was furrowed with anxiety, and remarked how unhappy he looked, Pauli replied, "How can anyone be happy when he's thinking about the anomalous Zeeman effect?" Conversely, the progress of science comes to a halt in any field where some explanation is put forward, and accepted, as the last word.

When is a scientific explanation 'satisfactory'? We do not now explain lightning by reference to the anger of the gods, or hereditary defects by reference to family curses, but some people might be tempted to say that the submicroscopic particles of the modern physicist or the modern geneticist are, if anything, harder to observe than devils were, and that the explanations of events in terms of them are less intelligible to the ordinary man than the unscientific explanations they are meant to replace. Nobody is likely to take such complaints very seriously, but they bring out the point that scientific explanations are not to be accepted or rejected according to whether or not they satisfy us in some psychological sense. It is true that the scientist, as a man, must be satisfied by what he does; if he is not, he does further work on the problem until he is, unless he dies first, or gives up in despair. This is the germ of truth in the pragmatist theory of inquiry. Scientific explanations, however, do not primarily satisfy a natural sense of plausibility, but rather they satisfy certain requirements as to the logical relations which must hold between them and the statements they are supposed to explain. It is the business of the philosophy of science to clarify the nature of these relationships. Explanation has become a logical rather than a psychological matter.

The most usual pattern of explanation is *deductive;* from a universal statement or statements (laws or principles) together with some particular statements of conditions (which together constitute the *explanans*) is deduced a sentence describing the event to be explained (the *explanandum*). The criteria for sound explanations of this sort are that the deduction should genuinely (and not merely apparently) involve the universal statements, and that those statements, and the statements of conditions, should be true, as nearly as this can be ascertained.[2] This possibility is already implicit in the theoretical structure erected in the foregoing chapters, and will become explicit in the logical exposition which follows. Explanations, however, are sometimes said to be *analogical, teleological, probabilistic, genetic,* and so on, and hence not deductive in the strict sense.[3] But it would be a pity if a rigorous definition of 'deductive' were allowed to conceal the outstanding feature which these other types share with deductive explanations, namely, their suitability for expression in logical arguments satisfying the criteria set out above. Analogical explanations borrow the logical form of a well-known relationship and apply it to a less well-known one; teleological explanations include statements of *future* conditions in the explanans; probabilistic explanations make use of somewhat looser logical relations than deductive ones, in which the explanandum is only one among a number of possible consequences of the application of the given laws to the given conditions; genetic explanations appeal to special sets of laws pertaining to the way in which given events are actually produced from others by means of processes which take time. But each of these types might be called *quasi-deductive*—the claim is always made that the explanandum can be inferred more or less accurately from the explanans, given the conditions of the case—so there is no serious danger in allowing the deductive pattern to stand as paradigmatic of them all.

But pseudo-science also can *claim* to provide explanations according to this deductive pattern. The test then is to get it to use the deductive technique of explanation on a future event, that is, to take the risk of being proved wrong by making a prediction. The argument involved in a prediction is a slight modification of that involved in an explanation. In a prediction the conditions—some antecedent event or events—are the starting point, working through a law to the predicted event, whereas in an explanation, the explanandum is the starting point, and only such conditions are involved as to make its following from the law plausible. The antecedent event and the predicted event are described in protocol sentences, and we suppose that some sequence of events, related to one another as causes to effects, links the two, matching in some way the sequence of propositions which links the protocol sentences via the body of theory. The usefulness of theory in prediction depends, of course, on the scientist's ability to trace out the sequence of propositions faster than nature traces out the sequence of causes, so that the scientist gets there first. (If he does not succeed in this, the best thing he can do is explain what happened, his abortive prediction being immediately convertible into an explanation.)

Newton considered this predictive activity the characteristic mark of science (which, according to the usage of his day, he calls "philosophy"): "For the whole burden of philosophy seems to consist in this—from the phenomena of motions to investigate the forces of nature, and then from these forces to demonstrate the other phenomena." [4] And he was right in this. 'Burden' here means the principal theme, or the refrain periodically repeated; and the question that must principally and repeatedly be asked of any candidate for the title of scientific theory is whether it can demonstrate the *other* phenomena—that is, not merely the ones on which it rests in the first place. If it is prepared to stake its reputation on this, its claim to scientific status is taken seriously, and accepted until the theory is refuted by contrary evidence; if not, it must be dismissed as pseudo-science.

Science was defined in Chapter 1 as the explanation of nature in its own terms; and it is perhaps profitable to ask here whether there are any systematic limitations on the kinds of event that can properly be submitted as explananda for science, or can properly be used as the basis for theory construction. Sometimes nature has been contrasted with the supernatural, so that it would include everything except gods, angels, devils, witches, and the like. In this way, the scientists would be included in nature, since they are certainly not supernatural, but then the distinction between the scientist and what he studies would be lost. Others, therefore, make a distinction between nature and man, but this would cut out the sciences which deal with man, such as psychology. On reflection, however, it is evident that each scientist is only one man; there is nothing to prevent his regarding other men as part of nature—they are, after all, only physical objects which behave in special ways. We might therefore say that the subject matter of science is nature, where nature means everything except the observer who is making the observations. But what is this observer? Not his body, certainly, since he can easily regard that as part of nature. At this point, it becomes necessary to change the mode of discussion; we can no longer talk about 'the observer' in the abstract, because we have experience of only one observer, namely the person we call 'I'. *I* can talk about and observe *my* body, even *my* thoughts, but whenever I regard myself as an object in this way, there is a sense in which I am still the subject who observes.

In any scientific activity an observer confronts what is observed, but sometimes the observation is *reflexive,* and the same person plays both roles. The only experiences of observation to which I have direct access are my own, and I cannot tell if the experiences of others are like mine, even if they are described to me, for the experiences themselves are private and *sui generis,* whereas the description is public and makes use of the categories of language.

This perhaps gives a clue to a better formulation of the subject matter of science; we will say that science studies everything which can be publicly inspected—its subject matter is the class of public events. All public events, however, are seen from the private point of view of an individual scientist (at least one may assume that each scientist has such a private point of view—the only one of whose existence I can be sure is again my own). These private points of view cannot be studied scientifically, and they are the only things which cannot. An analogous situation, which may throw some light on the question, would be a group of cameras constantly taking pictures of the world; apart from limitations of focus, and so on, the only place of which pictures could not be taken would be the inside of a camera. Even if some cameras were opened, there would still have to be at least one closed camera to take pictures of their insides, and that closed camera corresponds to the individual from whose point of view the whole thing is considered—in other words, the reader. The pictures stand, of course, for scientific knowledge.

One further restriction on the possible objects of scientific investigation may be necessary in the light of the foregoing remarks. The writing of a novel, the performance of a symphony, a conversation between friends, are all public events, but they are not ordinarily thought to be particularly fruitful sources of scientific data. While the point cannot possibly be proved, it seems probable that what all these things have in common is a close connection with exactly such a private individuality, or a number of them. The claim is highly controversial, turning as it does on the question of whether man is or is not a free agent, but unless one wishes to say that nobody can help doing what he does then one has to agree that chains of causes and effects which pass through the private region of choice and decision may not submit to analysis in terms of invariable principles. Of course very few causal chains do pass entirely out of the reach of scientific scrutiny; even if we have freedom, we certainly do not exercise it most of the time, and some people probably never do, besides which the behavior of man in large groups (like the behavior of atomic nuclei in large groups) is capable of statistical treatment. The modification of our previous characterization of the object of scientific inquiry to take care of this point would therefore make it read 'public events whose *im-*

mediate causal antecedents do not include a free subject'. It must be understood that this is a cautionary measure introduced to prevent the begging of the question of free choice by an appeal to science; if it were to turn out that we *could* give scientific explanations of apparently free activity, we would have to revise our notion of freedom and perhaps abandon it altogether. At the moment it can safely be said that this is not imminent.

REFERENCES

1. K. R. Popper, "Philosphy of Science—A Personal Report," in Mace (ed.), *British Philosophy at Mid-Century* (Cambridge, Eng., 1957).
2. C. G. Hempel and Paul Oppenheim, "The Logic of Explanation," *Philosophy of Science*, 15 (1948).
3. Ernest Nagel, *The Structure of Science* (New York, 1961).
4. Isaac Newton, *Principia*, preface to the 1st ed.

PART II

THE STRUCTURE OF THEORY

PROLOGUE

The second part begins with theory as a scheme of constructs accurately reflecting certain features of the world. Its public and communicable form is provided by a language system—couched in a standard language abstracted and refined out of the language referred to in the prologue to Part I—within which are distinguished descriptive, disposition, and theoretical terms and protocol sentences, empirical generalizations, and hypotheses. Empirical generalizations, when true, become laws, and these form the principal basis for the explanation and prediction of events. The task of this part is the systematic internal organization of theory.

Chapter 14

LOGICAL TRUTH

The protocol sentences, empirical generalizations, and hypotheses of the previous part were always considered to have empirical content and to belong to some particular branch of science. But theory, although sometimes spoken of in the plural, was in general considered to be something belonging equally to all the sciences, the relations between its parts being the same whether the empirical content happened to be that of physics, of biology, or of psychology. Whether or not this assumption was justified it is too early to say (that belongs in Part IV), but in this part it will be understood that scientific theory has a logical structure which can be abstracted from all empirical content and studied in isolation. All reference to actual objects and events will now, for the time being, be dropped, and theory will be considered as a structure of *sentences* without any accompanying scheme of constructs. The end in view is an efficient internal organization of this structure so that it can be used along with *any* scientific scheme of constructs for the purposes of explanation, prediction, and so forth.

In the second chapter, two kinds of truth—empirical and systematic—were distinguished. Most of what we know to be true, it was said there, we know systematically, that is, because of its following from true statements already known. But eventually there has to be some statement the truth of which is known empirically, since otherwise the chain of inferences would become infinite. We cannot always have *already* known a true statement from which the rest would follow. But in the logical study of the structure of theory which is now proposed, empirical truth is to be abandoned altogether. To make matters worse, the notion of one statement's following from another, or, as we should now be careful to say, one *sentence's* following from another, when examined closely, turns out to conceal an assumption which if challenged threatens the whole concept of systematic truth. It is assumed that the fact that one sentence follows from another can be known to be true. But what kind of truth might it have? Not empirical truth, certainly, since the relation of 'following from' is not something that can be observed; nor however systematic truth either, since that cannot be trusted until exactly this question has been settled. We therefore confront two serious problems: (1) the lack of any true sentence with which to get the formal system started, empirical truth having been temporarily given up; and (2) the lack of any justification for the following of one part of the system from another, even supposing a true starting point to have been found.

These problems are both to be solved by the introduction of an apparently new kind of truth which may be called *logical* truth. But this obviously cannot be done by a mere assertion. The straightforward sense of truth as the faithfulness of a statement to what it describes is the only sense about which we are all likely to agree, and logical truth can in fact be shown to be derived from that, just as systematic truth is. First, however, we introduce a convention of logic. A statement can be more or less faithful to what it describes, and we might therefore expect gradations of truth from true, very nearly true, and so on, down to hardly true at all, and finally untrue. In fact, the notion of truth reflected in ordinary discussion does have such gradations. But in logic it is customary to simplify this by saying: either a sentence is true or it is not, and if it is not it is false. Logic, we say, is *two-valued*—there are only two alternative truth-values available. There would be nothing especially objectionable in having more truth-values, and some attempts at constructing multivalued logics have in fact been made. The advantage of the two-valued convention is that in lengthy deductions truth does not trickle away in the sand, as it were; it is carried through at full strength, or not at all. Also it permits the simple conversion of true sentences into false ones, and vice versa, by negation. One reason why the convention is plausible is that the human brain is constructed in part like a digital computer, with elements which have just two alternative states (like simple switches, which are either on or off).

Given this convention, what kind of sentence can be found which will be true independently of any empirical consideration? At a time when philosophers believed that logic described the actual processes of thought, it was generally agreed that there were three laws of thought which enjoyed this privileged status. They appear very simple and dull: the first, or *law of identity,* says that everything is itself, or, if we let A stand for anything, no matter what it is, that A is A. The second, or *law of contradiction,* says, using the same language, that A is not not-A. And the third, or *law of the excluded middle,* says that everything is either A or not-A. We would not now call these statements 'laws', and certainly not 'laws of thought', but their truth in a two-valued logic does seem convincing. To put it differently, it would be hard to conceive of circumstances in which they could possibly be false. And here the possibility of getting logical truth out of empirical truth comes to light: a sentence is logically true if there is no state of affairs to which it does not correctly apply, in other words, if it is empirically true of every possible state of affairs. The sentence 'either it is raining or it is not raining', for example, is always true whether it is raining or not, and therefore one need not have any empirical data at hand in order to assert it.

Such a sentence is called a *tautology*—it 'says itself'. It says nothing *informative* about the world, but that does not invalidate the claim that its truth is a kind of empirical truth; it is just an extreme case of empirical truth whose range of application is universal. (At the other extreme is the *self-contradictory* sentence which can never be true of any conceivable state of affairs, for example, the sentence 'it is raining and it is not raining', which is always false whether it is raining or not.) Such universally true sentences provide a plausible, although so far weak, case for constructing logical systems with a total disregard of all particular matters of empirical fact.

We now confront the second problem, that of guaranteeing in terms of logical truth the step from one sentence to another in a logical system. The passage from one sentence to another which follows from it is called an *inference,* and the relation which holds between a sentence and another which can legitimately be inferred from it is known as *implication.* Now the minimum requirement for a valid inference is that it shall not lead from a true sentence to a false one. We may assume by now that we have a true sentence to start with, and we wish to find the implication which will guarantee, not necessarily that the sentence to be inferred from this true sentence has any intrinsic connection with it, but that it will in fact be true. The weak kind of implication involved here is called *material implication,* as distinct from strong implication or *entailment.* If one sentence entails another we can, given the first, *derive* the second from it by the application of suitable rules of entailment, whereas if one sentence materially implies another we need both sentences before the application of the rules of material implication can confirm the inference from the first to the second.

All this is brought into the realm of logical truth in the following way: Suppose we have a sentence p which, it is claimed, materially implies a sentence q. The condition for material implication is that if p is true, q must not be false, that is, since we are using a two-valued logic, q must be true. It is logically true that p is either true or false, and therefore if p materially implies q it must be logically true that either p is false or q is true. If this can be shown, the difficulty about sentences following from one another will be resolved. In fact, we accept only those inferences for which it can be shown; the methods by which this is done in particular cases are sketched in the next chapter.

Chapter 15

DEDUCTIVE LOGIC

The discussion of sentences which follow from others and may be inferred from them is facilitated by the formal theory of inference, that is, formal logic. It is called *formal,* as opposed to empirical or factual, because it is concerned not with the content or the meaning of sentences but with their structure and the relations between them. Formal logic, like traditional logic, has two principal branches, depending on whether the inferences dealt with are *demonstrative* or *non-demonstrative,* that is, whether they lead to certainties or only to probabilities. An example of a demonstrative inference would be the passage from an empirical generalization to an instance of it; if the former is true, the latter *must* be true, because, as we have seen, its not being true would refute the generalization itself. Demonstrative inferences are also called *deductive,* from a Latin expression meaning the drawing out of particular conclusions from general principles.

The simplest branch of deductive logic deals with relations between sentences taken as units; since it also serves for propositions it is often called 'propositional logic', but here for obvious reasons a better name is 'sentential logic'. A set of sentences in which the truth of the last (the *conclusion*) follows from the truth of the others (the *premises*) is called an *argument,* and every inference may be expressed in an argument. Sentential logic is interested in the forms which arguments expressing valid inferences may take, not in the particular sentences involved. It has adopted certain symbols to express sentences and the relationships between sentences, no matter what the sentences may say. For our purposes, it will be necessary to know only that the letters *p, q, . . .* are *vari-*

ables standing for sentences, and that they may be modified or combined by the use of the following symbols:

$\sim$ negation ($\sim p$ is read 'not p' or 'it is not the case that p');

$\cdot$ conjunction ($p \cdot q$ is read 'p and q');

$\vee$ disjunction ($p \vee q$ is read 'p or q');

$\supset$ material implication ($p \supset q$ is read 'if p then q').

These symbols are known as *sentential connectives* because they serve to connect sentences, and as *truth-functional connectives* because the truth or falsity of a compound sentence put together by means of them depends only on the truth or falsity of the simple sentences out of which the compound is made. (The connectives may of course be used also with symbols which stand for actual sentences, a, b, . . . and not only with the sentential variables p, q, . . .) The exact function of the connectives is expressed in *truth-tables,* one for each connective, which show the truth-values of compound sentences according to the truth-values of their simple components. In the following tables, T stands for 'true' and F for 'false':

I. Negation

p	$\sim p$
T	F
F	T

II. Conjunction

p	q	$p \cdot q$
T	T	T
T	F	F
F	T	F
F	F	F

III. Disjunction

p	q	$p \vee q$
T	T	T
T	F	T
F	T	T
F	F	F

IV. Material Implication

p	q	$p \supset q$
T	T	T
T	F	F
F	T	T
F	F	T

Any valid argument whatever can be written in the form of a material implication, since, if we call the set of premises $\{p\}$ and the conclusion q, the fact that it *is* a valid argument means that $\{p\} \supset q$.

Material implication, as we have seen, guarantees only a weak form of validity which says that in fact the conclusion of a valid argument is never false when its premises are true, although it does not say how, if at all, one can get by a series of plausible deductive steps from the premises to the conclusion. This apparent indifference on the part of the conclusion to the nature of the premises leads to some odd consequences, the so-called *paradoxes of material implication*. It can easily be seen that the sentences '$q \supset (p \supset q)$' and '$\sim p \supset (p \supset q)$' are true, by the construction of truth-tables, and thus represent valid arguments; translated into English they say, respectively, 'If the sentence q is true, then it is materially implied by any sentence p, whether p is true or false', and 'If the sentence p is false, then it materially implies any sentence q, whether q is true or false'. In other words, any sentence whatever materially implies a true sentence, and a false sentence materially implies any sentence whatever. These results do not seem quite so paradoxical, however, if the distinction made at the end of Chapter 5 between object language and metalanguage is borne in mind. Strictly speaking, the paradoxes should read:

> if 'q' is true, 'q' is materially implied by any 'p'
> if 'p' is false, 'p' materially implies any 'q'

We have to know the truth of 'q' and the falsity of 'p' before the paradoxes become operative, but then they are seen not to be functional cases of implication. For if we know 'q' to be true, we do not need to infer it from any 'p', and, if we know 'p' to be false, we shall not try to infer any 'q' from it. The *fact that* 'p' is false may lead to something significant, but that will be on the level of the meta-language where 'p' is *mentioned,* not on the level of the object language where it is *used.*

Material implication, in other words, is an external relation between sentences, entailment an internal one; if the arrow in the accompanying schema stands for the logical relation in question, we have:

metalanguage   'p' → 'q'   material implication
object language p → q entailment

The reasons for the retention of material implication as the principal truth-functional connective in sentential logic are, first, that it is of much wider applicability than entailment—every entailment yields a material implication, but the converse is not true; second, that, since logic is to be applied to cases, it is as well to make a minimum commitment in advance as to the nature of those cases, and certainly not to assume that they will involve internal relations; third, that it reflects what is common to many different uses of 'if . . . then . . .'; and fourth, because the attempt to introduce arguments based on strict implication is an extremely complicated and difficult matter. In particular, the formalization of 'q can be deduced logically from p' requires the introduction of *modal operators,* such as 'it is possible that' and 'it is necessary that', which can only be handled with the aid of highly sophisticated logical techniques.

For the moment, consider the following argument form:

Premises: 1. $p \supset q$
                2. p
Conclusion: q

This represents a valid inference and may be written in English as follows: 'if it is true that the sentence q follows from the sentence p, and if the sentence p is true, then the sentence q is true'. (That it is a valid inference may be seen from the truth-table for material implication—in the only case in which both $p \supset q$ and p are true, q is also true.) Now we may apply this argument form (which used to be called *modus ponens* by the medieval logicians) to the relationship between hypotheses and their consequences. A hypothesis is, after all, a sentence—call it h—and the empirical generalization that follows from it (and at least one must, as we saw, if it is to be a genuine hypothesis) is also a sentence—call it g. The argument then becomes:

$$h \supset g$$
$$\underline{h }$$
$$g$$

In other words, if we know that the consequences really follow from the hypothesis, and if we know that the hypothesis is really true, then we know that the consequences are true. But by the very definition of a hypothesis, we get evidence for its truth by way of its consequences, and we can test their truth directly, because they are empirical generalizations; this inference therefore gives us nothing. What we really want is an inference which will tell us that the hypothesis is true if we already know that its consequences are true, that is, an argument of this sort:

$$h \supset g$$
$$\underline{g }$$
$$h$$

This is in fact the argument we use most frequently in justifying scientific hypotheses: for example, we talk about atoms, which nobody has ever seen, and say, 'If there were atoms with such and such properties, then certain elements would show certain chemical properties; these elements do show such properties, therefore there must be atoms'. Unfortunately, this argument form is not valid— it commits a well-known logical fallacy, the *fallacy of affirming the consequent*. A sentence which is a consequence of one hypothesis may also be the consequence of another hypothesis, and if all we have is the consequence we do not know which hypothesis to choose. The sentence 'If a man takes arsenic, he will die', while certainly true for most people, does not allow us to conclude that if one of them dies he must have taken arsenic. There are many ways of dying. One of them must have occurred, but which, without further inquiry, we cannot say.

We have therefore to abandon the hope of using this argument form as a means of getting at the truth of hypotheses, and things begin to look rather desperate for science. The paradoxical situation has arisen that, if the consequences actually are what the hypothesis says they ought to be, they are automatically prevented from helping to establish the hypothesis. But it is not quite as bad as it seems. Suppose the consequences are *not* what the hypothesis says they ought to be. Suppose the man referred to above does *not* die: we may then conclude with certainty that he did not take arsenic, or at least not enough. The form of this argument is closely related to the fallacious one, but this time it is the valid form *modus tollens:*

$$h \supset g$$
$$\frac{\sim g}{\sim h}$$

In other words, while a hypothesis cannot be *verified* (that is, shown to be true) by reference to its consequences, it may be *falsified* conclusively if the consequences fail to occur. This enables us to eliminate some of the alternative hypotheses referred to above, and, while this does not finally establish the one we think is true—we can never be sure we have found and eliminated all the alternatives—still our confidence in it will grow if it continues to remain unrefuted. Of course, it might turn out that it could not possibly be refuted, but in this case it would not be of much practical use. One can make the statement 'Something will happen in the next five minutes' with absolute confidence, but just *because* it cannot be refuted, it is empty of concrete information. We want to know *what* will happen, and as soon as we commit ourselves to one view or another we are vulnerable—our prediction will be refuted if what we said would happen does not. Thus there is a very close link between the usefulness of scientific statements and the possibility of their being refuted, as was suggested in Chapter 13. For the moment, however, we are left with no means of getting at our hypotheses logically; they stand without any direct link to perception and form starting points of logical relationships, but they cannot be the terminus of any such relationship.

Although deductive logic is of no assistance in arriving at hypotheses as conclusions, it can be extremely useful when it is a matter of finding out whether or not some sentence arrived at by other means is a genuine hypothesis, and if so, what follows from it. What is needed is a technique of finding all, or as many as possible, of the logical consequences of a given sentence, regardless of

whether or not they are known in advance to be empirical generalizations. If some of them turn out to be empirical generalizations,
then the sentence was a hypothesis, and if furthermore one or more
of these generalizations is false, then the hypothesis must be rejected. If true empirical generalizations, but no false ones, follow
logically from some statement, it is not shown thereby to be a true
hypothesis, but deductive logic can assure us that the assumption
of its truth does not lead to any conclusions which are known to
be false, and that, in the case of a hypothesis, is a great deal. For
the purpose of finding the consequences of a sentence, logic, as was
remarked above, is not interested in what the sentence says, but
only in the way it is said. The same relations may hold, and the
same problems arise, in the case of hypotheses (or more usually sets
of hypotheses), together with the empirical generalizations that
follow from them, which deal with completely diverse aspects of
the world. What counts is the form of the sentence, whether, for
example, it attributes a property to an object or relates two objects
or asserts the existence of an object having some property, and so
on. Sentential logic, as dealt with above, does not look at the
internal structure of sentences but only at their external relations;
for the former, *predicate* logic is required.

In addition to the symbolism of sentential logic, predicate logic
adopts the convention of representing individual objects by the
small letters $a, b, c, \ldots$ (individual constants) and representing
properties by the capital letters $P, Q, R, \ldots$ (There are of course
many alternative notations, but this is one of the most common.)
'Pa' means that a has the property P, P being in this case a *one-
place* predicate, which applies only to one object at a time. '$Pa \cdot Pb$'
means that both a and b have the property P, '$\cdot$' being the sign for
conjunction in sentential logic; of course, 'Pa' and 'Pb' are themselves sentences. *Two-place* predicates stand for *relations;* 'Qab'
means 'a stands in the relation Q to b', and there may be predicates
with more than two places standing for more complex relations. So
far, only *singular* sentences are possible. In order to allow for universal and existential sentences, *variables* are introduced, for which
the small letters $x, y, z, \ldots$ (individual variables) and the capital
letters $F, G, H, \ldots$ (predicate variables) are used. 'Fx' means
that x has the property F, but it is not, as it stands, a sentence—
it is called a *sentential function,* that is, something which becomes

a sentence when the name of some object, say a, is substituted for the variable x, and the name of some property, say P, substituted for the variable F. The step to universal and existential sentences is taken by the introduction of symbols for *quantifiers*. The *universal quantifier* 'all' is represented by '(x)'—'$(x)Px$' means 'Everything has the property p', and is read 'For all x, Px'. The quantifier which asserts existence (the *existential quantifier*) is represented by '$(\exists x)$'—'$(\exists x)Px$' means 'Something has the property P', and is read 'There exists an x such that Px', or 'For some x, Px'. In most systems of predicate logic, there is no singular quantifier 'this', since the logically important thing about a singular sentence is the fact that it is a kind of particular sentence, whose quantifier 'some' is taken care of by the existential quantifier. There is an implicit assumption here that particular sentences have *existential import*, that is, that the sentence 'Some A's are B' is false if no A's actually exist. Singular sentences certainly have existential import. The universal sentence given above as an example—'$(x)Px$'—is a rather extravagant case, since there are very few properties, if any, which are shared by everything. A better illustration is provided by the empirical generalization 'All A's are B' which was dealt with in the preceding section. This would read '$(x)\ (Ax \supset Bx)$'—'If anything has the property A, then it also has the property B'. The protocol sentence which contradicts this generalization would, similarly, have to be written '$(\exists x)\ (Ax \cdot \sim Bx)$'. These expressions, although they contain variables, are genuine sentences and not just sentential functions, because what they assert is definite; the variables are said to be *bound* by the presence of the quantifier, instead of being *free* as in the case of 'Px'. A sentence cannot contain free variables, but the free variables in a sentential function can be eliminated by binding them under quantifiers as well as by substituting names.

Sentential logic and predicate logic are both very ancient disciplines; the first was developed in a restricted form (not, of course, using the symbolism given above) by Aristotle,[1] and the second by the Stoics.[2] (Their present formulation is due principally to Frege,[3] Russell and Whitehead.[4]) A much more recent development is the logic of classes, due to Boole,[5] out of which has grown the important discipline known as *set theory*. The basic ideas of set theory are membership, symbolized by 'ϵ'—'$x \,\epsilon\, A$' means, and is read, 'x is a member of A' (where A stands for some set), and in-clusion, symbolized by '$\subset$'—'$A \subset B$' means that every member of the set A is also a member of the set B (in other words, that A is *in-cluded* in B), and is read 'A is a subset of B'. Obviously, every member of a set is also a member of the same set, so that for any set A, $A \subset A$. *Proper inclusion* is symbolized by '$\subseteq$'—'$A \subseteq B$' means that every member of the set A is also a member of the set B, but that at least one member of the set B is not a member of the set A; in this case, A is a *proper subset* of B. A set is simply any collection of things taken together, and is represented by enclosing the names of those things in curly brackets; $\{a,b\}$ is the set whose only members are a and $b,$ and if we call that set A then $\{A\}$ is the set whose only member is the set whose only members are a and b. A most important set is the set Λ, which has no members, and is called the empty set. There is only one empty set, since if any two sets have exactly the same members, they are the same set.

Sets may be combined to make other sets. The two most impor-tant operations for combining sets are *union*, symbolized by '$\cup$'—$A \cup B$ is the set whose members are those things, and only those things, which are either members or A, or members of B, or both, and *intersection*, symbolized by '$\cap$'—$A \cup B$ is the set whose mem-bers are those things, and only those things, which are members both of A and of B. Equality between sets is symbolized by '$=$'—'$A = B$' means that A and B have exactly the same members. Some very obvious truths of set theory are that for every set A, $A = A$; that for every set A, $\Lambda \subset A$; and that for every set A, $A \cup \Lambda = A$, and $A \cap \Lambda = \Lambda$. Since every assertion about sets, such as '$A \cup B \subset C$,' is a sentence, such assertions may be combined by means of the connectives of sentential logic.

The foregoing exposition of logical terminology is included only in order to provide a minimum vocabulary, which will be needed in some later chapters and will also be useful in making other current literature intelligible. It is obviously not intended to teach logic, although it may serve to refresh the memory of those who have already studied it. A thorough grounding in logic is indispensable for anybody who wishes to understand recent work in the philoso-phy of science, and, although in this book only the most elementary use is made of it, the symbolic language of logic is something with-out which a student of the subject is virtually illiterate. With its aid has been developed the notion of a logical *calculus,* that is a system within which we can calculate, not necessarily with numbers but with the formal properties and relations of logic. The word *calculus* in Latin means a pebble, and it was with formal properties of sets of pebbles, namely their numbers, that men used to perform their elementary calculations.

REFERENCES

1. Aristotle, *Organon.*
2. See, for example, Benson Mates, *Stoic Logic* (Berkeley and Los Angeles, 1961).
3. Geach and Black (eds.), *Translations from the Philosophical Writings of Gottlob Frege* (Oxford, 1952) contains most of the important papers.
4. A. N. Whitehead and B. Russell, *Principia Mathematica* (Oxford, 1908-1911).
5. G. Boole, *The Mathematical Analysis of Logic* (Cambridge, Eng., 1857).

CHAPTER 16

AXIOMS AND THEOREMS

There are two senses in which the word 'calculus' is commonly used in connection with logic. In the first, it means simply a tool of calculation, and in this sense the foregoing chapter might be said to include a simple exposition of the sentential calculus and of the first-order predicate calculus (first-order because it permits quantification only over individual variables; the second-order predicate calculus permits quantification also over predicate variables). In the second, and stronger, sense a calculus is a formalized language system, that is, a consistent set of sentences containing only rigorously defined terms drawn from a limited vocabulary, such that every sentence in the system is either a member of a small set of sentences given as axioms or follows logically from members of that set. In the first sense, the calculus is really a set of rules for playing a game with logical symbols; in the second, it is the result of playing the game according to the rules, starting from the axioms. The sentential calculus, in the second sense, is a formalization of sentential logic using the sentential variables $p, q, r, \ldots$ together with the sentential connectives, taking as axioms some set of sentences, such as '$(p \cdot q) \supset p$' or '$p \supset (p \vee q)$' and laying down such rules of inference as *modus ponens* and a rule governing the substitution of sentential variables. A similar formalization can be carried out for first-order predicate logic and for set theory. In these cases, the axioms will be of a purely logical nature, and will not contain reference to any particular sentences, particular objects, or particular sets (except the empty set); it is of course possible to have axioms and theorems which do contain reference to particular cases. To avoid confusion, the following terms will be used through-

117

out this discussion: By a *deductive system* is meant any system of interrelated statements such that some of them follow deductively from others; by an *axiomatized deductive system* or *axiomatic system* is meant a deductive system in which every statemnt is either an *axiom* not following deductively from any other statement, or a *theorem* following deductively from one or more axioms; and by a *pure axiomatic system* or *calculus* is meant a system having the logical form of an axiomatic system, but making no reference to particular contents. A calculus is, of course, an axiomatic system, and *a fortiori* a deductive system; an axiomatic system is a deductive system but is not necessarily a calculus (although it always *has* a calculus, namely its logical form); and a deductive system is not necessarily either an axiomatic system or a calculus (although it always points to the *possibility* of an axiomatic system, namely a formalization of itself). A theory may then be a deductive system or an axiomatic system—in the latter case, we say the theory has been axiomatized—but it cannot be a calculus, since the calculus is purely formal, and can at best contain sentences, whereas the theory, strictly speaking, contains propositions, or more loosely speaking statements. If the theory has been axiomatized, however, the resulting axiomatic system has a calculus, as pointed out above. The purpose of this chapter is to show that the formal aspects of scientific theories can be exhibited as calculi in this sense, but before that can be done the structure of such a calculus must be sketched in more detail.

If one starts from scratch to build a logical calculus, the first necessity is a vocabulary. Since the system is to be purely formal, the terms which constitute the minimum vocabulary cannot be chosen because of their empirical meaning—they cannot have external definitions. Because the system is an entirely new construction, they cannot have internal definitions either. Consequently, these being the only two kinds of definitions available to us, we are not in a position to give them any definition at all. For the time being we will accept this restriction; the elements of the minimum vocabulary are just terms, and since they are at the very beginning of the calculus they are called *primitive terms*, or simply *primitives*. They must somehow be put together into sentences if any logical calculation is to be undertaken, and, as we have just seen, the sentences from which calculation begins are called *axioms*. Obviously not every sentence which can be put together by means of the primitives is an axiom. In particular, if any sentence can be inferred from another, only the latter can be an axiom because axioms have the property which before we attributed to hypotheses: they cannot be arrived at by any chain of logical inferences but constitute the starting points of such chains. Since they stand in the same uncomfortable isolation as hypotheses, we wish to have as few of them as possible. It is a matter of choice how many axioms one has, but they have to fulfill two conditions if they are to lead to a useful calculus: they must be *independent,* that is, none of them must be able to be inferred from any of the others; and they must be *consistent,* that is, no contradictions must follow from using them together.

Still we do not have quite enough material for our purposes. In addition to primitives and axioms we need two sets of rules: *formation-rules,* which specify how primitive or other terms may be put together to form acceptable expressions (*well-formed formulas*) of the calculus, and *transformation-rules,* or rules of inference, which show how one may get from one sentence or set of sentences to another. Any sentence arrived at according to the rules, starting from the axioms, is called a *theorem,* and the series of sentences, starting with axioms and ending with the theorem, which exhibits the steps in this process, is called a *proof* of the theorem. It is not, of course, necessary to go all the way back to the axioms every time in proving a theorem—one may start from another theorem— but it is always possible in principle to get back to the starting point of the whole calculus, that is, to the axioms. Also, to avoid making the theorems very long, it is often desirable to introduce *defined terms,* or abbreviations for long expressions containing only primitives. This is the only kind of definition which can be done within the calculus, and represents the third of the functions of definition spoken of in Chapter 7. Some writers have suggested that the axioms themselves constitute *implicit* definitions of the primitives, but this is not a very useful suggestion. Some of the primitives, it is true, may be defined to the extent that one knows (on the basis of the formation and transformation rules) *how* they fit into well-formed formulas, and furthermore one knows when the formulas into which they fit are true. (The truth-tables on page 108, for example, constitute definitions of the connectives, which are primitives of the propositional calculus.) This kind of definition, however, is not within the calculus; the notion of truth and falsity is something brought to it from without. In the same way, the formation and transformation rules cannot be stated without going outside the vocabulary of the calculus itself. We may exhibit the structure of any calculus as follows:

Terms: Primitives   Rules governing terms: Formation-rules
       Defined terms*

Sentences: Axioms   Rules governing sentences: Transforma-
      Theorems*   tion-rules

The asterisks indicate that these elements are not strictly necessary to the system. This is easy enough to understand for defined terms; we have already seen that they are introduced only to save space, and in principle any theorem could be stated in terms of primitives alone. But how are the theorems dispensable? The answer to this question is that the theorems never tell us anything new—they only repeat what was implicit all along in the axioms. The reason why we have to go to all the trouble of working out theorems is that few of us are perceptive enough to see everything that is implicit in the axioms without doing some calculation. An infinite intelligence, however, would be able to see at a glance all that was implied in any set of axioms, and would not have to bother with working out their consequences.

As a rule, there is not a unique set of axioms for a particular calculus, nor a unique set of primitive terms. It may be possible to take some terms which in one formulation of the calculus are defined terms, and make them primitive in another formulation (the original primitives being defined by means of them); in the same way, it may be possible to take some sentences which in one formulation are theorems, and make them axioms in another formulation (the original axioms becoming theorems derivable from them). There are some important restrictions on these possibilities which arise because the processes of definition are not always reversible, but some reorganization of this sort can nearly always be done. In particular, if one axiom is shown not to be independent of the others, it is not always that one which has to be given up—one of the others may be sacrificed instead.

Four points in the preceding account require further elucidation:

first, the nature of the formation-rules; second, the circumstances under which a well-formed formula is a theorem; and third and fourth, the criteria for independence and consistency of axioms. They will be taken up in order. Specification of the formation-rules is equivalent to defining the notion of a well-formed formula (*wff*), and this is generally done by means of a *recursive* definition. Any expression put together out of terms belonging to the system may be regarded as a formula—for example, '$p \cdot \sim q \vee$' is a formula of the sentential calculus, although it is not a *wff*. The definition of a *wff* begins by specifying some simple formulas which are *asserted* to be *wff*'s, and then goes on to specify what combinations of these simple *wff*'s will also be considered to be *wff*'s. For example, the definition of a *wff* in the sentential calculus might go like this:

> $p, q, \ldots$ are *wff*'s
> If p is a *wff* then $\sim p$ is a *wff*
> If p and q are *wff*'s then $p \cdot q$, $p \vee q$, $p \supset q$ are *wff*'s.

If it is remembered that in the second and third lines 'p' and 'q' can stand for compound sentences, it will easily be seen that these three lines are a complete statement of the formation-rules for the sentential calculus, and that any formula, no matter how complicated, can be analyzed one step at a time (the recursive procedure in reverse) in such a way that a judgment can be made as to whether or not it is a *wff*. The formation-rules of the first-order predicate calculus are not very much more complicated. In this connection it may be remarked that, following the discussion of the previous chapter, the notion of a *wff* permits the definition of 'sentence' as '*wff* containing no free variables'.

In a way, the procedure of using the transformation-rules to derive theorems from the axioms is parallel to this procedure of using the formation-rules to derive *wff*'s from other *wff*'s. The *decision problem* for a logical calculus is the problem of finding a method, which must be an *effective procedure* (that is, one applicable according to fixed rules which cover all cases), of discovering whether a given *wff* is a theorem or not. While the recursive definition of '*wff*' which constitutes the formation-rules may be applied in reverse, however, the reverse application of the transformation-rules is not possible. Given some *wff*, it is a theorem if it can be reached by a chain of logical deductions from the axioms. If in fact it *has* been reached in this way, then the problem is solved—it is a theorem. But suppose nobody has yet been able to derive it? That does not mean that it cannot be derived, since, as we saw earlier, finite minds have to go to a good deal of effort to find out what follows from the axioms. It is easy to see, in the case of a formula, whether or not it could have been arrived at by repeated applications of the steps of the recursive definition of '*wff*', but in the case of some *wff* which has not been derived from the axioms the decision whether or not it *could* have been so derived is much harder. A decision procedure does exist for the sentential calculus, although it is rather clumsy—it consists of constructing a truth-table for the *wff* in question and working out all the possibilities for its truth-value in terms of the truth-values of its simple components. But it has been shown, by the American logician Church,[1] that no effective decision procedure *can* be found for the first-order predicate calculus, and *a fortiori* for more complicated calculi (although such a procedure is known for a restricted version of the first-order predicate calculus, namely, one containing only one-place predicates.) This is, in one way, a serious limitation, but in another it keeps open the question of whether or not some *wff* of great interest, so far not proven, may yet be given a proof.

It has been said before that it is desirable to have as few axioms as possible (and the same remark may be made parenthetically about primitive terms); at least, some of the sentential connectives given in the last section for the sentential calculus are not primitive, since for example '⊃' can be defined according to the relation:

$$p \supset q =_{df.} \sim p \lor q$$

In order to achieve the reduction of the number of axioms to a minimum, it is necessary to have a technique for finding out, for a given formulation of an axiom set, whether all its members are independent of one another. (It is of course possible that some different formulation might still further reduce the number, but that is not the question at issue.) 'Independent of' means, in this case, 'not following logically from'. This problem is comparable to the decision problem, since what it amounts to is finding out whether something that claims to be an axiom is not really just a theorem derivable from the true axioms.

Now one of the devices available in tackling the decision problem, although it is not an effective procedure, is to search for an inconsistency between the denial of the *wff* being tested and some theorem of the system, for if such an inconsistency can be found the *wff* is a theorem. This is known as a *reductio ad absurdum* proof, and depends on the validity of the argument form $(\sim p \supset [q \cdot \sim q]) \supset p$, which admits as a theorem any sentence whose denial leads to a contradiction. A similar technique is usually adopted in testing the independence of axioms. Suppose an axiom set $\{a_1, a_2, a_3\}$, and the problem of showing the independence of a_3 from a_1 and a_2. If a_3 is *not* independent of a_1 and a_2, then it is a theorem of a calculus whose axiom set is $\{a_1, a_2\}$. Suppose now we form a new axiom set consisting of a_1 and a_2 together with the *denial* of a_3, that is, the set $\{a_1, a_2, \sim a_3\}$. a_3 will still be a theorem of this new calculus, since it is derivable from a_1 and a_2, and the new calculus will therefore contain a contradiction, namely the sentence '$a_3 \cdot \sim a_3$', formed by the conjunction of that theorem with the new third axiom. If, however, a_3 is *not* derivable from a_1 and a_2—in other words if it *is* independent—then there will be no inconsistencies in the new calculus which were not present in the old one, and that is assumed to have been consistent. The test for independence therefore consists of forming a new axiom set by taking the other axioms together with the denial of the axiom to be tested; if a contradiction can be derived, the axiom was not independent; if no contradiction can be derived, it was. An interesting consequence of this is that given any calculus whose axioms have been properly identified as such—that is, none of whose axioms is really a theorem in disguise—a whole new calculus may be generated simply by denying one of the axioms and taking it along with the other axioms as the starting point of the new system. In fact, every calculus with n axioms is a member of a family of 2^n calculi whose axioms are the assertions or denials of the same set of sentences. Most of these systems would probably be quite uninteresting to the person who had devised the original one, but it sometimes happens that the denial of some axiom leads to important discoveries. The most famous case of this is the development of non-Euclidean geometry as a result of denying the fifth axiom of Euclid, and this was done in an attempt to test the independence of the axiom.

If, when an axiom is denied, a contradiction does appear in the system which would not otherwise have appeared there, one can of course say finally that the axiom was not independent. But if no contradiction appears it cannot be said definitely that one never will; and if a contradiction does appear, it is perhaps not always easy to tell that it would not have appeared otherwise. This brings us to the notion of the *consistency* of the axioms. A calculus is consistent, and therefore its axioms are consistent, if it contains no contradiction, that is, if it contains no theorem whose negation is also a theorem. But unless we have derived *all* the possible consequences of the axioms, it is too soon to say that the calculus contains no contradiction. There have been two suggestions of ways in which this difficulty might be overcome. One of them involves the discovery of an interpretation for the axioms, and this will be dealt with in the next chapter. The other depends on one of the paradoxes of material implication mentioned in the last chapter, and on the discovery of some property of the formulas in a calculus, which is possessed by the axioms, and which is *hereditary*—that is, which, if it is possessed by any sentence, must also be possessed by any other sentence following from the first according to the transformation-rules. Suppose such a hereditary property to be found, and to belong to the axioms of a calculus. If now any *wff* can be found such that it does not possess this hereditary property, the system must be consistent; for on the one hand, any formula following from the axioms according to the transformation-rules must possess this property, and on the other, if the system contained a contradiction—that is, if it were inconsistent—all *wff*'s would follow from the axioms, according to the rule that a false sentence implies any sentence whatever. (If the system contains a contradiction, we know that one of the elements of the contradiction must be false.) This criterion of consistency has been used successfully for the sentential calculus but is otherwise of very restricted applicability. The axioms of the sentential calculus are tautologies (that is, compound sentences which are always true whether or not their simple constituents are true, such as '$p \supset p$', '$p \lor {\sim}p$'), and the property of being a tautology turns out to be a hereditary property, so that the theorems are also tautologies. There are obviously *wff*'s of the sentential calculus which are not tautologies, and therefore not theorems, for example, '$p \lor q$'; the sentential calculus is therefore consistent. But for more complicated calculi, the application of the criterion depends on the existence of an effective decision procedure. The criterion can be formulated as follows: 'Any calculus for which a *wff* can be found which is not a theorem is consistent'. The problem, however, as before, is to know whether or not a given *wff* is a theorem.

One further problem, not mentioned in the previous exposition, is that of the *completeness* of the axiom set and hence of the system. A calculus is said to be complete if all *wff*'s which are always true when the axioms are true are theorems, that is, if all such *wff*'s can be derived from the axioms according to the transformation-rules. This amounts to saying that there is no *wff* which is not a theorem and which, taken together with the axioms, would yield a consistent system—in other words, that there are no more possible axioms. (A test for completeness may also be regarded as a test of the adequacy of the transformation-rules to derive theorems from the given axioms.) This is an even more difficult question than the decision problem, but like that problem it has been solved for the sentential calculus and for the first-order predicate calculus. The solution for the sentential calculus depends on the possibility of showing, not only that every theorem is a tautology, but also that every tautology is a theorem, and this has been done. Since the only *wff*'s which are always true are tautologies (every other *wff*, such as '$p \lor q$', is false whenever certain of its constituent sentences [in this case, both 'p' and 'q'] are false), the fact that all tautologies are theorems guarantees the completeness of the system. The completeness proof for the first-order predicate calculus is due to the Austrian mathematician Kurt Gödel,[2] and will not be given here. Like the decision problem, the proof of completeness gets harder the more complex the calculus. Another proof due to Gödel,[3] the famous '*incompleteness* proof', shows that in the case of a calculus strong enough for the purposes of ordinary arithmetic there are infinitely many *wff*'s which are true but which cannot be derived from *any* finite set of axioms by means of any finite set of transformation-rules.

This brief introduction to the subject of logical calculi is sufficient for our immediate purposes; it is clear, from what has been said, that further construction might proceed by the addition of new terms, new axioms, and perhaps new formation and transformation-rules. One of the obvious additions to the first-order predicate calculus, for example, would be a term symbolizing *identity,* '=', and one might also wish to add terms like '1' and '0' and '+' to make arithmetical operations possible. (The formalization of mathematics will be taken up in a later chapter.) The limitations imposed on formal systems by the failure of decision procedures and completeness proofs at the higher levels of complexity are often thought to be fatal, and with respect to some over-ambitious programs for the formalization of everything they are, but they do not in the least impair the usefulness of the calculi for practical purposes. It must be remembered that, in the context of this book, the subject of calculi has been introduced not so much for the sake of making a logical exhibition as for the sake of acquiring tools for the analysis of scientific theories. Theories do not have to be formalized, although to the extent that this can be done it saves thought by shifting the locus of operation from the conceptual segment of Fig. 10.1 to the linguistic segment, where there are rules for moving from one sentence to another. If there were rules for all possible moves between all possible sentences, and also rigid techniques of protocol for generating descriptive sentences, we would not have to think at all. Few people, except perhaps some radical behaviorists, have ever thought such a state of affairs possible or even desirable. In a sense, the formal calculi are ancillary to scientific theory, showing expeditious ways of arranging theoretical statements; the theory never *becomes* a formal calculus, however, even when its statements are in fact arranged in this way.

REFERENCES

1. A. Church, article on "Logic, formal," in Runes (ed.), *Dictionary of Philosophy* (New York).
2. R. L. Goodstein, *Mathematical Logic* (Leicester, 1957), pp. 39-40.
3. See E. Nagel and J. R. Newman, *Gödel's Proof* (New York, 1958). Gödel's original paper appeared in the *Monatshefte für Mathematik und Physik* (1931).

CHAPTER 17

INTERPRETATION AND RULES
OF CORRESPONDENCE

The problem with which we began was that of finding as many as possible of the consequences of some putative hypothesis. Ideally, one would be able to abstract from any hypothesis its pure logical form, and fit this into a formal calculus; the discovery of its consequences would then be practically automatic, and only after all this work had been done would it be necessary to look at the content once again to see whether the theorem in question was in fact an empirical generalization. Pure logic, and pure mathematics, which is considered by some to be simply a branch of logic, and which in any case has the form of a logical calculus, are not really interested in whether or not their axioms and theorems have the form of hypotheses and empirical generalizations; they give us only *uninterpreted* calculi. The concern with content provides the calculus with an *interpretation*—it turns the calculus into an axiomatic system composed of statements about some determinate subject matter. These statements have the same logical form as the corresponding sentences of the calculus. In order to achieve this, the calculus has to be coordinated with the scheme of constructs (that is, with the theory whose logical form the calculus exhibits); correlations have to be set up between the terms of the sentences of the calculus and the names of conceptual or perceptual entities, and the rules according to which this is done are called *rules of correspondence*.

A rule of correspondence is in effect a kind of definition, and there has often been some confusion between this notion and that of a *coordinating definition*. The latter term has been used to mean a

127

special variety of rules of correspondence, namely, those which establish metrical units and standards of equality for spatial and temporal intervals.[1] Rules of correspondence involve more than that—they establish a relationship between the language we use to talk about the world and the language we use to exhibit purely logical truths. (They are, of course—at least at first—*stipulative* definitions; the correspondence is a conventional one, just as, in most cases, the relation between signs and what they signify is conventional.) Providing an interpretation is rather like turning an algebraic statement into an arithmetical one by the substitution of definite numbers for the variables, and the sentence 'let $x = 5$' is like a rule of correspondence. Figure 17.1, a three-dimensional

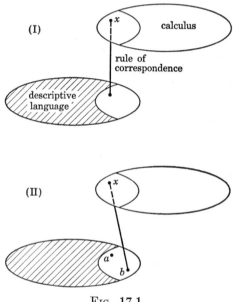

Fig. 17.1.

modification of the diagram in the Preface, shows the part played by rules of correspondence in interpretation, and shows also that by the manipulation of the rules (in the second part of the diagram) the relation between a logically unchanging calculus and a linguistically unchanging account of the world may be altered profoundly. The two parts of the diagram represent different theories, although this would not be evident if only the calculus or only the descriptive scheme were examined.

When, in connection with some scientific theory, one wishes to make use of a calculus in answering such questions as whether a particular empirical generalization does in fact follow from a given hypothesis, whether a particular hypothesis provides an adequate explanatory basis for a given empirical generalization or needs to be supplemented by other statements, or whether some hypothesis is not itself derivable from other even more basic hypotheses, the calculus required is one of which that scientific theory is an interpretation. It would be giving a false impression to pretend that there are many ready-made calculi available, and that all that is involved is selecting the appropriate one; more often than not the calculus is devised to suit the theory, which is then what Carnap has called its "customary interpretation." [2] The axiomatization of a theory consists in finding a minimum set of assumptions and showing that the rest of the theory follows from it; this, as is evident, amounts to constructing the calculus of which the theory is the customary interpretation, and is generally so understood. It would again be giving a false impression to pretend that such a calculus is known for every scientific theory, in view of the fact that very few theories have been successfully axiomatized. Apart from the difficulties mentioned before in constructing formal systems of the required degree of complexity there are difficulties in identifying primitive terms, choosing appropriate transformation-rules, and so on. Axiomatization in most cases remains a program, not an accomplishment. But most theories can be given a partial axiomatization, and the parts can be seen to be parts of a genuine axiomatic system.

The notion of interpretation is important for calculi quite apart from their being the representations of the formal structure of scientific theories; as indicated earlier, it can be used for demonstrating the consistency of an axiom set, and it can also be used for showing the invalidity of arguments. What is needed for an interpretation is a *domain of objects,* the empirical truth or falsity of statements about which is already known and which are related to one another in various ways. Such a domain might be, for example, the class of men, or the class of points on a line. A statement about members of this domain of objects is an interpretation of a sentence in a calculus if the following conditions hold: for every individual constant or free individual variable in the sentence, the statement uses the name of some object in the domain; for every predicate variable in the sentence, the statement uses the name of some property of or relation between objects in the domain; and the sentence may be obtained from the statement by substituting the former terms for the latter names. The test for consistency of an axiom set is then very simple: the set is consistent if some domain of objects can be found such that the interpretation of each of the axioms with respect to it is a true statement. (The restriction must be added that the domain be non-empty, to prevent one's choosing, say, the domain of unicorns.) For if the set were not consistent, a contradiction could be derived from it according to the transformation-rules, and in the interpretation we would then have the impossible situation that the rules, correctly applied to a set of true statements, produced a false one, thus infringing the fundamental requirement that no valid argument can lead from true premises to a false conclusion. The matter can be put even more simply by saying that no actual state of affairs can be inconsistent with any other, or that contradictions do not occur in nature. The latter sounds very metaphysical, but it is in fact the assumption on which this proof of consistency rests.

The way in which a scientific theory may be an interpretation of a calculus should now be clearer. Scientific theories, after all, are sets of propositions linking concepts derived from observations, or, to use a less extreme formulation, sets of statements about objects in some domain (electrons, atoms, molecules, genes, viruses, cells, organisms, families, societies); and if logical studies can use the properties of the domains for their own purposes, scientific studies of the domains are certainly free to use the logical structures for theirs. There is one qualification, however, that must be added to the definition of 'interpretation' given above. It was said there that the objects in the domain had to be such that the empirical truth or falsity of statements about them was already known, and of course in many scientifically interesting domains such matters are still under investigation. Also, empirically obvious relations are limited both in number and complexity, and consequently logicians often turn to non-empirical domains like the domain of integers or the domain of real numbers for purposes of interpretation. Statements about numbers are not, however, empirically true or false. They can be admitted only on one further assumption, namely that no inconsistencies can arise between systematically true statements about numbers by the use of the appropriate transformation-rules. But this is exactly one of the things that has not yet been demonstrated, and it begins to look as if the operation of interpretation is in danger of becoming circular. Nevertheless it may still be useful if the interpretation is intended to serve only a limited purpose, and as we have already seen it is too much to ask, for a calculus of any complexity, that it be shown to be complete or consistent. In the region where systems can be used to reinforce one another in this way, the ground of interpretation is familiar and safe—only at the outer limits does one run into serious trouble.

In the interpreted calculus, it is possible to raise once more the problem of definition of the primitives. At least some of the theorems of an interpreted calculus must be empirical generalizations; so far we have only envisaged the case in which the axioms would be hypotheses, but of course there is no reason why the axioms should not be empirical generalizations also. That would depend after all on the content, and what makes a sentence an axiom is simply its form. For that matter, there is no reason why some hypotheses might not be theorems derived from even more fundamental axioms. These possibilities are diagrammed in Fig. 17.2. In this illustration, a, t, h, g, and p stand respectively for axioms, theorems, hypotheses, empirical generalizations, and protocol sentences. Reading from left to right in each of the three parts of the diagram, the three columns represent first the calculus, second the scheme of constructs (that is, the theory proper), and third the observational basis of the theory—in other words, the realms of language, thought, and perception of the earlier diagrams. In the third case, it is clear that the primitives will correspond to elements of the perceptual situation from which the first empirical generalization (g_1) arises; they will therefore have external definitions. In this case defined terms also, if they enter into theorems which are empirical generalizations, will have external definitions, and from the point of view of the calculus the latter will take precedence. In the first case the defined terms will again have both kinds of definition, but the primitives will not have any definition at all, while the middle case shows a situation in which there may be defined terms, in a theorem which is hypothetical in its empirical aspect, which do not have external definitions. This case is added to avoid the impression that hypotheses must always correspond to axioms, and theorems to empirical generalizations.

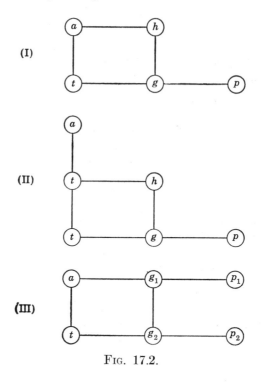

Fig. 17.2.

As remarked above, very few sciences have been successfully axiomatized; there are many hypotheses, but most of them would correspond to theorems if an axiomatization could be carried out. In the cases where the primitives do not have external definitions, it looks as if we have to abandon the attempt to give them any meaning at all. Strictly speaking this is true, but there are two ways of getting round the difficulty. If we can find an empirical generalization whose formal properties are the same as those of the axiom in question, we may understand the primitives as analogues of the perceptual elements about which this empirical generalization speaks; we then say that the state of affairs referred to by the empirical generalization is a *model* for the state of affairs (which we cannot examine in perception) referred to by the axiom. For example, the kinetic theory of gases talks about elastic particles, which we cannot see; we do not really know what they are like, but the equations which describe their behavior have the same form as the equations which describe the idealized behavior of billiard balls and other perceptual objects of this sort, and colliding billiard balls become a model for the particles of kinetic theory. The second way of giving a sort of meaning to primitives depends on finding some perceptual situation corresponding to a theorem rather high up in the theory, which follows very closely on the non-perceptual situation referred to by the axioms; one may then see direct effects of the primitives, and may take these for manifestations of them. The perceptual situation in this case is referred to as an *epistemic correlate* of the primitive.[3] Of course this procedure is just as much in danger from the fallacy of affirming the consequent as any other interpretation of the axioms, but it is satisfying to be able to point to the nearest thing to the primitives available in perception. A familiar case of this technique is the exhibition of tracks in bubble-chambers or on photographic plates as indications of the existence of fundamental particles, and it is certainly better to have these than to have nothing except rather remote consequences to reassure us.

REFERENCES

1. See, for example, Hans Reichenbach, *The Rise of Scientific Philosophy* (Berkeley and Los Angeles, 1957), pp. 132, 147. Reichenbach's term is 'coordinative definition'.
2. Rudolf Carnap, "The Interpretation of Physics," in Feigl and Brodbeck (eds.), *Readings in the Philosophy of Science* (New York, 1953), p. 310.
3. F. S. C. Northrop, *The Logic of the Sciences and the Humanities* (New York, 1947), p. 117.

CHAPTER 18

SYNTAX AND SEMANTICS

A parenthesis is desirable here to separate from one another two questions which are likely to become confused. In a discussion of the logical structure of science, such as the one in which we have been engaged, there are likely to be references to a contrast between the empirical and the formal, to distinguish the purely theoretical activity which goes on within the deductive system from the practical application of that system to observation. This contrast may be illuminated by reference to the interpreted and the uninterpreted calculus, or it may be illuminated by reference to the distinction, for example, between definitions and reduction sentences. These two approaches are, however, fundamentally different. What distinguishes an uninterpreted calculus from an interpreted one is nothing in the structure of the sentences which make up the calculus, but the existence or non-existence of rules of correspondence or coordinating definitions linking the terms of the calculus to terms of some theory having empirical content. The problem of interpretation is a problem of *semantics,* that is, of the meaning and interpretation of signs; and this problem, while it may lead from one sign to another sign at first, always, in the end (where the system of signs has any empirical relevance at all), reduces to a problem of the relation between sign and object. And just as in the case of individual signs, the empirical relevance of the theory as a whole is a semantic question. On the other hand, the distinction between definitions and reduction sentences is a question of the logical form of the sentences and not at all of what they mean, and the difficulty of conditional definition which led to the introduction of reduction sentences was a purely logical difficulty arising out of the paradoxes of material implication. Such questions are questions of *logical syntax,* that is, of the internal structure of sentences.

The reason why semantic and syntactic questions may become confused is that it is possible to make some distinctions within logical syntax which appear to have empirical significance. The most important of these distinctions is that between *analytic* and *synthetic* statements. According to Kant, a statement in subject-predicate form (for example, 'All A is B') is analytic if the predicate B is contained in the subject A, and synthetic if it is not so contained, but adds something to the subject. He therefore spoke of synthetic judgments as *ampliative,* whereas analytic judgments he called merely *explicative.*[1] Unfortunately, the notion of 'being contained in' is not clear, and an analysis of Kant's examples leads one to suspect that it has something to do with psychology rather than logic, a judgment being synthetic or ampliative if it surprises us with what appears to be new information, and analytic or explicative if it is already obvious. For example, Kant felt that the judgments of mathematics were synthetic, on the grounds that the equation

$$7 + 5 = 12$$

introduced a new concept, 12, which was not 'contained' in the concept of the addition of 7 and 5. There is, of course, a sense in which that is true, and it can be seen even more clearly with an example like

$$37842 + 129506 = 167348,$$

in which only people of abnormal powers are able to see at a glance that the right-hand and left-hand sides are equivalent, although we can all see it after a couple of seconds' calculation. But if the sum of 7 and 5 does not contain 12, it certainly does not contain 13 or 11 or any other number—12 is the only number that can be got out of it by the ordinary rules of arithmetic. And if the status of a judgment as analytic or synthetic is to depend on whether we can see the relation of containment, then from some points of view even apparently obvious cases of analytic judgments like 'All bachelors are unmarried' may turn out to be synthetic. Consider the situation of a child who has a bachelor uncle and is introduced to his other bachelor friends; the child might form a concept of 'bachelor' having to do with eccentricity, fastidiousness, and so on, and be quite surprised to find that in addition to *these* defining characteristics bachelors also have the property of being unmarried. In view of these ambiguities, more recent writers have adopted definitions of 'analytic' and 'synthetic' which do not involve the notion of containment but are concerned instead with the basis for assigning truth and falsity to the sentences in question. A sentence which is true solely by virtue of the formation- and transformation-rules and definitions of the language to which it belongs is called analytic, and one which is false in this way is called contradictory; sentences whose truth or falsity depend on external (for example, empirical) factors are called synthetic.

Clearly, in this latter sense, 'analytic' and 'synthetic' apply only in the context of a formalized language. The language does not have to be fully formalized—'All bachelors are unmarried' is analytic by this test if 'bachelor' is defined as 'unmarried man', and as was pointed out in an earlier chapter a degree of formalization (of which such a definition is a good example) enters into standard languages as they develop. It is also clear that, taken as an element of a formal system, a sentence can be analytic only if the axioms from which it ultimately derives are analytic. Every proof in a formal system is analytic—that is, the assertion that a certain theorem follows from the axioms is analytic since it obviously depends only on the rules —but the theorem proved is not analytic unless the axioms are. If this *were* the case, however, it would be absurd to look for empirical confirmation of the theorem; it would be true *a priori,* that is, independently of empirical test. Formal systems in which the axioms are analytic will therefore never serve as calculi for empirical sciences; for once a sentence is analytic, even the insertion in it of empirically meaningful terms makes no difference to its truth. For every empirical science, therefore, the calculus has to contain, in addition to the purely logical or analytic axioms, some non-analytic axioms which will enable the theorems to carry empirical truths. Conversely, these non-analytic axioms will have empirical significance to the degree that their consequences do, although they may have surplus meaning too which is not validated by their consequences.

The mention of empirically meaningful terms brings us back to observation. The language of a science may contain two different kinds of term, which may be called respectively logical and descriptive, the latter being, or being reducible to, observation terms, and the former not. A science which uses only logical terms cannot deal in empirical truth, so that the only true statements that could be made in it would be analytic ones. Such a science might be called a purely formal science; some people might refuse to call it a science at all, reserving that title for empirical studies, but there is good historical precedent for including mathematics among the sciences. A science containing both logical and descriptive terms, but having analytic axioms, would as we saw above be empty of empirical content, although its statements would be vacuously true of the world. 'Nothing can be a metal and at the same time not a metal' is analytically true, contains a descriptive term, and is also factually true, although in an empty or vacuous sense—it tells us nothing about metals or anything else. The fact that it is not always easy to tell whether or not a substance should be classified as a metal does not affect the status of the sentence. Such a sentence is still formal—the descriptive terms do not function as such, and the fact that they have empirical meaning is irrelevant. Finally a science which contains both logical and descriptive terms, and some of whose axioms are synthetic, may be called a factual science. Factual sciences offer something which may be confirmed or refuted; formal sciences do not.

This part of the book is, in fact, devoted to logical syntax, among other things; in the next part, the transition will be made to semantic considerations. It is a simple consequence of what has been said above that formal sciences have no semantic problems. The distinction must be kept clearly in mind, however, between a formal *science,* which contains only analytic statements, and a formal *system* or calculus, which is so called because the form is paid attention to to the exclusion of factual content, not because it is impossible for that form to carry any factual content. Every factual science has its logical form; it is a characteristic of formal sciences that they have nothing else. The logical form of the factual science (that is, the calculus of which it is an interpretation) may of course be a part of, or have much in common with, some formal science; and in this case it is obviously to the advantage of the workers in the former to make as much use as possible of the results of the latter. The most familiar example is provided by physics and mathematics; physicists commonly move into mathematics and stay there as long as possible, restoring physical meaning to their equations only when the approaching end of the work in question makes it necessary. It is always possible in any piece of scientific argument to get all the purely formal steps together—Braithwaite has called this "the separation of the mathematical apparatus" [2]— and this is clearly the most efficient way of going about it.

REFERENCES

1. I. Kant (tr. Kemp Smith), *Critique of Pure Reason* (London, 1956), p. 48.
2. R. B. Braithwaite, *Scientific Explanation* (Cambridge, Eng., 1953), p. 47.

Chapter 19

MODELS

The notion of a 'model', referred to in Chapter 17, is one of the most important in the philosophy of science. The possibility of having a model for a scientific theory depends on the fact that the same calculus may have more than one interpretation. The calculus of which the kinetic theory of gases is an interpretation (based on the domain of gas molecules) is the same as that of which the theory of elastic collisions in Newtonian mechanics is an interpretation (based on the domain of homogeneous spherical objects whose masses and elastic moduli are such as to allow them to undergo collisions without permanent deformation and without fracture); it is not only that the two calculi have the same form, but *they are the same calculus*. Of course the parallel between the theories does not extend very far, and the calculi of which they are interpretations become quite soon in their development different modifications of this basic calculus. But the parallel lasts long enough, when both theories are suitably simplified, to permit the transfer of understanding from one to the other, although never the transfer of content (gas molecules are not very small billiard balls, but they behave like them). Although we may say that the theories are analogous to one another, this formulation does not suffer from the main weakness of arguments from analogy, namely that the analogy is usually inexact. The analogy between a model and the theory of which it is a model cannot be inexact as long as both are interpretations of the same calculus. We may not be able to push the analogy very far, but there is all the difference in the world between a limited analogy and an inexact one.

It is important to notice that a model for a theory in this stricter sense is another theory, and *not* a state of affairs, just as an interpretation of a calculus is a set of statements, not the objects to which the statements refer. But the point of having a model is, of course, that one understands some theories better than others, usually through being acquainted in perception with the states of affairs accounted for by those theories. In view of this, one may define a model for a theory as another theory which is an interpretation of the same calculus, but which is better understood. The model helps in the understanding of the first theory; it does not make its use any easier—that depends on the calculus itself and on the kind of evidence available. If the assumption is made that the theory refers to actual, although unobservable, objects, then the objects referred to by the model are taken as 'models' for those referred to by the theory. There is no harm in such an assumption, and it may be true, but it is not necessary and is better not made if it leads to philosophical discomfort. We may speak of electrons as if they were planets, since there is a calculus which permits of two geometrical interpretations, one in terms of planets going round the sun and the other in terms of electrons going round a nucleus, gravitational relationships in the first corresponding to electrostatic relationships in the second (as long as the electron remains in the same state), and so on. But as Braithwaite says: "Hydrogen atoms are not solar systems; it is only useful to think of them as if they were such systems if one remembers all the time that they are not. The price of the employment of models is eternal vigilance." [1]

The best possible interpretation for a calculus would, of course, contain a statement for every sentence of the calculus, and the best possible model for a theory would match the theory at every point. These might be called respectively a *complete* interpretation and a *comprehensive* model, but they are extremely rare. Usually interpretations and models are *partial*, extending over part of the calculus in question or touching it only at discrete points. For example, an interpretation may be found for some theorems of a calculus, but not for its axioms; or some sentences of the calculus, especially those used in the course of proving theorems, may not have interpretations, although sentences from which they follow and to which they lead do have interpretations. As far as calculi are concerned, such incompleteness is not serious—the calculi themselves are indifferent to interpretation, which becomes important only when we want to use the calculus for some purpose extrinsic to it. When we come to models it is more disappointing, but a partial model is better than none.

Partial models may, however, sometimes lead to trouble if they are unwisely used. Suppose a complex calculus of which some very difficult theory was an interpretation, and of which two other simpler theories were partial interpretations. (They might be interpretations of quite different parts of the calculus, or they might be interpretations of closely related theorems, some of which followed from one subset of the axioms alone, and the others of which followed from a different, but perhaps overlapping, subset of the axioms alone.) Each of the simpler theories would then be a partial model for the more complex one. Suppose now that properties used in one partial interpretation were incompatible with those used in the other: injudicious use of the models might then make it appear as if the complex theory contained inconsistencies. A famous case of this mistake has been responsible for a great deal of confusion in the understanding of modern physics, namely the mixing up of the wave model and the particle model of quantum mechanics. In such cases, it has only to be remembered that the conflicting models are partial, and that they represent different interpretations of different parts of the calculus, so that there is no point in confronting the statements of one with the statements of the other, and no contradiction if they give apparently incompatible accounts.

In view of such dangers, it may be thought better to abandon the use of models altogether. It is quite true that they are dispensable, since as long as one can handle the calculus all the consequences of the theory follow, and nothing is formally added by comparing it with another theory. But the question is not on a formal level; it is a matter of using one theory to throw light on another where our understanding of the conceptual structure is concerned. The use of models will not enable us to derive logical consequences (among which might be contradictions) which we could not otherwise have derived, but it may enable us to see more clearly than otherwise what the logical extension of a theory into the realm of unobservables might mean, conceptually speaking. This the calculus by itself cannot do; it is not a model in the sense in which the term is used here, although it is sometimes taken as such by those who speak of 'mathematical models' in physics, for example. It is necessary to insist on the independent status of the model as a theory in its own right in order to avoid the claim that *any* isomorphic system will do as a model, when in fact such systems can be generated trivially at will. The tendency among scientists to speak of their theories as 'models', even when the relationship described in this chapter does not hold, probably arises out of their intuitive (and correct) belief that in some way theories are replicas of the world; in this way one might speak of wave theory and particle theory as alternative models, not of quantum theory, but of the world itself.

As a matter of fact, there is generally *some* sense, however minimal, in which the relationship does hold, even if the model is only a small part of a very general theory. Two alternative 'models' of the atomic nucleus, for example, the vibrating shell model and the rotating shell model, are so called because they contain terms suggestive of periodic oscillation and angular momentum, respectively. Any *visualization* of the vibrations or rotations in question would be quite inappropriate, but there is no doubt that this terminology helps the physicist to get a conceptual grasp of the situation. The invocation of the model brings with it all the paraphernalia of understanding associated with the model, and this then is at the service of the new theory.

REFERENCE

1. R. B. Braithwaite, *Scientific Explanation* (Cambridge, Eng., 1953), p. 93.

CHAPTER 20

THE FOUNDATIONS OF MATHEMATICS

In the last chapter reference was made to the domain of numbers as one frequently appealed to in the interpretation of calculi. Since earliest times numbers have occupied a special place in the interest of philosophers, because the relations between them seem to display a certainty never attainable in empirical matters, and yet they seem at the same time to be knowable in experience. Mathematics, which among other things is the study of numbers and their properties, has therefore exerted a great influence on the development of philosophy, and its already strong position among intellectual activities was enormously strengthened when it proved to be one of the most important factors in the development of science also. Only when Galileo turned his attention to accurate quantitative determinations did the laws of mechanics begin to be apparent, and he was so impressed by this fact that he said that the "book of nature" was written in the language of mathematics.[1] Plato had already gone even further; in Book VII of the *Republic* he says, "Number and calculation—do not all arts and sciences necessarily partake of them?" [2] It is reported that the audience at a lecture which he gave about the "Idea of the Good" was disappointed to find him really talking about mathematics. At times when theology was not called the Queen of the Sciences that title was held by mathematics, and geometry and arithmetic were included among the seven liberal arts. With such a history it would be surprising if the nature of mathematics were a matter of clear agreement; and it is not. Accordingly, we must look into the subject, and try to settle such questions as whether mathematics is a purely formal or also an empirical discipline, why its truths seem so certain, and so forth. The discussion of these problems has deliberately been left until after the treatment of scientific theories and their logical calculi, in spite of the fact that mathematics is often considered to be a prerequisite to the understanding of science, because as will be seen they may best be regarded as arising when the kind of process described in the last chapter is carried to extremes.

The points to be made here about the nature of mathematics can be illustrated much more clearly in connection with arithmetic than in connection with geometry, although if anything geometry is probably the older of the two. Certainly, the formal organization of geometry takes precedence historically—the geometry of Euclid represents the first attempt to construct an axiomatic system of the kind discussed above. But geometry, at least when it is quantitative, poses unique problems which have done as much as anything to cloud the understanding of mathematics generally, and these problems cannot be dealt with until the next chapter. We therefore begin with a study of the empirical origins of arithmetic, or, as it used to be called, the science of number.

The perceptual basis of arithmetic lies, like the perceptual basis of any science, in the properties and relations of objects and events. In particular, the percepts in question are those identified in Chapter 3 as *collections* of objects, which were said to generate numerical concepts. (The configurations referred to in the same place form, of course, the perceptual basis of geometry.) The special property of collections is that they can be *counted,* and when counted characterized by numbers. The terms which name numbers are called *numerals.* The process of counting a collection consists in finding another collection in which there is one element for each element in the collection being counted, and none left over; we then say that the two collections have the same number of elements. If on comparison there are some left over in one of the collections after this process of pairing, we say that that collection has the larger number of the two. The *integers* represent a series of numbers, the first being that of a collection having the same number as any collection containing a single member, the next being that of a collection having the same number as any collection consisting of a single-member collection to which has been added a single new member, and so on recursively. We can arrange these collections in order, such that each matches any collection matched by the previous one but to which a single new member has been added. Very early in our lives we learn the names of such a standard, ordered, set of collections, together with a technique of arriving at a collection which will match any finite collection with which we may be presented. This technique we are taught to call 'counting'—1, 2, 3, 4 . . .—although it is not really counting, but the recitation of a list of names (that is, the numerals) which becomes counting when it is applied to collections. The operations of addition, multiplication, and so forth are defined for such collections—the sum of two numbers is the number of a collection formed by combining a collection having the first number with one having the second, and so on. The possibility of doing this kind of thing depends on the fact that most objects of everyday experience preserve their properties unchanged over reasonably long periods of time (without breaking into parts, for example) and can be put in groups together without reacting upon one another (coalescing, for example).

It is already apparent that small numbers have a quality of precision lacking in other percepts. Suppose, for example, that one were confronted with two green cubes. Descriptive classification, as we have seen, is as a rule not rigid; disputes might arise as to whether the cubes were really green (whether they might not be blue-green, whether the light might not be deceptive) or as to whether they were exactly cubes, but, assuming that they were distinct and able to be examined closely, a dispute could hardly arise as to whether there were two of them, whatever they might be called. Every object whatever, and every event, whether or not it can be accurately described with respect to its other properties, can be said to be one object, a single event. To the charge that the object or event might be divisible into smaller units, the reply might be that it was then a single *complex* object or event, and the very term 'unit' used here testifies to the pervasiveness of this elementary numerical notion. It might be thought that this deprives it of real significance, and that to say of something presented in sense that it is a single thing adds no more to our knowledge of it than to say that it is an existent thing. But this would be to miss a most important point. Numbers describe collections, and to say of something that it is a single thing means that it is the only member of some collection; there are other collections, characterized by other numbers, to which it might belong, and the term *one* therefore serves to make a genuine distinction between the object regarded in its individual aspect and the same object regarded in its various possible collective aspects.

The system of numbers lent itself very early to formalization, although not to axiomatization. The important movement toward formal development did not, unfortunately, occur in Greece or Alex-

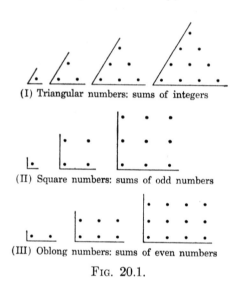

(I) Triangular numbers: sums of integers

(II) Square numbers: sums of odd numbers

(III) Oblong numbers: sums of even numbers

FIG. 20.1.

andria—if it had, the development of theoretical science might have proceeded very much more rapidly than in fact it did. In Greek mathematics, it is true, two steps were taken away from the immediate dependence of arithmetic on empirical matters. It was seen that the process of counting described above could be carried on, in principle, without limit, so that the concept of infinity was introduced and correctly defined (Aristotle says that a quantity is infinite if, however much has been taken, there is always more[3]), and the notion of proportionality, and hence rational numbers (that is, numbers which can be expressed as the ratio of two integers) were introduced. But the notation of the Greeks was clumsy, and in this connection they made one serious mistake. That was to represent numbers as sets of points *arranged in a special way*. The Pythagorean system, with its triangular, square, and oblong numbers, is well known (see Fig. 20.1), but it deserves further attention, since it can justly be said that what followed from it did more to confuse the understanding of the nature of mathematics than anything else in history. Consider the representation of numbers in Fig. 20.1. The number 3, for example, is shown as a collection of three dots, and so far this is very commendable. But it is also shown as a triangle, a *configuration,* and this, for the Pythagoreans, was equally important. As far as arithmetic is concerned, it is completely irrelevant, but arithmetic was to be saddled for 2000 years with such geometrical overtones.

Two things followed from this notion of numbers as sets of points located in space. One was physical—the idea that lines might be made up of large numbers of such points, planes of large numbers of such lines, and solids of large numbers of such planes—and it had metaphysical implications, since a world built up in that way would clearly be *pluralistic,* that is, made of many distinct parts. The Pythagoreans thought there were infinitely many points in a line, infinitely many lines in a plane, and so on, and this extravagant pluralism led a contemporary monist, the Eleatic Zeno, to refute the Pythagorean doctrine by showing that it led to absurdities. His famous paradoxes involve, in one way or another, the idea that if points have size, an infinite number of them will make an infinitely long line, while if they have no size, an infinite number of them will not make a line at all. In his own words, "If there is a multiplicity of things, it is necessary that these should be great and small—small enough not to have any magnitude, and great enough to be infinite." [4] No answer was found to these paradoxes, and they did not do much good because of the Pythagoreans' tendency to retreat into mysticism when attacked.

The other consequence of this kind of representation was of genuine mathematical interest, namely the development of important relationships like square and cube roots, harmonic and geometrical means, and so on. But this led to its own difficulties, since by a fairly simple proof it could be shown that $\sqrt{2}$, for example, cannot be expressed as the ratio of two integers. It was therefore called an unreasonable number—an *irrational.* It proved extremely difficult to bring such numbers acceptably into the scheme of arithmetic, and consequently the whole of arithmetic was shifted into geometry, where they could at least be exhibited—the hypotenuse of a right-angled triangle of side 1 is $\sqrt{2}$, according to the well-known Pythagorean theorem. This way of speaking, however, is fundamentally confused, and cannot be straightened out without a theory of measurement. The sides of triangles are not numbers, and geometry is not arithmetic, nor does it have anything directly to do with arithmetic.

The most important step toward formalization, without which modern mathematics would have been impossible, was taken in India; it was the invention of a name for a collection having no members, that is, the introduction of *zero*. This was done in order to facilitate calculation by means of numerals written in columns, one column representing units, one tens, one hundreds, and so on. A numeral was required to represent, as Dantzig puts it, an empty column,[5] and the invention of zero for this purpose (the actual symbol used does not matter) completed a vocabulary of arithmetic with a small number of primitive symbols (ten of them, since the system was based on ten, although any other base would have done) out of which could be constructed by an effective procedure a numeral for any number whatever, however large. The Greeks, when they were not using dots, used letters of the alphabet as numerals, and if one of them had been chosen to represent zero similar progress might have been made, although for the reasons given above it is doubtful.

At any rate, the combination of a positional notation with zero made possible the definition, starting with the integers, not only of the rationals but also of the negative numbers, the irrationals (as non-terminating decimals), and the complex numbers—the latter by performing, in the formal language, the empirically preposterous operation of extracting the square root of a negative number. Very early in this development the notion of a *variable* was introduced, thus making possible the algebraic treatment of arithmetical problems. Algebra was developed to a high degree of sophistication by Diophantus of Alexandria, and, when the Greek and Indian influences met in the Arab world, rapid advances began to take place. The development of mathematics from that period until the nineteenth century consisted of a continual elaboration of the formal symbolism and methods of demonstration. Geometry was still regrettably mixed up with other branches of mathematics, but Descartes' work on analytic or coordinate geometry helped to save modern mathematics from too great dependence on diagrams by arithmetizing spatial relationships.

Now arithmetic, since it deals (at least in its simpler branches) with actual properties of actual collections, is clearly an empirical science just as much as physics is. The equation '5 + 7 = 12' is an empirical generalization, a shorthand way of saying 'All pairs of collections of five and seven objects respectively yield when combined a collection of twelve objects'. This would have to be accompanied by a statement of conditions under which the generalization is valid, so as to rule out collections of objects likely to interact or run together, but when suitably qualified is a generalization of which no counter-examples are known, although nobody can say that none are possible. On the other hand, arithmetic as a formal system (part of a calculus, although no axiom set for this calculus was known until the Italian mathematician Peano constructed one in the late nineteenth century) is, like any other formal system, merely a language in which terms are defined by means of other terms and manipulated in such a way as to exhibit systematically true relationships. In this context, it is senseless to say that there might be a counter-example of '5 + 7 = 12', since its truth is merely a matter of the interrelations of its terms; given the meanings in the formal system of '5', '7', '12', '+', and '=', such a sentence cannot help being true. It is, after all, only a sentence—it does not assert anything which is open to confirmation or refutation. Unfortunately, it is impossible to tell, simply by looking at '5 + 7 = 12', whether it is intended to be merely a formal sentence or a statement belonging to an empirical theory. The theory is clearly an interpretation of the calculus in which the formal sentence occurs, and this confusion arises because no distinction is made between the vocabulary of the theory and the vocabulary of the calculus.

If this is understood, the controversies which have raged over mathematical statements—whether they are *a priori* or *a posteriori* (that is, whether their truth can be known independently of experience or requires empirical confirmation) and whether they are *synthetic* or *analytic* (that is, whether their denial is consistently conceivable or leads to a self-contradiction)—cease to be controversial. Three famous positions have been taken up with respect to these questions by three famous philosophers, all of whom were right. Hume maintained that mathematical truths were analytic and *a priori,* and so they are, within the formal calculus.[6] Mill maintained that they were synthetic and *a posteriori,* and so they are, within the empirical theory.[7] Kant maintained that they were synthetic and *a priori,* and this is a more difficult matter, but it amounts to saying that the theory which actually describes the world, and whose statements are synthetic, must be an interpretation of this particular calculus, whose sentences are true *a priori,* because if it had been an interpretation of any other calculus we would not have been able to understand it in the first place.[8] 'The world' here means the phenomenal world.

The development of mathematics has been represented in the foregoing account as the development of an empirical theory and of a calculus for which it provides a customary interpretation. The difference between mathematics and other empirical sciences, which arises, as indicated before, out of a certain simplicity and lack of ambiguity in the percepts which lead to its conceptual foundation, is that whereas most theories have great difficulty in extracting the formal structure of even a few of their hypotheses and empirical generalizations to arrive at even a partial axiomatization, mathematics found this task so easy that its calculus has long since outstripped the empirical theory from which it was originally extracted. The formal system of mathematics has hardly any interpretation at all, when one considers the extraordinary ramifications of the subject which have been developed in the last hundred years or so. What made this spectacular development possible, besides the facility of handling the symbolism which was stressed earlier, was of course the establishment of the calculus on sound axiomatic foundations. It is hardly surprising, after all that was said at the beginning of this section about collections, to find those foundations in set theory. Russell once went as far as to say that Boole's book *An Investigation of the Laws of Thought,* published in 1854, was "the first ever written on mathematics."[9] He meant by mathematics of course the calculus of which all mathematics in the traditional sense can be shown to be a partial interpretation. It is this calculus, with its various modifications, developments, and problems, which is today studied by mathematicians.

REFERENCES

1. Stillman Drake, *Discoveries and Opinions of Galileo* (Garden City, Anchor, 1957), p. 238. The quotation is from *Il Saggiatore*.
2. Plato, *Republic*, 522b.
3. Aristotle, *Physics*, 207a.
4. Zeno, fragment 1.
5. T. Dantzig, *Number, The Language of Science* (New York, Anchor ed., 1956), p. 31.
6. David Hume, *An Enquiry Concerning Human Understanding* (London, 1748), Section IV, Part I.
7. J. S. Mill, *A System of Logic* (London, 1843), Book II, ch. V.
8. I. Kant (tr. Kemp Smith), *Critique of Pure Reason* (London, 1956), p. 52.
9. Bertrand Russell, *Mysticism and Logic* (London, Penguin ed., 1953), p. 74.

Chapter 21

MEASUREMENT

The very natural question now arises, Why should this formalism be so useful to science? The answer to that question involves the notion of measurement, and provides incidentally a clarification of the relationship between arithmetic and geometry which so bemused early mathematicians.

The mathematical formalism is used to make predictions about collections; we know in the calculus that $5 + 7 = 12$, and we therefore know in advance that if we have \$5 in one pocket and \$7 in another there are altogether \$12 at our disposal. The arithmetical relation is the formal aspect of the empirical relation between the dollars. The general problem is to get numbers from perception *in association with* other percepts. Numbers in association with dollars are restricted to decimal values and combine in a limited number of ways; this use of the mathematical calculus applies to situations where many individuals can be counted. Most sciences get more benefit from situations where magnitudes or intensities can be *measured*. (It should be noted here that some sciences hardly involve measurement at all, and are nonetheless sciences; description, explanation, and prediction can all be done without ever referring to numbers, if the events being described, explained, or predicted do not have *quantitative* but only *qualitative* aspects.) It has often been suggested that measurement is simply a process of getting numbers, but this, while partly true, is not enough. Measurement means getting numbers, by means of various operations (putting a measuring-tape along a table, and reading what is marked on the tape where it coincides with the edge of the table), but at the same time observing the elements of the perceptual situation which accompany the operation (in this case, the fact that the table has extension). The result of the measurement might be 'the length of the table is 30 inches'. What does this mean? An analysis of the situation shows that an entity in perception, namely the table, has somehow selected a number, not known in advance; the method of selection was an operation of measurement. What are there 30 *of*? Since 30 is a numerical concept, it must apply to a collection; in this case the collection is a collection of inches—units of length—which, when laid end to end along a line parallel to the longest axis of symmetry of the table, reach exactly from one end to the other. Of course we did not lay down 30 inches, but one measuring-tape; the measuring-tape, however, is only a convenient way of carrying a collection of inches, already laid end to end.

The first advantage of having a technique of measurement is that we may *order* collections in a unique way. There are two requirements for obtaining an order: first there must be a *unit*, so that all the collections contain the same kind of thing, and then there must be an *operation*, the application of which will show whether one collection is larger or smaller than another. (Of course they may be the same size; if the operation does not distinguish between collections of the same size, we say it leads to a *quasi-serial* order. Two collections *A* and *B* having the same number will not be ordered uniquely with respect to one another—it makes no difference which comes first—but they will be ordered uniquely with respect to smaller and larger collections.) These two requirements are obviously met in the case of straightforward counting, and they may be extended to measurement in general. For example, suppose we are measuring the strength of electric current in a wire. A unit is available, namely the ampère, and we know the standard conditions under which it may be obtained. The operation for producing a quasi-serial order involves, of course, an ammeter; we say the current is larger if the needle on the ammeter goes further to the right, smaller if it does not go so far. We are now measuring, in principle, but our measurements will be more useful if we can calculate with them. We therefore calibrate the ammeter in terms of the standard conditions which determine the unit, and graduate it according to the physical principles which relate the current to other variables. For instance, if one cell produces a current x in a given wire, two such cells will produce $2x$. It is clear that choosing units and means of combining them is not a simple matter, because in cases like this the value obtained is never useful alone, only in combination with other values, and the technique of measurement must produce the numbers which will combine successfully and lead to predictions. The theoretical point, however, is clear: if we wish to make use of the mathematical calculus we must choose the means of generating numbers in such a way that the numbers obtained, when operated on by the calculus, produce other numbers which are also among those physically generated. Whether or not this actually happens is of course to be determined empirically— one may only use the calculus *after* it has been shown to apply.

When we measure, then, we do two things at once: first, *observation,* the identification of something in perception; and second, some *operation,* the extraction of a number from this perceptual situation. In simple cases it is almost impossible to separate the two; as we saw earlier, the judgments with respect to anything that it is the kind of thing it is, and that it is one of them, seem to be a single judgment. In the case of the ammeter the perceptual situation is much more complicated; what tells us that we are dealing with an electric current is itself a result of some sophistication in theory, and the operations necessary for getting numbers involve an equal sophistication in instrumental technique. It has sometimes been said that in cases such as this the concept, here *current intensity,* is nothing more than the set of operations required for its measurement; this view is known as *operationism* or *operationalism,* and the definition of concepts in this way as *operational definition.* Some writers, notable among them Bridgman,[1] have advocated this kind of definition as a means of avoiding such crises among concepts as that which followed the introduction of Einstein's theory of relativity. These writers suggest that if one never talks about concepts except as numerical values arrived at by specified operations there can never be any contradictions in theory, since there are none in nature, and one would never go beyond what was taken directly from nature (that is, from perception). But in taking the numerical values one has not taken enough from perception; theory does not consist merely of numbers, but also of qualitative determinations which give meaning to the numbers. From the operationist point of view, this directly apprehended qualitative aspect is overlooked—measurement is just the acquisition of numbers, and provides the only link between perception and theory.

Consider again the measurement of length. The extension of bodies is something familiar in experience—we may say of a wire that it is very long, or of one metal rod that it is longer than another, without thinking of measurement at all. Now the so-called 'mathematical' sciences are interested in phenomena *quantitatively,* and we wish therefore to add, to the judgment that a body has extension, a supplementary judgment as to how much extension it has in comparison with other bodies (in particular with a standard body, such as the international meter). This makes our concept of length more precise, but it cannot *define* length. One might say that what can be defined operationally in this case is *specific length,* that is, a measure of comparison of one body with a standard body in the matter of length, just as specific gravity and specific heat compare the properties of substances with those of a standard substance, namely water, in matters of density and liability to change in temperature. That would explain why the result of measuring operations is a mere number—the conceptual aspects cancel out, as it were, leaving simply a numerical ratio.

This point may be made clearer if the following problem is considered: Suppose somebody is given a six-inch ruler and asked to measure the length of some object in meters, and suppose he is also shown the standard meter, which is, however, too unwieldy to be used directly, and does not have subdivisions. The obvious thing to do is to measure the standard meter with the six-inch ruler, and then measure the object; its length in meters is the ratio of the latter result to the former. If all lengths were expressed in meters, and everybody understood this, there would be no need to report that the object was, say, 6.3 *meters* long—it would be enough to report that its length was 6.3, just as we may say that the specific gravity of a solution is 1.5, because everybody knows that the unit of specific gravity is the density of water. Again, the operations do not define length; we already have to know that the ruler has length in order to be able to use it in finding the length of other objects. There are some cases, it is true, in which it seems as if the conceptual status of some property is subsequent to its numerical status, as when the values of two familiar properties are combined in some way to give the value of a new property—mass and volume, for example, being combined (by dividing the latter into the former) to give density. *These* values would not be combined, however, unless there were already an idea of what the combination would signify (mass per unit volume, a measure of how tightly packed a substance is), and the attempt would immediately be made to exhibit this property independently of those in terms of which it was defined, which was done for density by studying floating bodies and the fluid displacements characteristic of them.

If operationism were correct, the emergence of numbers whereever it occurred would constitute measurement, and as soon as we knew how to get the numbers we would know what the concept was of which they were the values, so that no purely descriptive work would have to be done. Two examples will show the weakness of that view. When it was observed that the wavelengths of lines in the spectrum of hydrogen did not occur at random, but were in fact the solutions of an equation (Rydberg's equation), there was an almost perfect case of the discovery of numerical regularity, and some concept ought immediately to have been obvious, in the operational manner. Instead, scientists asked what accounted for the numerical regularity, on the assumption that its appearance reflected the regular behavior of something in the world, the answer in this case being provided by Bohr's modification of the Rutherford atom. This explanation had very little to do with the operations of measurement, which consisted of collimating beams and adjusting prisms and centering cross hairs in a field of view and reading vernier scales. Then there are some kinds of operation which, although they yield numbers, we would not call measurement or regard as definitions—for example, the spinning of a roulette wheel. It may be objected that a refusal to call that measurement is short-sighted, and that some important results may one day be obtainable from a study of numbers generated by roulette wheels. But of course there is nothing to prevent any apparently futile game—like sticking telephone numbers with a pin—from *becoming* measurement by the provision of a conceptual framework.

These latter examples really touch the crux of the matter. We do not say we are measuring unless we know what we are doing— that is, unless we know *both* how to get the numbers *and* what the numbers stand for. A set of numbers operationally generated means nothing unless it is taken as indicating a relationship between aspects of the world, which in their theoretical setting are concepts. And measurement does not establish a connection between theory and the world; it establishes a connection between two theories, a connection between the numbers and what they stand for. The two theories in question are seen to be the original thory based on concepts which correspond to perceptual elements and *an arithmetical model for it*. The congruence of the theory and its model arises out of the association of objects in collections and the relationships between the properties of objects and properties of standard objects.

We are now in a position to examine the relation between geometry and arithmetic drawn attention to in the last chapter. The Pythagoreans' discovery of the relations between lengths of harmonically tuned strings and between sides of triangles depended on measurement, and indicated nothing about the properties of numbers but rather something about the physical properties of strings and the geometrical properties of triangles. They were taken, however, as evidence of the harmonious nature of number, the numerical nature of space, and so on. In the case of geometry, the theory could be, and to some extent was, axiomatized in its own terms, but some of the terms used by Euclid in purely geometrical contexts also had arithmetical meanings, which did not help matters. The meanings of 'equals' in '2 = 2' and in 'the line AB equals the line

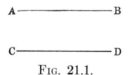

FIG. 21.1.

CD' (Fig. 21.1) are quite different. In the first case, the equality is based on a matching of collections; in the second, it is based on a congruence of configurations. It was not until much later that, as mentioned before, the work of Descartes permitted a complete translation of geometrical statements into algebraic ones, trigonometry and plane and solid geometry having before used quantitative methods only as an adjunct to descriptive ones. It was later still when Dedekind's work on the continuum[2] showed how irrational numbers could be represented by cuts on lines, and Cantor's work on infinity[3] resolved Zeno's paradoxes and made sense of the

view that lines were collections of points. Only when all this had
been done was it possible to unravel the confusion about number.
Descartes' work showed already that arithmetic and geometry were
both interpretations of the same calculus on a simple level, and
Cantor's work showed that they were both partial interpretations
of set theory, arithmetic using the domain of discrete objects and
geometry the domain of points in the plane, or more generally
points in an n-dimensional space. The outcome of these discoveries
is that, with suitable precautions, geometry can serve as a model
for arithmetic, and vice versa, since they are both interpretations
of the same calculus. Earlier mathematicians were not aware of the
dangers, pointed out in the last chapter, of confusing the language
of the theory with the language of its model, and consequently
switched from one language to the other as it suited them. As far
as the growth of mathematical techniques was concerned, these
switches were often very helpful—one can hardly imagine the development of the differential calculus, for example, without geometrical illustrations. The trouble lay in *confusing* derivatives with
slopes when in fact slopes are only one way of representing derivatives graphically. The use of such models in calculation is perfectly
justified in view of the economies effected by it, and it continues
to be useful (a familiar example in more recent times is provided
by vector analysis).

More generally, when techniques of measurement are known,
various branches of mathematics may serve as models for other
theories. The arithmetical case given above is suitable only to the
measurement of certain kinds of physical magnitude, namely, those
which combine additively. (This means that if there are two quantities A and B whose measured values are a and b, then the result
of a measurement carried out on the combination of A and B will
be $a + b$.) Clearly there will be magnitudes which do not combine
in this simple way, and the next chapter shows how the resources
of mathematics can be brought to bear on measurements of quite
different kinds. In these cases, the model also will be different—it
may be topological, or algebraic, or graphical. Such formal models
do not of course have the advantages of the empirical models
spoken of earlier, but they do have one great advantage, namely
that of clarity. It might indeed be said that mathematics is only the
calculus of which the theory is an interpretation, and not a model

at all, and if one were to agree that mathematics is merely an extension of logic that would be the case. At the moment, however, even if the logical nature of mathematics is admitted in principle, most branches of it are not, as it were, in place in the logical system; they are axiomatized theories, perhaps, but not as yet purely formal calculi, only interpretations of some parts of the ideal logical calculus comprising the whole. Mathematical interpretations of the calculus, however, have the least extraneous content, and come the closest to exhibiting the pure form, so that when used as models they serve to bring to the surface relationships which in the theory may be concealed or even unsuspected. Once measurement has been carried out, therefore, it is (as we have seen) the habit of scientists to cross over entirely into the mathematical theory for their calculations.

REFERENCES

1. P. Bridgman, *The Logic of Modern Physics* (New York, 1927), p. 5.
2. R. Dedekind, (tr. Beman), *Essays on the Theory of Numbers* (Chicago, 1901), p. 13.
3. G. Cantor (tr. Jourdain), *Contributions to the Founding of the Theory of Transfinite Numbers* (Chicago, 1915), *passim*.

CHAPTER 22

CALCULATION

Measurement presupposes a one-to-one correlation between constructs and elements of a mathematical system, this correlation being provided by *coordinating definitions*. These definitions make possible the writing of results of measurement in the form of equations, for example:

$$T = 273°\text{K.}$$

Such an equation may be interpreted in two ways: as an assertion that the temperature of a body or an enclosure is 273 degrees Kelvin, thus locating that body or enclosure in order among others with respect to the attribution of a property (here the *number* is incidental, serving only as a mark of the intensity of a variable property), or as an indication that a certain number, namely 273, is to be substituted for the letter T wherever it occurs in some equation or set of equations, such as:

$$pv = RT$$

In the first case, the '=' means a coordination: the reading was taken for such and such a body, or at such and such a time (there will often be a subscript, as T_1 or T_a, to indicate this), by such and such a means, under such and such perceptual conditions (there was perhaps an ice bath surrounding a flask containing a gas, and so on). All this has to be specified along with the simple statement,

$$T = 273°\text{K.}$$

In the second case, the '=' is a sign of the interchangeability of the two sides of the equation in certain algebraic contexts.

The double meaning of such a statement may lead to confusion, and in particular it may lead to confusion between the concept and the numbers used to express its quantitative values. Some people, confronted with mathematical sciences like physics, have concluded that the things with which they deal are only quantities, and that nothing more can be said about them. This we have seen above to be an error. Nevertheless it has to be explained, without simply saying that a coordinating definition has been stipulated, how these quantities can ever be operated on in such a way as to produce other quantities having empirical reference, which was seen in the last section to be the condition for useful measurement. The fact that this does happen has sometimes seemed a fortunate coincidence, and sometimes it has been taken as evidence that God is a mathematician. The equation given above,

$$pv = RT,$$

is a familiar example of a 'mathematical' law, due jointly to Boyle, Charles, and Gay-Lussac, and may serve as an illustration. What it says, in English, is that the product of the pressure and volume of a given mass of gas is equal to a constant multiple of the absolute temperature. But this is obviously nonsense: 'product' and 'is equal to' are algebraic operations, but 'pressure', 'volume', 'temperature', are properties of the gas, empirically determined. How would one go about multiplying a pressure by a volume? and supposing this possible, what could be meant by saying that the result was a temperature? The fallacy of speaking in this way is easily pointed out: the equation is not directly concerned with the physical properties, but only with numbers which stand for them, having been obtained by a process of measurement. The statement is not about the gas, but about numbers; it asserts a functional relationship between numbers generated by physical means. We often use such equations as substitutes for statements about objects and their properties, and even make definitions with their help, as when we interpret

$$f = ma$$

as a definition of 'force'—'the product of mass and acceleration', another curious physico-mathematical amphibian with no intelligible meaning as it stands. Such definitions represent a borrowing, by scientific theory, of mathematical precision. The question as to the validity of calculation then becomes a question of why there should ever be functional relationships of this sort between the measured values of properties of objects, and in order to answer it the notion of a 'function' must be clarified.

Suppose some property p of an object which varies with time. We might construct tables, such as those in Fig. 22.1, giving in the

Table 1			Table 2	
t	p		t	p
0	4		0	0
1	7		1	1
2	5		2	4
3	8		3	9
4	3		4	16
5	6		5	25

FIG. 22.1.

first column time in seconds, measured from some arbitrary starting point, and in the second column the values of p obtained at those times. An examination of Table 1 does not reveal any very obvious relationship between the values of t and of p. Still, if the figures given were reproducible—if every time we started taking readings under the same conditions, the same sequence of measurements followed—the table itself would enable us to make predictions, of a kind; if the process had been running for less than five seconds and the last reading was 5, for example, it could be predicted that the next reading would be 8. We could imagine the table extended indefinitely downward, so that for any number of seconds having elapsed since the start of the process, there would be available a value for p. The only requirement is that under similar circumstances the same sequence should be gone through again—in other words, that the behavior of the system should be uniform. This assumption is readily granted by most scientists; its validity cannot be defended here, but for the moment we can admit it. With that concession we are in a position to exhibit a functional relation between t and p.

It was said above that there was no very obvious relationship, but there is one which is obvious, though not in the sense naturally understood there: for every value of t, there is one and only one value of p. This is exactly the condition under which we can say that p is a function of t—in this case, a single-valued one. For a function is nothing more than a rule which enables us, given the values of the independent variables, to find the values of the dependent ones, where 'independent variables' means those variables whose values do not depend on the things to which they are related by the function, but on something else, such as the passage of time, and 'dependent variables' means those whose values are determined by the values of the independent variables, and thus depend on the values of those variables. Here t is the independent variable, p the dependent variable; there is only one of each, which makes the situation very simple. What is the function? One ordinarily expects an equation in answer to such a question—for instance, if told that y is a linear function of x, the equation

$$y = ax + b.$$

In this case, however, the function is not one that can easily be written as an equation, because that requires a constant relationship between the values. *The function is simply the given table of values.* The rule for finding the value of p which goes with any given value of t is simply: look it up in the table. This kind of function is of limited usefulness, it is true—if asked, for example, what is the value of p when t is 2.5, one can only answer that it has no value—the table does not provide for such a case. This is less than satisfactory, but there are times when it is the only answer that can be given, as recent work in physics has emphasized. One would prefer a function in which, instead of a table, one could write an equation and use it as the rule for generating values of the dependent variable. Such a function is illustrated in Table 2. What is given there is, it is true, only another table, but it can easily be seen that as far as the table goes the values of p are constantly related to the values of t according to the equation

$$p = t^2.$$

If the table continues in that way, then it may be dispensed with altogether in favor of the equation. The discovery of functional

relationships between measured values of physical properties always, however, begins with such a table.

In the case of the second, regular function, the inadequacy of the
first, unsystematic one seems to have been remedied. If we want the
value of p when t is 2.5, all we have to do is to perform a simple
operation on the latter value (square it) and come up with the
answer: $p = 6.25$. But a moment's thought will show that there is
a good deal taken for granted in this process. It will be easier to
see what is involved if we switch from representing functions in
tables to representing them on graphs, such as Fig. 22.2. A graph is

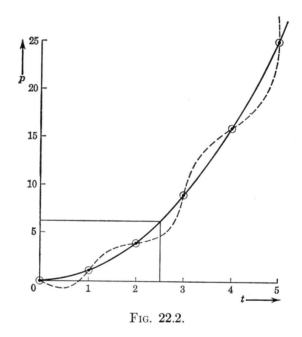

FIG. 22.2.

also a way of finding values of one variable when those of another
are given; the rule in this case is: look up the given value on the
appropriate axis, locate the point on the curve which has that coordinate, and read off the value of its other coordinate, which is
the value required. (If the curve does not have any breaks in it, the
function is said to be *continuous*, at least over the interval covered
by the graph.) The curve of $p = t^2$ is shown, and the six points
given in Table 2 are indicated on it. There is another curve—the
dotted one—which also passes through those six points, but which

is not the curve of $p = t^2$. If the function represented in Table 2 is indeed the function $p = t^2$, then the interpolation for $t = 2.5$ given above is correct. But suppose it should be this other, dotted function? From the table there is no way of telling, because the dotted curve gives all the correct values too. The best way of solving this problem is, of course, to take another reading for $t = 2.5$, which will remove all doubt as to that particular point. But this cannot be carried on indefinitely, since for any two points at which readings are taken there are, if the function is continuous, infinitely many points between. Further interpolation will always be possible, and the same question raised again, although in a less and less serious form.

Clearly it is impossible to avert the difficulty entirely, and in this case we invoke a methodological rule, the *principle of simplicity:* always choose the simplest function compatible with the data at hand. This, like the techniques of protocol discussed in an earlier section, is merely an agreement to do things in a certain way, not the solution of a philosophical problem, and for the time being no attempt will be made to defend it. It can easily be seen, however, that it is in keeping with the aim of science to explain events by referring them to general principles, simple functions having presumably a wider range of application than tables like Table 1. It might also be said that this is the least unreasonable assumption, that is, that any other assumption would strike one as unnecessarily complicated in the circumstances. Of course all this depends on an understanding of 'simplicity', the definition of which poses problems of its own. That too is a methodological problem, however. Although it used to be thought that the discovery of simple laws indicated simplicity in nature, so that a precise measure of simplicity would have been desirable as helping in the estimate of the *truth* of scientific statements, we no longer consider simplicity in itself such a virtue. The principle of simplicity given above contains a qualification ("compatible with the data at hand") which indicates that whenever there is a conflict between simplicity and fidelity to observation, the latter takes precedence. Science need not be easy, but it must be accurate.

It should now be clear how functional relationships may be useful in making scientific predictions. Such relationships may be derived from any repeatable and measurable event by an observer's merely taking readings and putting them in columns, and if equations can be written, that is only a convenient way of summarizing the contents of the table. Sometimes a correlation appears between readings taken in different contexts, for example, the consumption of cigarettes and the occurrence of lung cancer, and then a functional relation of a kind can be established between diverse phenomena. (The question is left open here of whether such functional relationships are to be taken as indicating causal relationships—all that is required is a constant, that is, repeatable, association between one set of data and the other. For some writers this is all that can be meant by causality, but others, as will be seen later, demand considerably more.) It may still be asked, however, why *simple* functions should appear so frequently among those found useful in science. The classic answer to this was given by Russell: If a simple-minded man is presented with a number of statements, some simple and some complicated, the simple ones will be the ones he understands.[1] As a matter of fact it nearly always turns out that the simple function is too simple, and has to be modified if the state of affairs is to be reflected exactly. As is well known, the gas law given above is hopelessly inadequate in most cases, and has to be replaced by Van der Waals' equation

$$(p + a/v^2)(v - b) = RT,$$

which is itself only approximately valid. The more closely we examine nature, the fewer the simple laws seem to be.

Measurement is a process of selecting, among an infinity of possible numbers, exactly those which characterize the state of affairs under observation. The numbers by themselves mean nothing for science—only the choice of units, and the specification of the measuring operation, make them significant. In a similar way, one might say that calculation is a process of selecting, among an infinity of functions, exactly those which link the measured values of the variables under observation with each other, or with the measured values of other variables in other situations. The functions in themselves mean nothing for science—only the empirically determined fact that they represent constant relationships makes them significant. The last surprise at the applicability of mathematics to science should be removed when it is realized that the set of operations which, when performed on the given data, lead to useful results, is a finite subset of an infinite set of possible operations, all of which fall within the province of mathematics. All one has to do is to locate the particular one needed for the problem at hand. Of course it is not as easy as that—mathematicians have not yet worked out all the functions, and it is out of the question that they ever should. But there are no limitations on mathematical imagination, whereas there are severe limitations on empirical observation. What we have to aim for is, therefore, to keep the set of mathematical operations larger than the set of empirical relationships to be accounted for at any particular time. In this we do not always succeed. Newton, for example, when he needed the differential and integral calculus in connection with his mechanics, had to invent them. In recent years, however, there have been many cases in which some function required for the statement of an empirical or theoretical relationship has been found already worked out in mathematics. Einstein found the Lorentz transformations at hand when he needed them, and the work of Hardy (who, as a pure mathematician, prided himself on never having done anything practically useful)[2] contained exactly the relationship called for by some quantitative results in genetics. Mathematics, as the study of the pure logical calculus without regard to whether or not it has any interpretation, ought therefore to be done first, so that when observations are made the functional relations which link them together may be immediately available. But if it had not been for the observations and their more obvious interrelations, mathematics itself would never have begun. And the impression should not be given that even now the process always works from the pure calculus to the application of it. Even the pure calculus has its limitations, and, from the point of view of the scientist, there is much truth in the following remark of the brilliant but eccentric English mathematical physicist Oliver Heaviside:

> I know mathematical processes, that I have used with success for a very long time, of which neither I nor any one else understands the scholastic logic. I have grown into them, and understand them that way. Facts are facts, even though you do not see your way to a complete theory of them. And no *complete* theory is possible. There is always something wanting, no matter how logical people may pretend.[3]

If the last sentence sounds unnecessarily harsh, it should be remembered that this comment was made thirty years before Gödel's proof confirmed it.

REFERENCES

1. Bertrand Russell, *Human Knowledge, Its Scope and Limits* (London, 1948), p. 497: "Obviously a simple law is easier to discover than a complex one."
2. G. H. Hardy, *A Mathematician's Apology* (Cambridge, Eng., 1941), p. 90.
3. O. Heaviside, *Electrical Papers* (London, 1892).

CHAPTER 23

RECAPITULATION: THE EXACT SCIENCES

We have exhibited in the foregoing chapters a structure whose function is to be the scientific explanation of nature. Some general conclusions may be drawn from a brief summary of its main features. First of all, its foundations lie in perceptual experience, which provides the raw material for all the activity of the human mind. At first automatically, and later deliberately, the mind seeks to bring order out of the chaotic and fragmentary data presented to it. To this end, after the initial stage during which objects and their properties crystallize out of the confused background of sensation, concepts are formed (the automatic process) which have the dual function of representing objects and providing criteria for their recognition, and, under the first impulse which can really be called scientific, constructs are refined out of them, or are invented (the deliberate process) to facilitate the exact treatment of results of observation. These results are reported in singular statements, which in suitable numbers suggest universal statements, first in observation language and later in theoretical language (using invented constructs). This development takes place on two levels, those of thought and language, which are to be distinguished for purposes of analysis, although the results of scientific work must be communicated in the latter. The realm of thought is as it were the dynamic field for theory, the realm of language a field of more or less fixed symbols in which theory can be publicly represented. The latter lends itself to conventional treatment, to the formalization of relationships between statements in terms of stipulated relationships between the sentences which express them, and the contents of the theory—universal propositions, asserted in universal statements by means of universal sentences—become in this way an articulated system, a deductive system or, if they are arranged in a special hierarchical manner, an axiomatic system.

The whole of the theory regarded as referring to the world of perception by the mediation of thought may be called the 'scheme of constructs'. The abstracted form of the theory, displayed as a network of sentences not referring to the world but capable of carrying such reference when suitably interpreted, may be called the 'calculus'. The interpretation of the calculus is its application to the world by the mediation of thought, which clothes the form with conceptual content so that it becomes a theory. There is a sense in which the theory is private, a set of propositions built of constructs not shared, as to their content, with other individuals, but each functioning as a *nexus* of relationships. There is a sense also in which it is public, a set of sentences composed of terms whose meaning is given by other terms or by conventional operations. Exclusive reliance on the former view would make scientific cooperation impossible, and exclusive reliance on the latter would make original, creative scientific work impossible. It is better to say that for the purposes of science both the scheme of constructs and the calculus, the privately understood and the publicly communicated elements are needed. It is true that the account given in these chapters allows more than the calculus to be communicated, since language contains more than merely logical terms, and there are other signs as well. But there is a sense in which no language is rich enough to convey from one mind to another anything more than a form requiring to be substantiated out of the private resources of the hearer or reader.

Depending on the aspects of its structure which are emphasized and on the contents to which it is taken to refer, the calculus may assume many disguises, among which mathematics occupies an especially important place. One such disguise may reveal more of the structure than another, and may serve then as a 'model' for the elucidation of the other. In particular, the precision of the constructs of mathematics makes its branches suitable for the clarification of qualitative relationships, the quantitative aspects of which belong to them by right. The agency of this clarification is measurement, which provides the necessary quantitative determinations in conjunction with qualitative observations. But a model may never be substituted for the theory of which it is a model, and this case is no exception; science is not merely mathematics, and its constructs are not merely mathematical variables. In its recent developments, however, mathematics approaches more and more the pure calculus of which all theories are partial interpretations. Mathematics, as Whitehead somewhere remarks, is the study of possibilities; science, on the other hand, is the study of actualities, but nothing can become actual which was not possible, and therefore there is no scientific theory which mathematics cannot, in principle, anticipate.

This remark sounds like a claim that any science worth the name must in some way be 'mathematical'. Clearly, some sciences have not progressed so far in their formalization as to be able to make use of mathematics in the sophisticated sense envisaged in the last chapter. It has been customary, in fact, to distinguish between the exact or mathematical sciences, which have reached this stage, and the other sciences which have not; and this has led sometimes to anxiety on the part of sciences in the latter class, which, feeling themselves not yet quite 'scientific' enough, have artificially speeded up the process of quantification by the introduction of numerical coefficients and indices, statistical tables, and the like. This appearance of numerical precision unfortunately often conceals *conceptual* vagueness in the foundations.

Exactitude, however, is not by itself of any use, and if aimed for too soon it may hinder the development of a science. All sciences are of course as exact as possible—that goes without saying—and they are all more exact than everyday opinion and belief, so that in one sense 'exact science' is tautologous. But there is an ambiguity in it nevertheless. In sciences where numerical quantities are obtainable, those quantities should be as exact as possible, that is, they should have standard errors as small as possible. And in all sciences which have progressed to the point where analysis reveals a logical structure, the fit of the science to its calculus should be as exact as possible, that is, the categories of classification, the definitions, and the rules of correspondence should be as free as possible from vagueness and ambiguity.

What are the obstacles in the way of this goal? First of all, at the level of observation, there may be difficulties of identification and classification of elements, and consequent difficulties in obtaining protocols. Astronomy and medicine are the oldest sciences, but astronomy reached the status of an exact science long before medicine did, because stars are very easy to identify as units and fall neatly into two classes—those which, relatively speaking, stay where they are and those which wander about (the planets)—while the symptoms of disease are complicated, changing, and elusive. (It may be remarked parenthetically here that there has to be an *interest* in what can be observed before a science is likely to arise from it, and that is another reason for the antiquity of these two.) Then there may be difficulty in detecting any regularity in the protocols, and difficulty in devising hypotheses which are relevant and which genuinely produce *these* protocols as deductive consequences. There may also be difficulty in *ordering* elements in observation according to suitable criteria. And there will always be, eventually, difficulty in the numerical refinement of the results of measurement. Long before this stage is reached, most of the biological and social sciences have fallen by the way at the greatest hurdle of all, namely, the *exact* definition of constructs—of the emergence of *constructs* at all. What concepts in everyday use are suitable for refinement into constructs? What new theoretical constructs ought to be introduced? These are the questions of classification and the devising of hypotheses put in a slightly different way, and *these* are the problems to be solved if a science is to qualify as exact in the only sense which is really important. Numerical exactitude, if it is required, will come later. No statistical tabulation of the results of questionnaires will make a sociological investigation exact if the questions themselves (or the questions as they are understood by the person answering them) make use of poorly defined categories, and if the theory they are designed to support or refute contains poorly defined constructs.

The logical calculus is exact; it cannot be anything else, even if it is merely an elementary set-theoretical structure with no numerical elements at all, and in this it embodies the highest mathematical virtues. It is in the interpretation—in the rules of correspondence and the elements of the scheme of constructs—that difficulties arise, that is, in the application of the logical calculus to specific contents. Interpretations too could be arbitrary if it were not for the fact that most scientists are concerned about the applicability of their work to a world given intractably in perception. It is the task of the next part of this book to show how, among so many possible and self-consistent theories, those which are empirically relevant and empirically useful are selected.

PART III

THE VALIDATION OF THEORY

PROLOGUE

The third part begins with theory as a logical calculus of which the scheme of constructs referred to in the prologue to Part II is the customary interpretation. This calculus has been developed to a point where, given suitable techniques of measurement, all the resources of mathematics may in principle be brought to bear on the solution of scientific problems. The truth of the calculus depends deductively on its axioms, which, with the exception of the purely logical ones, are asserted only hypothetically. The task of this part is to inquire how such a hypothetical system can be grounded in observation in such a way as to render it reliable as an instrument of explanation and prediction.

Chapter 24

THE EXTRAPOLATION OF EXPERIENCE

Part II was devoted to the completion of a formal system, a framework for scientific theory. This formal system requires interpretation in order to become an actual theory, and it has already been shown how such interpretation is to be done. But even when interpreted in this way, there is something unsatisfactory about the resulting theory. For all we have so far ascertained to the contrary, it is as it were suspended in mid-air from a point arbitrarily established. And while the ultimate consequences of an interpreted theory have an appearance of empirical significance, we have taken no pains to examine their empirical status, or to determine whether the same sentences might not equally well be the ultimate consequences of some other theory.

Taken merely as a framework for theory, the formal system cannot of course be tied down to empirical contents. It has to serve for more than one science, and each interpretation brings with it unique problems. What is possible, however, is a specification of a *method* for tying the system down so that it can serve as the framework for a particular science with its particular empirical reference. This amounts to a method of rendering the formal system factually operational, and reliably so, by founding it on a basis of observation and measurement and working up from this basis to the hypotheses, instead of in the reverse direction. Such a process may be called the *validation* of theory. It is not exactly a validation of the deductive system in itself, which would be superfluous, since we have taken care to ensure its formal validity; it is rather its validation as serviceable for particular ends. In a somewhat analogous way, we may speak of the validation of a passport by its having the bearer's name entered in it and being stamped by the appropriate official. It was already a perfectly good passport, but until validated in this way nobody was entitled to use it as such.

But a serious difficulty arises immediately. The theory developed in the first half of the book is arranged deductively; truth belongs to the axioms by their logical nature or is conferred on them hypothetically, and it descends unimpaired through the various levels of the theory, emerging in the form of protocol sentences which, as far as their status in the theory is concerned, are true. But are they really true? Such parts of the theory as depend only on the *logical axioms* are eternally and irrevocably true, but as we have seen they can have no empirical significance that can be of the slightest use. The rest of it is true only if the hypotheses are true, and their truth is only provisional. Of course, for any protocol sentence referring to present experience or to the remembered or recorded past, a simple test of truth—examination, or comparison with the record—is available. But the usefulness of scientific theory lies in its ability to *explain* these statements by reference to higher-level truths, and in its ability to produce protocol-type sentences referring to the future or to events which are contemporary or past but concealed or unrecorded. We do not need it to tell us truths which we already know directly.

Such directly known truths are all we have on which to base the theory, however. What we need then is some way of turning the theory upside down, so that the empirical truth of observation will flow back to the hypotheses, or a method of forcing this truth up through the theory. The difficulty in the way of this program was pointed out in Chapter 15: arguments from consequences to antecedents commit the fallacy of affirming the consequent. A possible remedy was pointed out there too: if a theory leads to protocol sentences which on examination turn out to be false, then we can reject it. This, according to Karl Popper, is the only solution to the problem.[1] We must build the philosophy of science, he says, on the notion of falsification or *falsifiability,* and entertain only those theories offering predictions which stand an honest chance of being refuted. The importance of this view in providing a criterion for demarcation between science and pseudo-science was referred to in Chapter 13, and this is the function which Popper intended it to serve. But it is not of the slightest use here. We will all agree in rejecting theories shown to be incompatible with the evidence; it may be that this leaves us with one theory only, which we accept *faute de mieux,* or it may be that a number of alternatives escape refutation (or none). What we now want to know is whether we have a *true* theory, and, if so, which? It does not help to point out that there are some false theories which we no longer accept. The ones we have may be false too, although as yet unrefuted.

The problem is only partially one of arriving at suitable hypotheses; its most challenging aspect is logical. The brain *automatically* constructs the conceptual outlines of a world which we experience only in disconnected fragments, and our expectation that there will not be gaps or irregularities in those parts of the world we do encounter is generally fulfilled. However, we know too that the brain sometimes jumps to unwarranted conclusions—what looks like a log may turn out to be a crocodile, and if it does we are thereafter timid about stepping on logs. We are easily tempted to jump from a few observations to a generalization, and we invent hypotheses on the slightest excuse. Psychology studies these tendencies as characteristic of human behavior, but even if it turned out that the habit of universalizing experience was quite incurable we could still ask what philosophical justification such a habit might have. And on the face of it, that appears to be very little. What is involved is always a passage from particular premises to general conclusions, from past experiences to future expectations, from what is known directly to what is not yet known at all.

There is one circumstance which puts things in a better light. Events are not static entities. As we have seen, our awareness of them is colored by time; they might be called *vectorial,* since they contain within themselves a certain directedness toward the future and toward other events, of which we are immediately conscious. Our knowledge of the past and present points with a kind of impetus to the future, and our knowledge of local events to events happening elsewhere. Sir Roy Harrod has made this experience of continuity, with its implied suggestion of extrapolation beyond the spatial and temporal boundaries within which it is obtained, the basis for a solution to the difficulties with which this part of the book deals (this will be discussed in a later chapter). It is not a finally satisfactory solution, but there is a certain plausibility in the notion that an object moving out of our range of observation in a straight line will continue, for the time being, along the same path. At least there is no obvious reason why it should not do so. And while, when we jump to a generalization on the basis of a few confirming instances with no contrary ones, we have no compelling reason to expect that future instances will justify the jump, we have less reason to expect that they will show it to have been mistaken. Of course, dealing in the reasonable and plausible is less satisfactory than dealing in the rational and compelling, but it may still be better than nothing. There is a principle, once of great importance in philosophy, called the *principle of sufficient reason,* which maintains that nothing happens rather than another thing if there is not some reason for it to do so. This principle used to be illustrated by the story of Buridan's ass, which, being equally hungry and thirsty, starved to death exactly halfway between a bale of hay and an equally attractive pail of water, there being no reason for it to start eating rather than drinking or vice versa. Poised between the alternatives of expecting the rest of the world, elsewhere and in the future, to have the same characteristics as the part we know, and expecting it to have surprisingly different characteristics, we are strongly impelled toward the former.

The strategy then should be to organize the knowledge we do have in such a way as to make its vectorial aspects as obvious as possible, so that plausible routes of extrapolation offer themselves. We may speak of this direct knowledge, for any given scientific theory, as the *observation basis* for that theory. The observation basis must consist of carefully formulated protocol sentences constructed out of a vocabulary of carefully chosen and defined observation terms according to a precisely specified syntax. These, while they must emerge as the lowest-level consequences of the theory, must be capable of standing alone and carrying the weight of the theory into the bargain. To do this, they must satisfy certain criteria which will be set down in the next chapter.

REFERENCE

1. K. Popper, *The Logic of Discovery* (London, 1959), *passim.*

CHAPTER 25

RELEVANCE AND RELIABILITY

The elements of the theoretical structure, whose firm establishment on a foundation of observation is now occupying our attention, are sentences. It would be very satisfactory and inspire us with confidence in the theory if we could find some way of testing sentences one by one to see if they qualified as sound structural elements. There are three indispensable qualifications which any sentence in the theory ought to possess: (1) it should fit in with the rest of the theory; (2) there should be some point in having it there; and (3) it should be capable of bearing whatever weight (in the way of deductive consequences, and so on) may be put upon it without breaking down, that is, without leading to wrong conclusions. These three desiderata may be summed up by saying that the sentence should be *formally correct, relevant,* and *reliable.*

A criterion for formal correctness is already available in the notion of a well-formed formula discussed in Chapter 17, and need not preoccupy us further. For some sentences a beginning has also been made on the notion of relevance, since the whole point of the interpretation of formal systems is to make them relevant, at least in their lower regions, to empirical contents. The question of reliability has hardly been touched on. In a formal system, a sentence is as reliable as the axioms from which it follows, but since the axioms are arbitrary, and even when interpreted only hypothetical, nothing better can be said for their consequences. We have first to decide, therefore, what makes a sentence relevant and reliable, and then to inquire how to determine, in the case of any given sentence, whether or not it meets these standards.

A sentence may be said to be relevant to a state of affairs **if it** asserts or denies something with respect to that state of affairs. Knowledge of the state of affairs will thus permit one to say of the sentence that it is true or false. The sentence is irrelevant if knowledge of the state of affairs does not provide a basis for saying anything about it one way or the other—with respect to that state of affairs, it is meaningless. If we rule out ignorance, then meaninglessness is the only alternative to truth and falsity for the truth-value of a sentence. It looks therefore as if the notion of relevance is intimately involved with the notion of meaning, and as if we should find our guarantee of relevance in the satisfaction of a *criterion of meaning*. As to reliability, it is obvious that the only condition which a sentence must meet if it is not to lead to mistaken results is that it should be true, and that the guarantee of its reliability is to be found in its passing some *test of truth*. And these two things are seen to be interrelated, since in the context of this discussion 'having meaning' is equivalent to 'being true or false'; one might say that the point of having a criterion of meaning is to decide which sentences are worth submitting to the test of truth.

It will be remembered from Chapter 2 that the truth of a statement (or of a proposition) may be either empirical or systematic, and that empirical truth is taken to consist in some kind of correspondence between statement and fact. This idea must now be made more precise. Let us suppose, to use the terminology established earlier, some state of affairs in the perceptual world, consisting of an interrelated group of percepts. The statement corresponding to this state of affairs will be the assertion of a proposition, that is, an interrelated group of concepts, and the empirical truth of this proposition will depend on an identity of form between it and the state of affairs. An empirically true proposition is then *isomorphic* with the state of affairs it represents: for every perceptual element in the state of affairs there is a conceptual element in the proposition, and for every perceptual relation there is similarly a conceptual one. On the other hand, should there be no state of affairs exhibiting such an isomorphism, the proposition would be empirically false. True propositions may be generated merely by the confrontation of an observer with a state of affairs; what he observes are just those percepts in those relationships which bring that set of concepts into play. But when the question arises as to whether the proposition concerned is true or false, something else besides the proposition itself is involved, namely, the recognition of its truth or falsity, and this is the province of judgment. Judgment may be defined as the assent to a proposition as true, or its rejection as false. Judgment of empirical truth depends on a direct awareness of the isomorphism between the proposition and its corresponding state of affairs. It is to be noted that the isomorphism may not extend, at least not in such a way as to be easily recognizable, to the statement in which the proposition is asserted, nor in consequence to the sentence by means of which the statement is made, since these involve language, and the structure of language is not necessarily such as to parallel the structure of the world in detail. A complex sentence may be needed in order to assert some proposition which is intuitively simple.

The term 'intuition', introduced here, is a dangerous one, since it has been used to suggest that empirical truth can be arrived at by introspection. It is very difficult, however, to find a substitute for it. What is meant is of course not introspection, but the immediate grasping of a relation which is presented to consciousness transparently. One *sees* the truth of the proposition as soon as it is formulated. One does not *say* that it is true unless challenged, but when this is said there is nothing that can be pointed to as a ground for the claim to truth, other than the state of affairs itself. If someone were to say, "But how do you know that the proposition corresponds to the state of affairs?" there would be no way of answering him—it is directly known, there is no 'how' to be explained. (We are not here speaking of any state of affairs beyond the phenomenal.) It is of course possible to be mistaken, to apply the wrong concepts; if this kind of mistake showed up in the statement which was made as a report of the observation, disagreements might arise which would be very difficult to settle. It was for this reason that one of the conditions laid down for an observation's yielding a protocol sentence was 'invariance between observers'. The point to be made here is that no statement can be made which is of any use to theory unless it is preceded by a judgment—a proposition cannot be *asserted* as true unless it has been *assented to* as true. This is the case, at least, with empirical statements. Some systematic statements, on the other hand, may be made before it is known whether or not they are true, that is, when there has been a suspension of judgment. Hypotheses are a case in point, and one of the great questions of inductive logic is exactly when the suspension of judgment may be revoked, when, that is, there is enough evidence to justify assent to a hypothesis as true.

The mention of hypotheses brings up the question of systematic, as opposed to empirical, truth. Judgments of empirical truth or falsity require only powers of observation; judgments of systematic truth or falsity require powers of reasoning. Both kinds of judgment are amenable to training—naive persons make neither good observers nor good theoreticians—and both share the quality of immediacy spoken of above. This being the case, it is important to see that nobody can coerce judgment, which arises spontaneously or not at all. Lewis Carroll illustrates this point vividly in his fable of Achilles and the tortoise[1]—a logical variant of Zeno's paradox of motion which goes by the same name. Zeno pointed out that if Achilles enters a race with the tortoise, which is given a start, then by the time he gets to the place from which the tortoise started it has moved ahead by a finite, although short, distance; by the time Achilles has covered this distance, the tortoise has once more moved on, a shorter distance, but still a finite one; and this goes on infinitely many times, the result being that Achilles never catches the tortoise. In the logical version, Achilles and the tortoise are discussing an argument from Euclid involving two propositions A and B from which a third proposition, Z, is said to follow. If Z follows from A and B, says the tortoise, then "anyone who accepts A and B as true, must accept Z as true?" Achilles agrees, and the tortoise proceeds as follows: Let the proposition, 'If A and B are true, then Z is true', be called C. Before accepting the truth of Z it is possible to formulate another conditional proposition, 'If A and B and C are true, then Z is true', on the grounds that if the acceptance of A and B forces the acceptance of Z, then if A and B are in fact true, Z follows. Then let this conditional proposition be called D, and another conditional immediately follows by the same line of argument: 'If A and B and C and D are true, then Z is true'. And there is no reason why this process should ever stop; it is always possible to put off the acceptance of Z by the formulation of another conditional. Carroll calls this "a race-course, that most people fancy they can get to the end of in two or three steps, while it *really* consists of an infinite number of distances, each one longer than the previous one"; and Achilles is represented as an ineffectual logician, just as in Zeno's paradox he is represented as an ineffectual runner.

In each case there is a trick, and in each case the conclusion of the paradox contradicts common experience. With respect to Zeno's paradox, Carroll makes Achilles say, *"Solvitur ambulando"* (it is solved by walking)—everybody being perfectly confident in his practical ability to overtake tortoises. In the case of Carroll's own paradox, one might equally well say, *"Solvitur judicando"* (it is solved by judging)—everybody being perfectly confident in his practical ability to draw logical conclusions. The trick is to make running races and drawing conclusions appear to be more complicated than they are. One can, of course, imagine the race between Achilles and the tortoise instantaneously suspended, as it were, each time Achilles gets to the point where the tortoise was at the beginning of that section, so that it proceeds by distinct, finite stages, and so never ends. And one can imagine a simple argument conducted by the perpetual formulation of conditionals, so that the conclusion is never accepted. In fact, however, neither races nor arguments are carried on in this way. Given A and B and the fact that Z follows from them, we move to Z with immediate conviction. If a person cannot *see* why Z is to be accepted as true, nobody will be able to convince him that it should. Such a person, however, could still accept the *rule* 'Given A and B and the fact that Z follows from them, move to Z', and this would enable him to do logic just as well as somebody who did see it. Indeed, it is sometimes maintained that logic is nothing more than the formal application of rules to premises, and that judgment has nothing to do with it; but it is safe to say, I think, that what makes the rules themselves acceptable is just seeing that they lead to the required conclusion. How much one can see in this way depends on one's experience and education; the very advanced worker will often take great steps involving many complex inferences at once, and may forget that for persons of less experience such steps must be broken down before they can be understood. The lecturer who says "Clearly it follows that . . ." or "Obviously . . ." when his students see no connection is a familiar figure. The logical analysis of a process of inference consists in showing that it can be reproduced by the serial application of a small number of steps (for example, the transformation-rules of a logical system), but the validity of these steps themselves cannot be further analyzed, and rests on a primitive judgment.

No criterion of reliability, then, can be laid down, which does not rest on the judgment of individuals; this cannot be coerced, although it can certainly be educated. Relevance, on the other hand, can perhaps be judged according to some criterion of meaning or empirical significance. There has been in the last few decades a vigorous debate as to what form such a criterion should take.[2] Some writers feel that the establishment of any criterion tends to exclude sentences which are significant at least to some person at some time in some circumstances; others feel that this kind of protest is really an attempt to subvert philosophy to "metaphysical" ends, where metaphysics means, roughly, nonsense, that is, something that would be rejected by the criterion it is sought to introduce. There have been constructed examples of typically meaningless nonsense to provide practice, as it were, for meaning criteria, and surprisingly enough these have sometimes produced perfectly sensible, if poetic, results: Russell's example was "Quadruplicity drinks procrastination," which can be simply interpreted to mean that people who try to do four things at once have to be adept at putting them off.

The Vienna circle, a group of philosophers who were associated with Moritz Schlick at Vienna in the 1920's and 1930's, in considering this problem, proposed at first that a sentence should be said to be empirically meaningful only if it was *verifiable*. According to this view, which became known as the *verifiability theory of meaning*, the meaning of a sentence was identical with the method of its verification, which in the end amounted to the method of confronting it with an observable state of affairs. Only if one knew how to do this could one have any guarantee that anything was meant at all. The unfortunate thing about this criterion was that it prevented universal sentences from having any meaning, since all that can actually be confronted in experience is particular. Otherwise, it worked fairly well—it did not after all demand that the sentence be *verified,* only verifiable—and Schlick was able to show by means of it that sentences about the other side of the moon and even about immortality were meaningful, while sentences about absolute goodness and similar things were not.[3] Even universal sentences could be accommodated if one did not mind infinite classes of observations leading to infinitely long observation statements. Objections to these led, however, to the modification of the criterion in the direction of *confirmation* rather than of verification. The altered view held that a sentence was meaningful if one knew what observations would support it, or at least be relevant to its truth or falsity; under these circumstances it was said to be *confirmable*. The confirmability criterion was a good deal weaker, as far as the exclusion of meaningless sentences was concerned, than the verifiability one, but at least it allowed the universal statements which are so necessary to science. There was added to it by Carnap the supplementary notion of *testability,* which applied when one knew not only what would count as confirmation of the sentence, but how to achieve the state of affairs in which the required observations could be made.[4]

The introduction of confirmability raised the question as to how much evidence was required in order to say that a sentence was actually *confirmed,* and led to the notion of *degrees of confirmation.* But this development, while it gave rise to an important new branch of inductive logic, had nothing directly to do with the problem of meaning. And there were still some cases in which even confirmability seemed too strong a requirement, notably those involving theoretical or disposition terms. A further modification in the direction of *reducibility* or *translatability* has since taken place. A sentence, according to this last view, is meaningful if it can be translated into a confirmable sentence, or if its confirmation can be reduced to that of a confirmable sentence. Once again, however, translatability brings its own problems. In order to translate one sentence into another, one must be in possession of a criterion of *likeness of meaning,* and if translatability is to be used as a criterion for meaning proper then this other criterion must precede it. Likeness of meaning (for terms, *synonymy*) can be handled either intensionally (sentences or terms with the same meaning may be substituted for one another without altering the truth or falsity of any compounds in which they occur) or extensionally (sentences or terms with the same meaning have the same denotations, either states of affairs or objects). In both cases, there appear to be insurmountable obstacles. Intensionally, problems arise with *modal* statements—sentences preceded by *modal operators* like 'X believes that . . .', 'X knows that . . .', 'It is probable that . . .',

'It is possible that . . .'. For example, it might seem that the two sentences 'Carnap was a member of the Vienna Circle' and 'The author of *Testability and Meaning* was a member of the Vienna Circle' were identical in meaning, and yet the sentence 'Smith knows that Carnap was a member of the Vienna Circle' might be true while the sentence 'Smith knows that the author of *Testability and Meaning* was a member of the Vienna Circle' was at the same time false. And for every pair of sentences claimed to be alike in meaning there can be imagined a Smith who knows one but not the other. Extensionally, a problem arises with terms which have no denotation, which according to the criterion must therefore all mean the same thing. It may be said that science is not interested in modalities, and yet, as we shall see, at least the last two of the four given above are of crucial importance. Or it may be said that there is no place in science for terms having zero denotation, but this supposes that we know far more than we actually do about the contents of the world. It was pointed out in Chapter 8 that the surplus meaning of theoretical terms is, if not a necessary, at least a very useful part of science, and it would be regrettable to have to say that every theoretical term meant exactly the same thing.

Is a criterion necessary at all? The scientist often feels that philosophical problems of this sort, raised under the auspices of the philosophy of science, have very little to do with the science he knows, either in its practical or its theoretical aspect. It is quite true that in the majority of cases the criterion will be of no practical use to the scientist, but then one does not study the philosophy of science with a view to its practical usefulness, or at any rate not primarily for that end. The genuine service rendered by such criteria, apart from the intrinsic interest of the problem which a search for a criterion poses, has been to draw attention to the high standards of empirical discourse set by science, almost automatically applied and lived up to by the majority of working scientists, but easily liable to abuse and easily lost if attention is not sometimes drawn to them. Even scientists, who have learned such standards as rules of thumb in some particular branch of science, are often remarkably gullible in other branches. It is a mark of the importance attached by philosophy to the way of approaching the world which is characteristic of science that such questions should have been the object of so much recent philosophical discussion.

As a matter of fact, a straightforward criterion of empirical significance for the sentences of scientific theory can be constructed out of the definitions, given in Chapter 11, of 'protocol sentence', 'empirical generalization', and 'hypothesis'. Because of the manner of its construction it will be called the *recursive criterion*. In order to state it, we introduce two further logical terms. A sentence will be called *atomic* if it contains no sentential connectives, *molecular* if it is made up of a number of atomic sentences joined by such connectives. In sentential logic 'p' is atomic, '$\sim p$' and '$p \cdot q$' molecular; in predicate logic 'Px' and '$(x)Px$' are atomic, '$Px \lor Qx$' and '$(x)Px \supset Qx$' molecular, and so on. The recursive criterion then is as follows:

(1) Every atomic protocol sentence is significant;

(2) Every molecular sentence, each of whose atomic components is significant, is significant;

(3) Every universal or existential sentence, which on instantiation yields a significant sentence, is significant; and

(4) Every atomic sentence which, together with any set S of other significant sentences, has as a consequence at least one significant sentence which is not a consequence of S alone, is significant.

The distinction between atomic and molecular sentences is required in order to avoid getting nonsense into the realm of the significant by conjoining it with what is genuinely significant.

The last element of the criterion (4) brings to light an important feature of those scientific theories in which hypotheses play a dominant role. The sentence whose significance is to be shown will in this case very probably be a hypothesis, and the set S of other significant sentences will be drawn from the rest of the theory. But it may happen that the hypothesis in question is indispensable to the theory, in the sense that the significance of some of the sentences of S can be shown only if they in their turn are conjoined with *it*. But then the recursive criterion will not work, since it requires that the sentences of S should already be significant in their own right. The best that can be done is to weaken the criterion by admitting the necessary sentences of S as *conditionally* significant, in which case the hypothesis itself will be conditionally significant too. To say of the sentences of a theory that they are conditionally significant means that they are significant *in the context of that theory*, but that if the theory itself should be superseded, and shown not to lead to the sentences to which it claimed to lead, *all* the sentences in it would be excluded by the criterion. This amounts to saying that hypotheses may be hypothetical, not only with respect to their truth, but also with respect to their significance, which seems an altogether plausible extension of a familiar idea.

The restriction of the criterion to the sentences of scientific theory is important. There would be no point in denying that sentences like "Issues from the hand of time the simple soul, Irresolute and selfish, misshapen, lame" may be profoundly significant, even empirically so in the broad sense, but nor would there be any point in trying to include such sentences in a scientific theory. The logical empiricists, who maintained that any sentence which was neither logically true nor empirically significant according to their own criterion could be dismissed to the province of "lyrical verses," took in this matter altogether too parochial a view.

REFERENCES

1. Lewis Carroll, "What the Tortoise Said to Achilles," *The Complete Works of Lewis Carroll* (New York, Modern Library ed.), p. 1225.
2. C. G. Hempel, "Problems and Changes in the Empiricist Criterion of Meaning," *Revue Internationale de Philosophie*, 11 (1950), pp. 41 ff.
3. M. Schlick, "Meaning and Verification," in Feigl and Sellars, *Readings in Philosophical Analysis* (New York, 1949), p. 157.
4. R. Carnap, "Testability and Meaning," *Philosophy of Science*, 3 (1936) and 4 (1937).

CHAPTER 26

INDUCTIVE LOGIC

A validated theory requires statements which are both significant and true, the significance being taken care of by agreement as to what constitutes meaning, and the truth by a judgment that what the statement means is or is not in fact the case. The recursive criterion developed above solves the problem of significance in the theoretical context, but the analysis of judgment, as far as empirical truth is concerned, has so far covered only the case of *particular* statements. Even a large number of particular statements—of which all observation statements are necessarily examples—cannot by themselves constitute a theory, which requires universal statements. We have somehow, therefore, to extend the notion of empirical truth to generalizations and hypotheses.

The problem is: Given a set of true particular statements, to deduce the truth of a general statement. This is the reverse of the process with which by now we are familiar, namely deducing the truth of a set of particular statements from that of a single general statement. Put in this way, the problem is insoluble, except in the case (mentioned below) in which the general statement is equivalent to the conjunction of the particular ones. For deduction has been said to be demonstrative, that is, to lead to certainly true conclusions, whereas the inference from particular to general with which we are now dealing can, as long as the generalization covers *one* case not included among the particulars, be shown to lead to falsity if that case proves to be an exception. We ought therefore not to speak of *deducing* the truth of a general statement, but rather merely of inferring it, in some other, non-demonstrative way. The most common name for such non-demonstrative inference is *induction*. One might define deduction as a process of inference in which one never goes beyond the given facts, and in which therefore there is never any loss of certainty. Induction, on the other hand, does go beyond the given facts, and therefore runs risks that deduction does not. We shall find these risks at the root of scientific theory.

Induction is sometimes restricted by definition to inference from the particular to the general. This, however, is inadequate; there are some inferences from particular to general which we do not wish to call inductive, and there are some inferences which we do wish to call inductive which have particular conclusions. An example of the first is what is sometimes called 'complete' induction. Suppose a series of protocol sentences: 'This A is B', 'This A is also B', and so on. Suppose we are able to examine *all the A's there are;* we may then conclude that 'All A's are B', which has the form of an empirical generalization. We would not, however, say that this was an inductive conclusion, for nothing was added to the separate statements about A's when the generalization was made; since the inference did not go beyond the given facts it is, according to the definition above, deductive. Furthermore it is useless, since any prediction ('This A must be B') made on the basis of it can only repeat what was already known from one of the particular statements. (Of course the generalization makes it unnecessary to look up the particular statement, and to this extent it is an economical way of summarizing such statements.) For an illustration of the second case, one need only refer to the first prediction of a particular fact that comes to mind—for example, that it will rain tomorrow. This does not conclude with a generalization, but it unmistakably goes beyond the given facts, which include only what can be determined today. We therefore classify it as an inductive inference. Carnap elaborates this classification of inferences as follows:[1] Call the set of objects or events to which a generalization refers the *population,* and any proper subset of this set a *sample;* for instance, three rainy days in a row would form a sample from the population of rainy days, or of days in general. Three kinds of inference can then be distinguished at once: *direct* inferences, from the population to a sample (more strictly from statements about the population to statements about the sample); *inverse* inferences, from a sample to the population; and *predictive* inferences, from a sample to another sample. (The latter can be regarded as a two-stage inference, first an inverse inference and then a direct one. But it is not necessary, and is sometimes undesirable, to pass through a generalization on the way from one protocol sentence to another.) Here both inverse and predictive inferences, which share the property of asserting in the conclusion something which is not warranted by the premises, are forms of inductive inference; direct inferences, on the other hand, are deductive if the assertion about the population is of the form '*All* A's are B', which is the only form we have so far considered. Complete induction is excluded from the classification by stipulating that the sample shall be a *proper* subset of the population.

Complete induction is in fact quite rare, except in very small populations. As we have seen, a characteristic of perceptual experience is its incompleteness, and induction becomes a genuine problem whenever we try to remedy that incompleteness. Starting from observation statements there are two possible ways of complicating matters, and thus of rendering oneself liable to error: one may retain the observational vocabulary but alter the logical syntax, by introducing the universal quantifier, forming conditionals, and the like; or one may retain the syntactical form but alter the vocabulary, by introducing theoretical terms, and so on. Both of these are matters for induction. It is helpful to distinguish between them by calling one *primary* induction and the other *secondary* induction. Primary induction is concerned principally with the transition from protocol sentences to empirical generalizations, while secondary induction is concerned principally with the transition from generalizations to hypotheses. We may also introduce, as Peirce did, a third case (called by him *abduction* or *retroduction*)[2] to cover the transition from protocol sentences directly to hypotheses, which in keeping with the others might be called *tertiary* induction. Peirce himself, however, did not consider this a kind of induction, and it poses problems which will have to be dealt with separately.

Inductive inferences are problematic in three ways. The first problem is to account for their happening at all, and this may be called *the psychological problem of induction*. What induces us to go beyond the facts, and to go beyond them in these particular ways? The second is to describe the logical relationship between protocol sentences and the generalizations and hypotheses to which they lead; this may be called *the logical problem of induction,* and will occupy our attention in the remainder of this chapter. The third is to justify our confidence in inductive inferences; this goes beyond the purely logical scope of the second problem, and raises the most profound philosophical questions, the answers to which are still in dispute. It may be called *the metaphysical problem of induction,* or *Hume's problem.*

The logical problem of primary induction is the apparently simple one of inferring a universal statement from a number of particular instantiations of it. It must be said at once that this was held by John Stuart Mill to be a disguised problem of deduction, in which one premise of the argument is suppressed.[3] The suppressed premise was his Principle of the Uniformity of Nature, so that a typical inductive argument, properly exhibited, would be:

> All A's so far observed are B
> Nature is uniform
> Therefore all A's are B.

But on the other hand, Mill also held that deductive arguments themselves rest on inductive ones, the principles of logic and mathematics being for him empirical truths learned by long observation of this very uniformity of nature.[4] If nature is uniform (and it is true that we are all disposed to believe that it is), then the problem is solved. But of course that is just what the problem of induction calls in question, and dispositions to belief will not do as foundations for philosophical conclusions.

The kind of inference under discussion here is known as 'induction by simple enumeration', that is, induction resting on the examination, one by one, of a series of confirming instances. It is often supposed that this was the procedure advocated by Bacon, but in fact it was only the first step in his inductive method, and led by itself to nothing. Strictly speaking, there is nothing it *can* lead to, logically; the generalization may be perfectly obvious, but we are not *entitled* to make it. 'All A's so far observed are B' seems very close to 'All A's are B', but a great logical gulf separates them. The 'all' in the first is misleading; it is not the universal 'all' but simply represents a summary of a number of particular statements. And even if, instead of this inverse inference, we try the more modest predictive inference from 'All A's so far observed are B' to 'The next A observed will be B', we find no better warrant for that.

Suppose now we go on observing more and more confirming instances, and still no contrary one turns up. Unfortunately, the situation does not change, unless we have some reason to suppose that the number of instances as yet unobserved is decreasing appreciably, which can only happen in those rare cases (some animal species, for example) when the population is known to be finite and not too large. We have no more logical right to make the generalization than before. An impartial observer might at this point reasonably ask, Why go on observing, if it makes no difference? Why not stop after just a few observations—or, for that matter, why not stop after only one? The only honest response to a challenge like this, I think, is to admit that in fact the generalization *was* made, illegitimately, after the first observation, or after a very few, and that the further observations are made not so much to strengthen it as to give nature a chance to produce exceptions to it. If this does not happen, our confidence, which rose quickly at the beginning, remains high; if it does, then we have to reconsider the generalization. But even this is not as disastrous as it was made to seem in Chapter 11. There it was said that one protocol sentence of the form 'A$_i$ is not B' is enough to ruin the empirical generalization 'All A's are B', and strictly speaking so it is. If now, however, the impartial observer were to say "You see, it is not the case that all A's are B," the response might very likely be "No; but most of them are." And the expectation that in spite of a few contrary instances the *next* A observed would be B might be almost as strong as ever.

We are now plunged into considerations of an entirely different kind. Clearly, something less than full logical certainty may be acceptable as the conclusion of an inductive inference—the conclusion may in fact be only *probable*. As a rule we do not demand more than this, and it may have been only the grammar of universal statements which ever led us to expect anything else. In logic it is all very well to talk in such extremes as 'all' or 'none', but in practical matters things rarely work out so neatly—a point of which Aristotle was so well aware that he usually qualified universal statements about actual events by saying "always or for the most part." But how is this probability of the conclusion to be taken? There

seem already to be two alternative meanings: one in connection with
the repetition of observations with *no* contrary instances, when the
argument runs 'If after so many opportunities no exception to the
generalization has appeared, probably none will' (which is equivalent to 'All A's so far observed [and there have been many] are B,
therefore probably all A's are B'); the other in connection with the
appearance of a *few* contrary instances, when the argument runs
'Most of the A's so far observed are B, therefore the next A to be
observed will probably be B'. Of these, the first case is an inverse
inference, the second a direct one. The difference between the
meanings of 'probability' can however be made clearest by complicating matters enough to make the cases parallel, that is, by making
the first inference predictive and inserting a middle step in the
second, as follows:

I	II
All A's so far observed are B	Most A's so far observed are B
Therefore all A's are B	Therefore most A's are B
Therefore the next A will be B	Therefore the next A will prob-ably be B

But it is evident at once that this is not a fair rendering of the
original arguments—probability has disappeared from the first one.
On examination, however, the parallel still seems exact, so that if
probability is restored to the first argument it will have to be *added*
to the second one:

I	II
All A's so far observed are B	Most A's so far observed are B
Therefore (probably) all A's are B	Therefore (probably) most A's are B
Therefore (probably) the next A will be B	Therefore (probably) the next A will probably be B

It is in the double 'probably' of the conclusion of the second argument that the fundamental difference between the two meanings of
probability becomes apparent. The first has been put in brackets
throughout to indicate that it modifies, without being part of, the
statement which follows it; it represents the confidence we have in
the truth of our generalizations and of the predictions we deduce
from them. The second, on the other hand, is an integral part of the

statement, and represents an estimate of the likelihood of the event referred to by that statement. The first descends deductively from generalization to protocol sentence—the probability that the next A *will* be B cannot be less than the probability that all A's *are* B (this universal *are* is of course timeless); the second is the conclusion of an inductive inference. There is one new feature here: the inference from 'Most A's are B' to 'The next A will probably be B' is a direct inference, from population to sample, but a non-demonstrative one. Finally, the first 'probably' belongs to a metalanguage, since it characterizes a sentence of the object language, while the second belongs to the object language, since it characterizes an event.

Probability is a variable quantity, and both types range from low to high. A high probability of the first type means many observations and great confidence, and a low one correspondingly few observations and only slight confidence. For the second type, the degree of probability depends on the interpretation of 'most' in 'Most A's are B'—and this 'most' can of course be replaced by other terms: 'Nearly all A's are B', 'Hardly any A's are B', the probability of the next A's being B rising and falling accordingly. And inductive arguments may be strong or weak, depending on the probability of their conclusion.

REFERENCES

1. Rudolf Carnap, *Logical Foundations of Probability* (Chicago, 1950), pp. 207-208.
2. C. S. Peirce, *Collected Papers* (ed. Hartshorne and Weiss) (Cambridge, Mass., 1935), vol. VI, p. 324.
3. J. S. Mill, *System of Logic*, Book III, ch. 3.
4. *Ibid.*, ch. 21.

CHAPTER 27

THE CALCULUS OF PROBABILITY

As we have seen, inferences whose conclusions are merely probable permit of distinctions among themselves on the grounds of reliability: some have conclusions which are almost certain, and others conclusions which are little better than no conclusions at all. The fact that such inferences may have to do with samples of known size drawn from populations of known size suggests at least the possibility of expressing these distinctions numerically, and that suggests a *calculus* of probability. Logical calculi we know to be deductive systems, and what is proposed therefore is a deductive meta-logic for inductive logic. Instead of saying 'If a then probably b, less probably c', and so on, this would enable us to say 'The probability of b, given a, has such-and-such a value', and so on. A convenient notation for this last statement is

$$p(b/a) = x.$$

(Some writers use simply b/a for 'the probability of b, given a'.) It would obviously make no sense to speak simply of 'the probability of b' in the context of inductive inference; probability here always means a relation between a consequence and its antecedents. If such an expression were used, it would have to be interpreted as meaning 'the probability of b given the available evidence'. In ordinary speech, "He'll probably come" is implicitly referred to the habits, promises, and so on of the person referred to.

A calculus requires a set of axioms, and a suitable set of axioms for the calculus of probability is as follows:[1]

(1) For any given a and b there is only one value of $p(b/a)$.
(2) $0 \leqslant p(b/a) \leqslant 1$.
(3) $(a \rightarrow b) \supset (p[b/a] = 1)$.
(4) $(a \rightarrow \sim b) \supset (p[b/a] = 0)$.
(5) $p(b \cdot c/a) = p(b/a)p(c/a \cdot b)$.
(6) $p(b \vee c/a) = p(b/a) + p(c/a) - p(b \cdot c/a)$.

Although such an axiom set may be left uninterpreted, its customary interpretation is of course just the set of statements which enter into probable inferences. But a quite different problem, or set of problems, of interpretation arises when it is asked what is meant by saying that a statement has a certain probability—does this really mean that the event described by the statement has that probability? or that we are entitled to a certain degree of confidence in the statement? or that the relation expressed in the inference has held true a certain number of times in the past? or that a rational gambler would accept certain odds in a bet on the truth of the statement? These problems are the object of current controversy, and they will be taken up in a separate chapter. For the time being we will restrict attention to some consequences of the axioms in the customary interpretation.

First of all it is easy to show that

$$p(b/a) = 1 - p(\sim b/a) \tag{7}$$

from (6) (substituting $\sim b$ for c) together with (3) and (4), and this agrees with our expectations. Also simple substitutions in (3) and (4) give

$$(a \rightarrow \sim b) \supset (p[\sim b/a] = 1) \tag{8}$$

and

$$(a \rightarrow b) \supset (p[\sim b/a] = 0) \tag{9}$$

Then from (5) we have by substitution

$$p(c \cdot b/a) = p(c/a) \times p(b/a \cdot c);$$

but since obviously

$$p(c \cdot b/a) = p(b \cdot c/a)$$

then

$$p(b/a) \times p(c/a \cdot b) = p(c/a) \times p(b/a \cdot c)$$

and hence

$$p(b/a \cdot c) = \frac{p(b/a)p(c/a \cdot b)}{p(c/a)}. \tag{10}$$

This is known as *Bayes' theorem*, or the *inverse probability theorem*. In the special case where $b \to c$, it becomes

$$p(b/a \cdot c) = \frac{p(b/a)}{p(c/a)}. \qquad (11)$$

From (6) it is clear that if b and c are mutually exclusive then

$$p(b \lor c/a) = p(b/a) + p(c/a) \qquad (12)$$

(this is most clearly seen if c is replaced by $\sim b$). Hence for any series of mutually exclusive alternatives

$$p(b_1 \lor b_2 \lor \ldots \lor b_n/a)$$
$$= p(b_1/a) + p(b_2/a) + \ldots + p(b_n/a). \qquad (13)$$

Now if such a set of mutually exclusive alternatives which are jointly exhaustive (that is, such that

$$b_1 \lor b_2 \lor \ldots \lor b_n$$

is true) are distributed in conjunction with c, we may write

$$p(c/a) = p(b_1 \cdot c \lor b_2 \cdot c \lor \ldots \lor b_n \cdot c/a)$$
$$= p(b_1 \cdot c/a) + p(b_2 \cdot c/a) + \ldots + p(b_n \cdot c/a) \quad \text{from (13)}$$
$$= p(b_1/a)p(c/a \cdot b_1) + p(b_2/a)p(c/a \cdot b_2) + \ldots$$
$$+ p(b_n/a)p(c/a \cdot b_n) \quad \text{from (5)}$$
$$= \sum_{i=1}^{n} p(b_i/a)p(c/a \cdot b_i) \qquad (14)$$

which on substitution in (10) gives, for one of the mutually exclusive b's,

$$p(b_j/a \cdot c) = \frac{p(b_j/a)p(c/a \cdot b_j)}{\sum_{i=1}^{n} p(b_i/a)p(c/a \cdot b_i)}. \qquad (15)$$

This is clearly an alternative statement of Bayes' theorem.

　　Without attempting to settle the vexed question of the meaning of probability statements, we can try a simple interpretation of the two forms of Bayes' theorem. In (11) let $b \equiv h$, a hypothesis, let $a \equiv e$, the accumulated evidence for h, and let $c \equiv f$ (for forecast), a prediction made on the basis of h (thus satisfying the condition for the simplified form of the theorem, namely that $h \to f$). We have

$$p(h/e \cdot f) = \frac{p(h/e)}{p(f/e)},$$

that is, the probability of the hypothesis when the prediction has in fact been fulfilled is given by the ratio of its probability given the prior evidence to the probability of the prediction on the basis of the prior evidence alone, without the intervention of the hypothesis. This value will be higher the less probable the prediction—that is, the successful prediction of an *unexpected* and therefore surprising event does more for the hypothesis on the basis of which it is made than the prediction of some event which might have been expected in any case. This is a very comforting result, since it vindicates the view that the more risks a theory takes in prediction (that is, the more startling the events it prophesies) the more it deserves to be believed after its predictions come true. There is a concealed limitation, however—the value of the ratio, by axiom (2), can never be greater than 1, and it must therefore be the case that

$$p(f/e) \geqslant p(h/e);$$

in other words, the prediction must generally be *less* startling, on the available evidence, than the theory which makes it. However, if $p(h/e)$ is low enough to start with, $p(f/e)$ can still become quite small, which is again reasonable: the less plausible the theory, the more bizarre what it predicts.

Turning now to (15), the situation is a little more complicated, but the interpretation follows similar lines. We have now $b_j \equiv h_j$, one among n mutually exclusive hypotheses which are jointly exhaustive, that is, one of which is true; $a \equiv e$ and $c \equiv f$ as before. This gives

$$p(h_j/e \cdot f) = \frac{p(h_j/e)p(f/e \cdot h_j)}{\sum\limits_{i=1}^{n} p(h_i/e)p(f/e \cdot h_i)}.$$

The prediction f is now assigned various probabilities according to the various hypotheses, and these are assumed known. The hypotheses themselves have various probabilities on the available evidence, called *initial probabilities*, and these are also known. If now f actually comes true, this event changes the probabilities of the hypotheses, and these changes are given by the equation above. In general, a hypothesis on which the probability of f was high, by comparison with its probability on one of the alternative hypotheses, becomes relatively speaking more probable with respect to that alternative, whatever their respective probabilities were according to the prior evidence.

The calculation will not work, however, unless these initial probabilities are known, and here lies the whole difficulty. It is all very well to work out *changes* in the probability of a hypothesis on the fulfillment of some prediction, but how did it acquire a probability in the first place? Some writers dismiss this question by calling the initial probabilities *a priori* probabilities, and saying perhaps that all the hypotheses were equally likely, and that since one of the h_i is known to be true

$$\sum_{i=1}^{n} p(h_i) = 1$$

so that *a priori*

$$(h_i)[p(h_i) = 1/n].$$

This is certainly one way of getting things started, and as various predictions of various probabilities on the various hypotheses actually come true, some hypotheses will gradually get stronger and others weaker, until eventually one emerges as so much more probable than the others that it is, for practical purposes, accepted as true. In the absence of other techniques this is the best that can be done. But a serious question remains: How can we be sure that we really have a set of jointly exhaustive hypotheses? And to this there is only one answer, namely that we cannot be sure.

We have then a calculus of probability which, when given its customary interpretaton in terms of scientific statements, allows us to calculate relative probabilities of alternative hypotheses in the light of changing evidence. Two problems stand out: how do we get the first probability into the calculation? and what does 'the probability of a statement' mean?

REFERENCE

1. These axioms are translated from B. Russell, *Human Knowledge, Its Scope and Limits* (London, 1948), p. 363. Russell in turn took them from Broad. "It is immaterial, for our purposes," says Russell, "whether these axioms are all *necessary;* what concerns us is only that they are *sufficient.*"

CHAPTER 28

RELATIVE FREQUENCY

The first serious work on the theory of probability was done by Pascal, although the idea goes back to the Stoics. In Pascal the problem is that of acting on uncertainties; his interest in the subject was stimulated by the gambling of his worldly friends, and in his famous wager he turned it to account in an attempt to convert them. The great classical work on the subject is by Laplace,[1] and contains, curiously enough, the great classical statement of strict causal determinism. This becomes more intelligible when it is realized that until quite recently it was always assumed that recourse to probabilities was necessary only because of our ignorance; if we could only know everything—all the facts, and all the laws governing them—then we would be able to deal always in certainties, and estimates of likelihood would be superfluous. But since that is impossible we do the best we can by calculating chances.

The simplest interpretation of the calculus is the *a priori* probability of Laplace, in which the numerical value is defined as the ratio of favorable possibilities to all possibilities. Suppose a coin to be tossed; what is the probability that it will turn up heads? There are two possibilities—heads and tails—of which one, namely heads, is favorable to the turning up of heads; the probability of this event is therefore 1/2. Similarly, the probability of a six on the throw of a true die is 1/6, and the probability of a double six on the throw of two such dice is 1/36. (The latter gives a simple illustration of the truth of axiom 5.) The difficulty with this interpretation lies in the meaning of the term 'possibility'. Suppose instead of tossing the coin we were to try to throw it into an eggcup at a distance of twenty feet; there are still only two possibilities—getting it into the eggcup, or failing to do so—one of which is favorable, but nobody would now say that the probability of success was 1/2. Of course, in this case there is lacking a certain symmetry present in the simple toss. But the symmetry even there may be only apparent—somebody might have weighted the coin in such a way that it was more likely to turn up heads. On the *a priori* view, this could be known only to the person who arranged it; but he could know it only on the grounds of actual prior experience of the tossing of coins tampered with in this way, and by a simple test anybody else could discover if the coin in question had in fact been tampered with. The test of course would be to toss it a number of times and see how often it turned up heads.

From the *a priori* view, then, the simple transition is made to the view that probability is a measure of a property of a sequence, namely of the *relative frequency* of the occurrence of some event in that sequence—for example, the occurrence of heads in a sequence of tossed pennies. It turns out that for a true penny this value, the ratio of successes to trials, is just the value 1/2 obtained on the *a priori* theory. To put the matter more precisely, we *call* a penny true if it gives this frequency, and biased if it gives some other value. The importance of these questions to gamblers can hardly be overestimated, since if one possessed a penny for which this value was even slightly greater than 1/2 one could, assuming sufficiently stupid opponents to be found sufficiently often, make a living by always calling heads, just as one could make a living by placing even money, at *every* birth, on the baby's being a boy. According to the relative frequency theory, the existence of two mutually exclusive alternatives only occasionally, and by no means necessarily, leads to a probability of exactly 1/2, and this can be known only by empirical test. When the value lies very close to such a simple fraction we shall not, of course, be surprised to find an apparent symmetry, but we do not count on it even then. Whether, if all the internal workings of nature were known, *a priori* probability together with the principle of sufficient reason would enable us to predict accurately the observed relative frequencies, we cannot be sure. Probably it would; but if anything went wrong we would have to trust the relative frequencies rather than the *a priori* probabilities.

But this is a crucial point. If probability *means* relative frequency, then the probability of heads in a sequence of ten tosses in which there were five heads would be 1/2, but in a sequence in which there were only four heads it would be 2/5. For any finite sequence there is this danger of fluctuation. On the other hand, if one takes averages over the long run no *reliable* estimate is possible; the run is never long enough—perhaps tomorrow heads will begin to turn up 4/5 of the time?—and in any case in the long run (Keynes is often quoted as saying) we shall all be dead. Probability must surely, if it is to be of any use, *have* some value, and this value must at least be approachable after a finite time. It cannot therefore *be* the relative frequency; we have to change the initial formulation round and say that the relative frequency is a measure of the probability, and not vice versa. But then the search for a meaning of 'probability' has to begin again from the beginning.

At this point it is common to invoke a result due to Bernoulli, known as the *law of large numbers*. Let a be the protocol sentence 'This is an A', and let b be the protocol sentence 'This A is B'; let α be the number of times a is true, and β the number of times b is true; and suppose indefinitely many A's, some of which are B, to be available for observation. The law of large numbers then states simply:

$$(p[b/a] = x) \supset (\exists n)(\exists \epsilon)(\alpha)(\alpha > n \supset |x - \beta/\alpha| \leqslant \epsilon).$$

In other words, if the probability is known, then there is some number n (presumed large) of observations after which the relative frequency cannot differ from the probability by more than a certain amount. The significance of this result is often taken to be that if we observe the relative frequency for a long enough sequence we shall know, within very narrow limits, what the probability is—or to put it bluntly

$$(\exists n)(\exists \epsilon)(\exists x)(\alpha)(\alpha > n \supset |x - \beta/\alpha| \leqslant \epsilon) \supset (p[b/a] = x).$$

But of course that is not the same thing at all. *If* the antecedent of this conditional could be known to be true for any reasonably small ϵ, we would certainly accept x as a good approximation to the probability. But it can *never* be known to be true. The trouble lies in

$$(\alpha)(\alpha > n \ldots);$$

it may always turn out that the n is too small, and that at some disastrous point

$$|x - \beta/\alpha| > \epsilon.$$

We are back, therefore, more or less where we started. If we know the probability all is well; if not, there seems to be no way of finding it.

This probability, of course, is the *second* kind of the two in Chapter 26—the probability that some given A will be B, that is, that given 'This is an A', 'This A is B' will also be true. Perhaps relative frequency will work better for the first kind, the probability of the generalization. The probability of a generalization must depend in some way, after all, on the *number* of confirming instances of it which have been observed; the more instances have been accumulated (in the absence of any contrary ones), the more probable the generalization. That at least is what we would intuitively expect. Hempel, however, pointed out in 1950 a serious difficulty in the way of this notion.[2] Suppose we are accumulating evidence for the generalization 'All crows are black'; we observe a crow, and it turns out to be black; then another, and another, and so on. The generalization begins to look reasonably strong, but we are a long way from observing even most of the crows there are, and its probability increases only slowly. Hempel showed that by a logical device we can generate at will indefinitely many confirming instances of the generalization, and make its probability approach as nearly as we like to 1, without the necessity of observing a single crow—in fact, we could do it if there were no such things as crows. The device is the perfectly proper logical one of turning 'All crows are black' into the equivalent statement 'All non-black things are non-crows', of which white shoes, green books, and so forth are confirming instances. Scores of non-black things lie ready to hand, and sure enough every one of them, on examination, turns out not to be a crow.

This looks like a red herring, and it is. Hempel's paradox is possible only on the assumption that the generalizations of science must be phrased in the simple Aristotelian way—'All A's are B'. For purposes of discussion this is often very convenient, but an examination of scientific texts produces surprisingly few examples of this sort, or of any sort on which logical tricks can be played.

Scientists tend to avoid quantifiers altogether, except in the case where some definite statistical assertion can be made; in other cases the universal quantifier is implicit, but there would probably be objections to making it explicit. The principal reason for this is that, as we have seen, the generalization has to fulfill two functions, one of which is retrospective—the description and explanation of what has been observed—and one predictive. This means that there is an irreducible ambiguity in the universal quantifier; retrospectively it stands for 'All so far observed', but predictively it stands for 'All' without qualification. And while the first might be acceptable, the scientist is understandably cautious about the second. Even to the first would usually be added some such qualification as 'within the limits of experimental error'. In fact, if any logically convenient form for a scientific generalization were required, it would probably follow the statistical pattern suggested on page 78. In this form, Hempel's paradox cannot arise. While it is true that 'All crows are black' is logically equivalent to 'All non-black objects are non-crows', it is certainly *not* true that 'In every sequence of α crows $\beta \pm \epsilon$ are black' is logically equivalent to 'In every sequence of α non-black objects $\beta \pm \epsilon$ are non-crows'. By making explicit reference to the series of observations the pitfall is avoided.

But the successful survival of this shock leaves us no nearer to an answer to the question, In what sense does the number of confirming instances contribute to the probability of the generalization which they support? In the absence of contrary instances we would hope to find that probability approaching 1, whatever the generalization might assert. (The paradigm just given is a statement about a relative frequency, so that the case in which $\alpha = \beta$ corresponds to a probability of 1, and smaller values of β to smaller probabilities, in the second sense of 'probability'.) So far, however, while the number of confirming instances helps to establish the probability asserted by the generalization, it has no connection whatever with the probability *of* the generalization. We could obtain a value of this latter probability in an *ad hoc* way by making it equal to $1 - \epsilon/\beta$, which has the advantage of increasing as β increases and decreasing as ϵ increases. This draws attention to a peculiarity of the statistical paradigm given above: in order to take advantage of the sheer number of observations we would want long sequences, perhaps even a single sequence in which α is equal to the total number of observations made—in this case there would be no sense in giving any value at all to ϵ, and the attempt to get a probability of the generalization would be defeated; conversely, in order to get a realistic value of ϵ, and to reflect the fluctuations in the sequence, we would want to break this long sequence up into many short sequences. The former of these alternatives was selected by Reichenbach, who, instead of trying to assign any probability to the generalization, argued that the relative frequency value β/α should be accepted, provisionally, as the true value of the probability asserted by the generalization.[3] Reichenbach called this value a *posit*, and claimed that if the value of β/α in the continued sequence in fact converged to some limit there could be no better estimate of this limiting value than the best, that is, latest, posit—in other words, just the relative frequency so far observed. Of course this estimate might be quite wrong; but this could only be discovered by making more observations, and these would automatically lead to the emergence of a new posit. Reichenbach's claim is simply that if in the long run a series of posits converges then, also in the long run, the method of best posits is the quickest and surest way of arriving at the true value. *If* the series converges, this is true. If it does not converge, we are wasting our time—and the snag is that we cannot know whether it converges or not. To this Reichenbach would reply that unless the world is constructed in such a way as to insure that such series do converge we are wasting our time anyway. This is just the uniformity of nature argument again, and represents no forward progress. And since generalizations in Reichenbach's form are quite unfalsifiable (any finite amount of evidence is compatible with any statistical generalization whatever) we have to conclude, according to Popper's criterion of demarcation, that this is not really a scientific account at all.

At this point a clear separation must be made between two quite distinct ideas. The practice of science requires, of course, just the acceptance of best posits on which Reichenbach insists—there is after all no alternative to the policy of making use of all the data so far gathered. But such scientific practice cannot possibly be taken as a solution to a problem in the philosophy of science, the philosophy of science consisting as we have seen exactly in the analysis and criticism of scientific thought and practice. *Obviously* the latest relative frequency value is the best posit, but that is not the point. The philosophical question is not whether it is the best posit but whether it is a good posit, that is, whether we have any grounds for accepting it as a close estimate of the final outcome. Even if all the posits were bad, there would still be a best one. This argument applies just as strongly to the statistical paradigm as to Reichenbach's case. It is true that a generalization couched in terms of discrete sequences can be falsified, by finding a sequence in which the number of B's observed differs from β by more than ϵ (this assumes that ϵ is a whole number—it would not work if ϵ were, for example, the standard deviation of β computed for the whole set of sequences, which would look like Reichenbach again); but it will usually be possible to break up the sequence of A's in a new way so as to get round this difficulty. We are in fact once again driven into the by now familiar philosophical impasse—from observations already made there is no legitimate way of deducing anything about the results of observations not yet made. We may say that there is a reasonable way of *conjecturing* something about these results, but that is a very different matter. To act reasonably in the face of uncertainty is at the same time to realize that the unexpected may occur and all one's calculations be vitiated.

We now appear to be caught in a dilemma: either our knowledge of probabilities rests on the measurement of relative frequencies—but in this case we always have to wait for further measurements before we can be sure that our estimate of the probability is tending in the right direction; or our knowledge of probabilities is derived from *a priori* considerations—but these cannot be known to be correct unless tested by relative frequency measurements. As far as theoretical construction goes, the latter alternative has been fully worked out by Carnap.[4] He supposes a world in which there is a finite number of things, each of these things having a finite number of properties. Such a world can have only a finite number of states, each state being characterized by the assignment of some of its possible properties to each thing. At first each of these states is considered to be equally possible, so that, if there are n states, each of them starts out with an *a priori* or initial probability of $1/n$. From these *a priori* probabilities other probabilities can be constructed by eliminating certain states as inconsistent with one another, or giving weights to some in preference to others. Eliminations and weightings would be done on the basis of empirical observations. A whole set of possible worlds—that is, of possible states of the aggregate of all the things there are—might be eliminated at a stroke if it proved to be inconsistent with some observation; and among those consistent with this observation, the ones which actually entailed it would become stronger by the application of Bayes' theorem. The practical difficulty with this scheme, apart from the fundamental criticism that a world fully describable in terms of things and their properties would not be like *this* world, lies in the postulation of a finite world. One of Kant's antinomies of pure reason concerns this point, his conclusion being that either assumption (that the world is finite, or that it is infinite) leads to contradictions.[5] For some mathematical purposes, especially where very large numbers are involved, it seems desirable to have an infinite world, in order that there shall be something for such large numbers to refer to no matter how large they get; for Carnap's purposes it is desirable to have a finite world. In such logical exercises we might make the world quite small, for example, containing ten things, each of which had five properties; but the real world, although it may be finite, is certainly not small, and for practical purposes 'finite but very large' is tantamount to 'infinite'. Aristotle's definition of an infinite quantity already referred to in Chapter 20 is still essentially satisfactory; a quantity is infinite, he says, if, however much has been taken, there is always more. The world will be infinite for us in that sense as long as it extends, spatially and temporally, just beyond the bounds of our conception and comprehension. And a world like Carnap's, large enough to reflect with any fidelity the complexities which we actually encounter, might turn out after all to be infinite in this sense. The same kind of criticism can be leveled at Keynes's principle of limited independent variety, which suggests, not that the world itself is finite, but that any property in it can enter only into a finite number of combinations.[6] If this number is small enough to be conveniently manipulated, it will probably be too small to reflect the complexity of the world of experience. And neither of these methods surmounts the initial difficulty that when it comes to *measuring* probabilities we still have, so far, to fall back on relative frequency.

REFERENCES

1. P. S. Laplace, *Essai Philosophique sur les Probabilités* (Paris, 1921, ed. Gauthier-Villars), p. 3.
2. C. G. Hempel, "Studies in the logic of confirmation, I," *Mind*, LIV (1950), p. 14.
3. H. Reichenbach (tr. Maria Reichenbach), "The Logical Foundations of the Concept of Probability," in Feigl and Brodbeck, *Readings in the Philosophy of Science* (New York, 1953), p. 466.
4. See S. F. Barker, *Induction and Hypothesis* (Ithaca, N. Y., 1957), p. 83.
5. I. Kant, *Critique of Pure Reason*, p. 396.
6. J. M. Keynes, *A Treatise on Probability* (London, 1921), p. 258.

CHAPTER 29

PROBABILITY: INTERPRETATIONS

We must now, in order to escape from the dilemma of the last chapter, take up the question of the interpretation of probability in a more fundamental sense. What in fact is it whose value is known *a priori*, or reveals itself through relative frequency measurements? Measurement, as we saw in an earlier chapter, does not simply produce numbers, but produces numbers in association with definable characteristics, and the question therefore is what characteristics of the world find their numerical expression in probability.

It must always be remembered that probability is not absolute, but expresses a relationship between two statements—the probability of *a, given b*. In view of this Keynes suggested [1] that probability is not a measure of anything in the world at all, but is simply an indefinable logical relationship between the two statements involved, a relationship whose extremes are entailment on the one hand (when the probability is 1) and incompatibility on the other (when the probability is 0). If language is descriptive of the world, there is presumably some actual relationship to which this logical relationship corresponds—perhaps a causal relation of some sort, looser or tighter as the value of the probability approaches 0 or 1. It is to be noticed that while a probability of 1 corresponds to contingent truth in the empirical statement, it does not mean that the statement is logically necessary, and that a probability of 0, similarly, while it means the contingent falsehood of the empirical statement, does not mean that the statement is logically impossible. There is in fact no reason why an event which had a probability of 0 might not nevertheless happen. After all, any statement which *was* contingently false may *become* contingently true by the supervention of a new state of affairs. The philosophical issues raised by this possibility are far-reaching, and cannot be pursued further here —the crucial question is whether the world is determined or whether it has room for novelty. Alternatively the strict notion of causality might be retained, and the logical relationship made a function of our ignorance as before.

A radically different proposal as to the nature of probability is associated with the names of Ramsey, De Finetti, and Savage,[2] who claim that probability reflects neither a knowable objective state of the world nor a merely logical relation between statements, but a state of the knower, best characterized not negatively as his ignorance of the future, but positively as his expectation with respect to it. The probability of an event is measured by the degree of confidence we have in its occurrence; the probability of a generalization, or of a hypothesis, is measured by the degree of confidence we have in its truth. This is not in itself such a novel idea. The serious contribution of these workers lies in their success at devising a measure of subjective probability. One form of this measure[3] is based on the behavior of a fictional being known as the rational gambler. One discovers the probability of a statement by proposing a bet to the rational gambler, and basing the calculation on the odds which he is prepared to accept. The rational gambler is not out to make money, but he is not prepared to lose it either; his pleasure in gambling is intellectual, and there is nothing under the sun on which he is not prepared to bet. The calculation of probabilities, once the rational gambler has been found, is extremely simple. The probability of an outcome E is x, if for every dollar to be paid off in the event that E occurs, the rational gambler is prepared to stake x dollars. Probability retains its character as a relation between two elements, the second being always the state of knowledge of the gambler himself.

The subjective point of view makes it possible to obtain values for the probability even where relative frequency breaks down. According to relative frequency we would have to conclude that the probability of b given a was 1 if, after three trials, no A had been found which was not B, and this explains why relative frequency theorists always insist on large numbers. The rational gambler, however, realizing that such a sequence of three successes may very well be fortuitous, will adjust his bet accordingly. Of course, if relative frequency measurements for large numbers were in fact available, even a rational gambler would make use of them—we would hardly believe him to be rational if he did not. But while the relative frequency theorist will always be plagued by doubts as to whether his number of observations is large enough, the actual size of the sample becomes for the rational gambler just one of the things which he takes into account.

The principal difficulty with subjective probability is that it does not give us the information we want, but something else instead. We wish to describe the world, and to attribute properties to things in the world, and in these matters the rational gambler is no help— unless indeed we believe that he has privileged access to knowledge about the world (such as divine revelation) which is denied to us. God would be the rational gambler *par excellence,* and scientific activity may be viewed as a kind of game of chance played against God; the only trouble with such an opponent is that he never reveals in advance what the odds are, but simply collects when the game is over. Even if the rational gambler could be found, it would be impossible to recognize him as such, and we would always be unsure as to the state of his knowledge, the values which he might inject into his calculations, his serious interest in the outcome, and so on. And the theory collapses at once if the gambler himself shows any interest in questions *about* probability; for if we inquire why it is he wishes to know about probabilities we certainly cannot give it as an answer that he wishes to know about his own state of mind. Presumably he wants to know about the world. As Popper remarks, men who bet on horses try to find out about horses, not about their feelings about horses.[4] This of course is not entirely fair—in the absence of direct information about horses we may still learn a lot about them by analyzing the behavior of gamblers. What subjective probability in fact offers us is an alternative mode of approach; when people are interested in the world, we may learn about the world by watching the reactions of the people. But it would undeniably be better to be able to get at the world in a more straightforward way.

Popper sees no reason why this should not be done. Probability, as applied to anything except a retrospective sequence of observations, is a theoretical construct; and the business of science is exactly to advance hypotheses in which such theoretical constructs occur, and offer them as accounts of the way the world is, beyond the limits of our observation. What might the probability which emerges in observation as a relative frequency stand for in such a world? Popper's answer is that it stands for a *propensity* of objects to behave in certain ways.[5] The properties of objects are not invariable, but ambiguous; under test an object has a certain propensity to reveal itself as having one property, and other propensities to reveal itself as having other properties, the strengths of these propensities being measured, as we might expect, by the relative frequency with which the properties in question appear. According to this view, we are justified in regarding propensities as real elements of the world to the same extent as we are justified in regarding, for example, Newtonian forces in this way. It is the argument of *natura naturans* and *natura naturata* again—if we are prepared to use theoretical constructs in our account of the former, and if these lead deductively to a correct description of the latter, there is no reason why we should not treat all our theoretical constructs as having the same status. *If* there are objectively real electrons, there may just as well be objectively real probabilities, that is, propensities.

The possibility of this interpretation is of the greatest importance in certain recent controversies in quantum mechanics. The difficulty is that probabilities enter into the formulation of quantum mechanical statements in an apparently fundamental way—we cannot say where an electron is, but only where it is likely to be; we cannot say when an atom will pass from one state to another, but only when it is likely to do so. One view, the 'Copenhagen interpretation', holds that there is no way of escaping these probabilistic formulations, since both observation and theory are subject to certain inherent limitations expressed in the uncertainty principle of Heisenberg, and the complementarity principle of Bohr. (According to the former principle, there is a limit to the accuracy of determination of certain pairs of properties, like position and momentum, or energy and time. According to the latter, we have to choose between the accurate description of systems in terms of geometry, and their accurate description in terms of energy exchange—we cannot have both.) But these limitations are limitations of ignorance; they are built into the theory, and even if the world is fully determinate it is impossible, according to the Copenhagen interpretation, for us to give a fully determinate account of it. This view is challenged by the Paris group, whose chief spokesman is de Broglie, which insists that it is wrong to impose *a priori* limitations on the success of theory, and which looks for a fully determinate account of a level of events underlying those whose observational description is now couched in probabilistic terms. Popper's approach provides a third alternative. While Copenhagen resigns itself to probability in theory, and Paris holds out the hope of determination in the world, the propensity theory suggests that there may be probability in the world.

This view—that probability, or as it would once have been called, chance, may be a real element of the real world—is a very ancient one; and it has been returned to again and again in the history of philosophy. Its last important proponent was C. S. Peirce,[6] whose doctrine of *tychism* allowed for the unexpected play of freedom in an otherwise orderly world. The scientific prejudice against admitting such a possibility seems to stem from a fear that the only alternative to a strictly determined scheme of things is complete chaos. There is a curious ambivalence among philosophers of science in this matter; the same man, on the one hand refusing, like a good empiricist, to admit that any scientific law can be known to be certainly true, may on the other hand recoil with horror at the suggestion that such a law might permit of chance exceptions. It is quite true that if such exceptions did occur we would always look for a higher level formulation of the law which would incorporate them—but this of course is just what the propensity theory does. The higher level law asserts that there is a more or less fixed proportion of exceptions, this proportion giving the relative frequency probability. What follows is not chaos, but a weighted alternation between possible outcomes. The situation may be illustrated by means of the following thought experiment, due to Landé:[7] Suppose a stream of particles arriving at a filter, which will pass particles if and only if they are in state B, all others (which are then in a state not-B), being rejected. Suppose it to be known, now, that all the particles approaching the filter are in fact in a state A, which is identical neither with B nor with not-B—but suppose further that one-third of these A-particles in fact pass the filter. What must have happened? Landé's answer is that on arrival at the filter all the particles underwent a transformation, either to state B, or to state not-B; evidently the probability of the transformation of A to B was one-third, and the probability of the transformation of A to not-B was two-thirds. Originally, all the particles were unequivocally in state A, but it is now clear that the description of state A must be supplemented by a reference to the particle's propensity to change its state from A to B or to not-B under suitable conditions, such as the presence of a B-filter. Landé, as a matter of fact, is prepared to show this kind of probability at work in much more ordinary contexts—for example, in another experiment in which balls are dropped on to a knife-edge.[8] If the knife-edge is moved, under the point from which the balls are dropped, from one side to the other, there will be a region in the center where it cannot be told in advance on which side of the knife-edge the ball will eventually come to rest—it may do so on either, in different trials, with measurable frequencies.

Now the reaction of the Paris group to all this will clearly be that micro-determinations of the position of the knife-edge, and of the various small disturbances in the system as a whole, will give determinate reasons for the ball's dropping on one side or on the other; similarly, a more precise knowledge of what it means for a particle to be in state A will show that there are internal grounds for distinguishing between the particles which jump to state B and those which jump to state not-B. But this is a program which they have not yet carried out, although it is being busily worked at. Until a determinate solution is found there is nothing to prevent our seriously entertaining the hypothesis that probabilities may be an objective feature of the world. And this hypothesis receives further support from an analysis of the simple tossing of a penny, with which our discussion of probability began. Suppose all the micro-determinations to be made, so that for any individual toss of the penny, given the initial conditions—the position, energy, angular momentum, and so on of the penny when tossed, the turbulence of the air, the nature of the surface upon which it falls—the outcome (heads or tails) can be completely predicted. This will still not tell us why it was that all these conditions arranged themselves in such a way as to produce the outcome heads half the time and tails the other half. It seems in fact quite extraordinary that this should be the case.

All this has had to do with probability of the second kind, the probability of events; and it can all be summed up by saying that we have now added to the old notion that probability is a measure of our ignorance of the world, a new notion that it may be a measure of some objective feature of the world. But none of these interpretations, with the exception of subjective probability, can reasonably be extended to cover the first case—the probability of generalizations. If propensities are features of the objective world, then generalizations (which do not belong in that world) cannot have propensities to be true; and while the relationship between a generalization and the evidence which supports it might be considered a kind of quasi-entailment, the step from full entailment to probability seems too great to be accounted for by the difference between 1 and some number very close to it, unless indeed we suppose that very high probability approaches truth asymptotically. As logic, at any rate, this kind of thing is highly unsatisfactory. But subjective probability enables us to measure the degree of confidence which scientists have in their generalizations, or for that matter in their hypotheses. As is true in the case of the probability of events, while subjective probability is more especially useful in the absence of clear quantitative evidence (relative frequency for the probability of events), we would not consider the rational gambler worthy of his title if he failed to make use of quantitative determinations if they happened to be available; and measures have been devised by which generalizations and hypotheses may be ranked in order of acceptability. What they measure has in general been called *degree of confirmation*.

Before proceeding to a discussion of methods which have been proposed for estimating degrees of confirmation, it is essential that a very common confusion should be cleared up. It would be absurd to speak of the probability of a hypothesis, if by 'probability' is meant the relative frequency of confirming instances, since by definition hypotheses have no confirming instances. It would be equally absurd to speak of the degree of confirmation of an observation statement. When we come to generalizations the situation is more complicated. It is, as we have seen, possible to assign to generalizations numerical probabilities calculated on the basis of relative frequencies, namely the frequencies of their confirming instances; and it is clearly also possible to assign to them degrees of confirmation descending deductively from the hypotheses which explain them. But these are not the same thing at all, although they have often been mistaken for one another. There is in fact no single interpretation of the notion of probability that is capable of being carried through from observation statements to hypotheses without leading to absurdity; and nobody would have thought that there could be, if it had not been for the fact that generalizations enjoy a double status, on the one hand resting inductively on their instances—being generalizations *of* those instances—and on the other depending deductively on hypotheses. It is therefore always necessary to decide, when asserting a generalization, whether this is done on the grounds of direct empirical evidence, or on the grounds of the generalization's fitting into some highly confirmed theory.

REFERENCES

1. J. M. Keynes, *Treatise on Probability*, p. 5.
2. F. P. Ramsey, *The Foundations of Mathematics* (London, 1931), pp. 178 ff. For de Finetti and Savage, see J. J. Mehlberg, "Is a Unitary Approach to Probability Possible?" in Feigl and Maxwell (eds.), *Current Issues in the Philosophy of Science* (New York, 1961), p. 287.
3. Mehlberg, *op. cit.*, p. 298. This is essentially de Finetti's system F II.
4. Karl Popper, "The Propensity Interpretation of Probability," *The British Journal for the Philosophy of Science* (May, 1959), vol. 10, no. 37, p. 29.
5. *Ibid.*
6. C. S. Peirce, *Collected Papers* (eds. Hartshorne and Weiss) (Cambridge, Mass., 1935), vol. VI, p. 86.
7. A. Landé, *From Dualism to Unity in Quantum Physics* (Cambridge, Eng., 1960), p. 8.
8. *Ibid.*, p. 5.

CHAPTER 30

DEGREE OF CONFIRMATION

Generalizations, it was said in the previous chapter, may be trusted either because numbers of instances of them have been observed, or because they follow from hypotheses which form part of an accepted theory. The former case is simple enough, and it was even found possible to make some sense of the meaning of the first p in the expression

$$p(p[b/a] = x/\{a\}) = y,$$

which is, in effect, a measure of the accuracy of the second p. The value of the first p was calculated on the basis of the regularity of a statistical proportion of confirming instances in a series of sequences of observations. (It must be noted here that if the proportion in every sequence is always exactly the same the probability which estimates its accuracy either cannot be calculated or has to be arrived at on the basis of some conventional statistical theory.) If we let g stand for the expression $p(b/a) = x$, and e stand for the expression $\{a\}$—g and e indicating respectively a generalization and the accumulated evidence for it—then the expression given above becomes

$$p(g/e) = y;$$

and this has just the same form as $p(b/a) = x$—which suggests that this kind of probability also applies to hypotheses. But this, as we have seen, is far from being the case. This impossibility of assigning to hypotheses probabilities which have even a remote connection with relative frequency must now be further explained.

The definite assignment of some value to y in the expression above will be called *verification*. This is a departure from normal usage, in which the term verification would be restricted to the case in which $y = 1$; but if values of probability can vary continuously between 0 and 1 there would seem to be no difference in principle between the exact assignment of a value 1 and the exact assignment of some other value. The point is academic, since the value of y, whether it is 1 or anything else, is never known exactly. The best we can usually do is to say that the probability of the generalization or the hypothesis lies between certain more or less well defined limits. When these limits are known, the generalization or hypothesis will be said to be *confirmed*. Again, the confirmation of a statement whose probability is 1 (or thereabouts) is not different in principle from the confirmation of a statement whose probability is some other value (or thereabouts), as long as the 'thereabouts' represents a comparable degree of vagueness in each case. The degree of confirmation of a hypothesis will be represented by a function $c(h/e)$, obeying the axioms of the calculus of probability. According to this definition of confirmation, all hypotheses whatever will be confirmed, in a vacuous sense, since for all of them we know that

$$0 \leqslant c \leqslant 1.$$

In order for the function to be practically useful, therefore, a range of values of c lying somewhere between 0 and 1 will have to be defined; and the narrower this range the more precise the degree of confirmation. It is fairly easy to get the limits of such a range away from the extremes, by showing that the hypothesis in question is neither impossible nor certainly true, but the process of converging on some reasonable value becomes rapidly more difficult as the range narrows. There are two alternative ways of going about this task: one may define the range either by approaching its upper and lower limits from the direction of 1 and 0, respectively, or one may define it by calculating a definite value of c by some method, and surrounding this value with a band of values representing its indeterminacy.

The latter method would be the obvious one if there were some way of calculating values for c on the basis of probability. Reichenbach, whose system of posits for the relative frequency of samples in a population was dealt with earlier, attempted to extend this system to the probability of hypotheses in the following way:

Given a hypothesis h and a class $\{a\}$ of observations, a class $\{b\}$ of predictions can be obtained by using the members of $\{a\}$ in turn in conjunction with h; for the observation a_i we have the relation

$$a_i \cdot h \supset b_i.$$

Obviously, the usefulness of h in making the predictions is in some way measured by the number of b_i which are actually found to be true; $a_i \cdot b_i$ will be a confirming instance, and $a_i \cdot \sim b_i$ will be a contrary instance. If we let the number of observations be α and the number of confirming instances be β, then, according to Reichenbach's theory of posits,

$$p(b_i/a_i) = \lim \beta/\alpha.$$

Reichenbach proposed to use this as the value of the probability of the hypothesis given all the available evidence, or at least as the basis for computing such a value. This is intuitively plausible, but it cannot be carried through. In fact, if we substitute these values in the simplified version of Bayes' theorem given on page 202 they lead to paradoxical results. We have

$$p(h/a_i \cdot b_i) = \frac{p(h/a_i)}{p(b_i/a_i)},$$

the second term in the numerator dropping out, as before, because $a_i \cdot h \supset b_i$. Substituting the value β/α in the denominator yields

$$p(h/a_i \cdot b_i) = \frac{\alpha p(h/a_i)}{\beta},$$

which increases as β decreases. The reason for this is easy enough to see—clearly if the b_i are true very rarely then the few occasions when they *are* true constitute a much-needed boost for the hypothesis, but that hardly helps to establish it as a reliable tool of prediction. Even with the abandonment of the identification of degree of confirmation with probability we are not much better off. We might assert that

$$c(h/e) = \lim \beta/\alpha,$$

where e stands for the observations and the tested predictions taken together, but we can still never know whether we are approaching the limit, and the law of large numbers, as we have seen, is of no help. We might adopt a convention similar to that adopted earlier for generalizations and write

$$p(h/e) = 1 - \epsilon/\beta,$$

but this, while a little more sophisticated, still has the same fundamental flaw.

If we suppose that there is some sense in talking about the probability of generalizations, then a more hopeful approach to the confirmation of hypotheses might be to get at them by way of the generalizations which are their deductive consequences. Again, at first, we might try for the probability of the hypothesis too. Consider a hypothesis h, of which an empirical generalization g is a deductive consequence; the problem now is to assign to h a quantity $p(h/e)$, analogous to $p(g/e)$, and to determine the relationship between these two quantities. It must immediately be observed that, just as a single observation statement cannot by itself generate an empirical generalization, a single empirical generalization cannot by itself provide confirmation of a hypothesis. The hypothesis might still be worth looking into, in that theorems deduced from it might, on further investigation, turn out to correspond to as yet unknown empirical generalizations, but until this proved to be the case one could not claim that it was *confirmed* by the generalization in question, no matter how highly probable the generalization itself might be. Any number of other hypotheses might be advanced which had the same generalization as a deductive consequence. Some of these might be eliminated on the grounds that they led to false or poorly confirmed generalizations, but however many were so eliminated one could never be sure that all the alternatives had been entertained. This restriction reflects the necessity of having at least two independent links between any theoretical entity and experience; in the context of concept formation it has been called the "requirement of multiple connections" by Margenau.[1]

As soon as h is shown to lead to two or more empirical generalizations $g_1, g_2, \ldots g_n$, as deductive consequences it loses its 'peninsular' character, and the generalizations begin to reinforce one another. It is apparent that n in this case is unlikely to become large, which is one of the reasons why relative frequency is not particularly useful for secondary induction. Suppose there are two such generalizations, g_1 and g_2, where $p(g_1) = 0.97$ and $p(g_2) =$

0.88. (These probabilities, and those that follow, are of course to be understood as relative to the available evidence.) What value should now be assigned to $p(h)$? and to what extent do g_1 and g_2 become more probable by virtue of their place in the system

In this simple situation it might seem at first as if $p(h)$ ought to be the mean of the other two probabilities, that is $= 0.925$, and as if g_1 gains nothing by its place in the system but $p(g_2)$ goes up to 0.925 also, by virtue of its deductive relationship to h, which entails that it must share any probability conferred upon h. But a moment's thought will show that, just as a single empirical generalization was not allowed to stand as confirmation of a hypothesis, so the excess of $p(g_1)$ over $p(g_2)$, with respect to which g_1 *does* stand alone, cannot contribute to $p(h)$, which can therefore be no higher than 0.88. Both generalizations are required before $p(h)$ can have *any* value, and consequently that value cannot be higher than the probability that they have in common. Suppose now a third generalization g_3, which is also a deductive consequence of h, and for which $p(g_3) = 0.82$, is discovered. There is no reason for $p(h)$ to drop below 0.88, since there are at least two generalizations following from it which are confirmed to this degree; but this seems to mean that g_3 adds nothing at all, and yet surely it is better to explain three generalizations than two. Any calculation one might carry out involving $p(g_3)$ could, however, only tend to *reduce* the value of $p(h)$. On the other hand, g_3 itself appears to be strengthened because of its link, via h, with g_1 and g_2; we might now wish to put $p(g_3) = 0.88$, by virtue of its deductive relationship to h. Even so, a difficulty remains. $p(g_3)$ is a measure of the degree of confirmation of g_3 *as an empirical generalization,* and as such is equivalent to an assertion about sets of observed instances; it seems odd to say that this is altered because of a deductive relationship to something that is not an empirical generalization and of which an instance has never been observed. We might feel more confident in g_3 because of its place in theory alongside g_1 and g_2, but the empirical evidence for it is not affected thereby.

It becomes clear, then, that the attempt to speak of a quantity $p(h)$, analogous to $p(g)$, fails to reflect what we mean by the degree of confirmation of a hypothesis. The trouble is that $p(h)$ does not seem to be a function of the number of generalizations that h explains, and that the wrong kind of quantity descends from it deductively to those generalizations. It certainly cannot be a relative frequency function, since g_1, g_2, . . . are not instances of h in the way in which observation statements are instances of g; and no attempt to combine the probabilities of the g_n can give an indication of the value of n. We therefore introduce a new concept, the *strength* of the hypothesis h, whose value is to be given by an ordered pair of numbers $\langle p,n \rangle$, where p ranges, like $p(g)$, between 0 and 1 and $n = 1, 2, 3, \ldots$. The reason for using an ordered pair is that there are two factors involved and they are not commensurable. It is as if we were attempting to define the intellectual strength of a family, and were faced with the problem of two families, one with five fairly intelligent children and the other with two brilliant ones. Which family would come higher in the scale? It would be hard to say, although one could say that a family with five fairly intelligent children would come higher than one with four, and a family with two brilliant children higher than a family with two fairly intelligent ones. In the case of the hypothesis, we have to take account both of its fertility and of the quality of its offspring. The tight logical relation between the hypothesis and its derived generalizations leads us to interpret $s(h)$ as follows: if n generalizations are appealed to as providing a confirmation basis for h, p will be equal to the *highest value of* $p(g)$ *that these generalizations have in common*. In the case discussed above, there are two alternative values for $s(h)$: if we take into account only g_1 and g_2, $s(h) = \langle .88,2 \rangle$, whereas, if we consider all three generalizations, $s(h) = \langle .82,3 \rangle$. This, strictly speaking, destroys the value of $s(h)$ as a *measure* of the degree of confirmation of h, since it does not arrange all hypotheses in a quasi-serial order. The development of a strict measure would depend on a decision to emphasize one member of the pair at the expense of the other, and this would raise the question why one wished to measure degree of confirmation in the first place. Of course, in any scientific theory, it is desirable to have both p and n as high as possible. Consider the following generalizations, with the values of their probabilities as shown:

g	$p(g)$
g_1	.97
g_2	.91
g_3	.93
g_4	.92
g_5	.78
g_6	.88

Suppose now a hypothesis h_1 of which the first four of these generalizations are deductive consequences; we then have $s(h_1) = \langle.91,4\rangle$. In this case we decide to place emphasis on n, since the highest p would occur in $s(h_1) = \langle.93,2\rangle$, and the loss in p would seem intuitively to be more than offset by the gain in n. Consider now another hypothesis h_2, having the first *five* generalizations as deductive consequences. On the level of $n = 4$, h_2 is just as strong as h_1; it also has a value of $s(h)$ on the level of $n = 5$, although this involves a considerable drop in p. This additional scope, however, makes it clearly preferable to h_1. How will it compare, though, with a third hypothesis, h_3, which has all but the fifth of the listed generalizations as deductive consequences? On the $n = 4$ level, $s(h_3) = s(h_2) = s(h_1)$; but on the $n = 5$ level, $s(h_3) = \langle.88,5\rangle$, as against $\langle.78,5\rangle$ for $s(h_2)$. It therefore emerges as the strongest of the three.

It is obvious that $s(h)$ is a rather cumbersome quantity, with limited possibilities for further calculation. The rules for combination of strengths will not form a calculus with the formal elegance of the probability calculus; if $s(h_1) = \langle.93,3\rangle$ and $s(h_2) = \langle.94,5\rangle$, then $s(h_1 \cdot h_2)$ will clearly be $\langle.93,8\rangle$, but only if none of the g_i explained by h_1 belong to the g_j explained by h_2. If there is an overlap, more information will be needed before the calculation can be carried out. On the other hand, zero strength, unlike zero probability, does not imply falsehood; and there is no need for the sum of strengths of exclusive alternatives to be less than any given value, so that problems about 'initial' values do not arise.

The two numbers in the ordered pair reflect, respectively, the *scope* and the *reliability* of the hypothesis. Both of these are essential in computing a degree of confirmation. The assumption that there are two kinds of probability, one of them being degree of confirmation, which establishes a whole-part relationship between 'probability' and 'degree of confirmation', is seen to be mistaken. One might be tempted to turn this round and say that there are two kinds of degree of confirmation, one of them being probability; but this would be equally wrong—the true relationship between these concepts is more symmetrical: there are probabilities which are not degrees of confirmation, but there are also degrees of confirmation which are not probabilities.

Although the concept of strength of hypothesis is a somewhat more realistic one than the concept of probability in assigning degrees of confirmation, all approaches of this kind suffer, in the end, the same fate—they all turn out to be affirmations of the consequent. This does not mean that they have to be abandoned altogether, but the difficulties into which their proponents are perpetually running lead to the suspicion that there may be something fundamentally wrong with the strategy of justifying hypotheses which are to be used predictively by reference to experiences which are known only retrospectively. Whatever may be the intellectual satisfactions of reflecting on theories considered merely as explanatory devices, there is no doubt that a great proportion of the motivation for science would be lost if theories did not lead to action; but if, when confronted with the necessity for action, we were always to wait for a satisfactory solution to the problem of confirmation for the theory in question, it is to be doubted whether anything would ever actually be done. All that is required for action is *decision;* and it may therefore be better to approach the problem of the validation of theory in terms of its usefulness in arriving at decisions rather than in terms of its status as true or false, probable or improbable, confirmed or disconfirmed. Many workers have accordingly turned away from the inverse probability approach to induction, and have begun to pay serious attention to decision theory and the theory of games. The questions which have now to be asked are no longer: Is the theory well confirmed? What is the strength of the hypothesis? but rather: What would be the consequences if we were to act as if this theory were true? Suppose we were to act as if it were true, and it happened to be false; how serious would the mistake be? Would that be worse than refraining from action even though the theory happened to be true?

A simple illustration of the difference between the old and new attitudes is given by the gambler referred to at the beginning of

Chapter 28, who had a penny which turned up heads rather more than half the time. The traditional scientist would be interested in the exact value of the relative frequency; he would fix on some posit and calculate degrees of confirmation. The gambler's theory is much simpler—he treats the penny as if it were all heads, in the confidence that when it turns up tails, as it will, his losses will be more than covered, and in the realization that no other strategy guarantees this. His theory is manifestly *not* true, and yet it works better than mixing the calls according to the scientist's best posit. He has not solved the problem of induction, but he is making fewer mistakes, and from his point of view that is all that matters. Gamblers, of course, have always behaved in this rather dubious way; what is new is the endorsement of it as rational by philosophers.

The introduction of notions like the seriousness of a mistake, or one mistake's being worse than another, changes the whole ground of the discussion. Instead of truth and falsity we have gains and losses, and the magnitude of these will depend on the values which individual scientists attach to the outcomes of their actions—the *utilities* of those outcomes. To regard a theory as highly confirmed is to trust it to a great degree, and thus at the same time to have a chance for a great gain and to run the risk of a great loss. Conversely, a low degree of confirmation, while it minimizes losses, also lessens the likelihood of gains. The boundaries of the range in which c lies will now represent the maximum tolerable loss and the minimum useful gain, respectively; and the width of the range will give (inversely) a rough estimate of the seriousness of the hypothesis in question. If it made no difference whether the hypothesis was true or false the range could extend from 0 to 1 without any unfortunate consequences, and nobody would take the hypothesis seriously.

This change of emphasis must not be allowed to leave the impression that the truth or falsity of the hypothesis is no longer a matter for concern. It matters very much whether the hypothesis is true; the trouble, as we have seen, is that there often seems to be no way of finding out whether or not it *is* true. Inverse probability gives us plausible hints, but these are without logical force. This being the case, we abandon the purely logical approach, and adopt instead the view that in the face of uncertainty we must make realistic estimates of risk, and act accordingly. The important thing is to act, but to do so with a degree of skepticism which arms us against the possibility of disappointment.

The mechanism by which this kind of degree of confirmation is arrived at is complex, and there is still controversy as to its details. It makes use of a ramified calculus of subjective probability like those of Ramsey and Savage, in which instead of a rational gambler we have a subject who attaches different utilities to different outcomes. There must exist some pair of alternatives with respect to which this subject is indifferent; if two rewards, one of which he values more than the other, are attached to these two outcomes, he will not mind which way round this is done. This establishes the equivalent of a probability of one-half (the toss of a true penny satisfies this condition) which serves as a fixed point in the calculation of utilities. The value of actions can then be judged according to the subjective probabilities and utilities of various outcomes, and theories awarded greater or lesser degrees of confirmation according to their success in leading to actions which maximize these values, giving due consideration to the information available when the theoretical recommendation is made.[2] The danger is that the *logical* character of the concept 'degree of confirmation' may be lost sight of. The validation of theories in this way is a pragmatic and utilitarian business, far removed from the traditional austerity of the search for truth; but then any inductive argument is bound to get mixed up with practical realities, and it may be all to the good to be honest about it.

REFERENCES

1. H. Margenau, *The Nature of Physical Reality* (New York, 1950), p. 84.
2. For a systematic development of this theme, see R. Carnap, "The Aim of Inductive Logic," in Nagel, Suppes, and Tarski (eds.), *Logic, Methodology and Philosophy of Science* (Stanford, 1962), p. 303.

CHAPTER 31

THE CHOICE BETWEEN ALTERNATIVE THEORIES

It would be absurd to pretend that, with all the critical apparatus at our disposal, we are usually confronted with a number of theories, each as well confirmed inductively as the others, and all providing acceptable explanations of a given set of states of affairs. As a matter of fact we would count ourselves lucky if one survived. It occasionally happens, nevertheless, that we are in doubt as to which among some small number of theories we ought to prefer; when this happens, further criteria are needed which go beyond ordinary inductive considerations.

So far our discussion has been kept more or less within the bounds of logic. If extra-logical reasons are to be admitted, there will be seen to be indefinitely many ways in which one theory might be held up as superior to another. Given two theories of equal logical strength, it might be that one of them led to consequences which were emotionally unacceptable to certain people; or that one had a more novel approach to the subject than the other; or that one was propounded by a person whose political views were suspect; or that one was more consonant with some widely held philosophical position than the other. No scientist, it might be thought, would actually make use of distinctions of this sort—but in the absence of other distinctions, what grounds for choice does he have? There are two ways of answering this question: on the one hand we might examine the grounds which have actually been put forward for choices between theories, and on the other we might look for rational grounds. The contrast is intentional; in the absence of a sound empirical basis for choice, decisions have been made all too frequently without good reason and for unworthy ends. Preferences

for Ptolemaic over Copernican astronomy, for the theory of creation over the Darwinian theory, for an ideological economics over
an empirical one, for special eugenic theories, and so on have often
rested, and sometimes still rest, on irrational prejudice. (It is quite
possible, of course, to prefer the right theory for the wrong reason.)
The preponderance of bad reasons for non-empirical choices is to
be explained by the fact that most choices between theories can be
made on logical or empirical grounds—the issues are usually clear
enough to be definitely settled in this way, and it is in fact quite
rare for any other mechanism to be called for. But that makes the
importance of its being provided all the greater.

We are to imagine, then, two theories, both supported by the
evidence, each incorporating a number of well-confirmed generalizations together with hypotheses from which these generalizations
follow, and each having been put to the test of prediction and
emerged successfully from it. Which shall we choose? Popper
answers unhesitatingly that we should choose the more improbable
of the two, that is, the one which makes the riskier predictions
about still future events.[1] His reason for this rather odd recommendation is that in his view a probability of 1 means not merely
truth, but analytic truth, so that (since analytic truths are empirically empty) the nearer the probability of a theory approaches
to 1 the less the theory says, whereas we naturally want theories
which say as much as possible. Since probable theories, in this
sense, are weak, and improbable ones are strong, a theory which
offers more than another for possible refutation is to be preferred.
The difficulty here is the familiar one, where Popper is concerned,
of not knowing (until the refutation has actually been done)
whether the theory is not in some sense bluffing. Any theory, after
all, could be made very strong indeed by the addition to it of one
or two hypotheses leading to wildly improbable predictions which,
however, were most unlikely ever actually to be put to test. If a
test were feasible, and the decision between the two theories a
matter of any importance, there would be little excuse for not making it; and even if it applied only to one of the theories, that theory
would be either refuted or more strongly confirmed by its outcome.

This last point leads to an older and more familiar strategy for
choice between theories; the search for a *crucial experiment*. A
crucial experiment is exactly one on which the choice between two

theories hinges; it is so designed that either of two possible outcomes refutes one of the theories in question—at least that is the
intention. In practice, theories are a good deal harder to refute
than a simple logical account would lead us to expect, and their
proponents manage to keep them alive by resorting to various devices such as redefining their scope of application or making *ad hoc*
changes in their structure. But occasionally, when the setting is
clear enough, single experiments can have an enormous influence
on the direction in which science develops by indicating, at a point
where two alternatives present themselves, which one ought to be
adopted. It was said earlier that an experiment is only a means of
creating artificially a certain kind of opportunity for observation;
and in this sense not only cases like Wu and Ambler's experiment
which demonstrated the non-conservation of parity, but also ones
like the eclipse observations of 1919, which settled an open question
in favor of the general theory of relativity, may be counted as
crucial experiments.

But even if tests are not actually feasible, so that the crucial experiment strategy breaks down, it is still possible to consider what
would be observed if some ideal experimental situation *could*
be devised. In arguments between different theories, therefore,
thought-experiments (*Gedanken* experiments) are sometimes re-
sorted to. Such hypothetical situations may help to make clearer
the difference between the two theories in question, but it would
be very dangerous to rely on them in *choosing* between the two.
The point of a crucial experiment is that it gives new data; the
limitation of a thought-experiment is that it *cannot* give new
data—it is, in fact, only a dramatization of some consequences of
one theory or the other which would be just as true or false whether
or not the thought-experiment was "carried out." (If it were *really*
carried out, it would not be a thought-experiment.) For example,
the uncertainty relations of Heisenberg have been dramatized in
this way by imagining a special microscope for the observation of
electrons, in which light of shorter and shorter wavelength is used
in order to approach with some accuracy the position of the electron; unfortunately, it is found that the energy of the photons
whose reflection from the electron is to tell us where it is gets
greater and greater as the wavelengths become shorter, until it is
great enough to knock the electron out of its path. This is true,

however, only if we accept the fundamental quantum relation between energy and frequency, from which, together with the rest of quantum theory, Heisenberg's relations follow without any thought-experiment. Something similar could be said about other attempts to show the inadequacy of the Copenhagen interpretation, such as that of Einstein, Podolski, and Rosen.[2] It would be better, of course, not to call thought-experiments *experiments* at all; they can never have any of the empirical surprise of genuine experiments, such as the double-slit experiment in electron diffraction.

When the empirical and quasi-empirical possibilities for choice between theories are exhausted—when, that is, the question can no longer be decided on grounds external to the theory—we are forced to turn to other approaches, such as the internal organization of the theory. The comparison between two theories would then take the form of ranking each of them on an objective scale—logical consistency, fertility, simplicity, elegance—and choosing the one which came higher in that scale. Of these characteristics the only one really useful for this purpose is simplicity. It is hard to see how one theory can be *more* consistent than another, since *any* inconsistency would be grounds for abandoning the theory. Fertility, like Popper's improbability, is something the proof of which lies in performance rather than in potential, which reintroduces empirical considerations. And elegance, although it might have something to do with the motivation of scientists to work in one theory rather than another, and thus be of some practical importance, is not really the sort of criterion we are after, if indeed it can be made into a criterion at all. What the scientist finds aesthetically satisfying about a theory may in fact be some balance between consistency and fertility, for example *invariance* in a physical theory, the possibility of rigorous transformation to fit a range of empirical conditions. Of course, it is often thought that simplicity is a just kind of elegance, but I do not think that this is true. As we shall see, the question of simplicity is in fact a rather complex one.

Credit for having introduced the criterion of simplicity usually goes to William of Ockham, the familiar form of whose 'razor' is *"Entia non (sunt) multiplicanda praeter necessitatem."* There seems to be some doubt whether he ever actually said this, although he would certainly have recognized and sympathized with the principle, which he applied with great effect. But it is not accidental that it should have been attributed to him and not to some other medieval philosopher. The word 'entia' is perhaps misleading, suggesting as it does economy of *things*. Ockham would not have minded multiplication of *things* in the least, and it certainly would not have made his world any more complex. For him, as we saw earlier, the world is neither simple nor complex, consisting as it does of unrelated individuals, contingently dependent on God, who is not to be limited by conventions—in fact Ockham, like Leibniz, would probably have thought the more things the better. What is to come under the scrutiny of the principle is the description or explanation of the world; economy is to be effected in our thought about nature, but there is no suggestion that nature is simple.

Ockham's razor, then, is a principle of economy, which may or may not lead to simplicity. It will almost certainly lead to an *appearance* of simplicity—after all, Thales' account of the world seems to be as simple as possible, and exhibits the most rigid economy of entities; but it does nothing to relieve the complexity of events, whereas the ninety-two elements of the pre-nuclear periodic table lead to an enormous simplification by comparison. Properly speaking, of course, the *simple* is to be opposed to the *compound,* not the *complex.* But there is an easy transference of meaning when, in an epistemology like that of Locke, for example, simple predicates are associated with simple ideas, and these are assumed to correspond to simple qualities in the world. A simple predicate may be simple only with respect to the logical system in which it occurs, and this simplicity does not preclude the possibility of its having a complex referent.

We now know, of course, not only how extremely complicated a simple datum (such as a monochromatic color) can be on the physical side, but also what highly developed organs are needed for its reception, and what intricate behavior it stimulates in the cortex; it is evident that a high degree of complexity underlies the production of even one of Locke's simple ideas. This suggests a solution to the problem of the apparent simplicity of the world. The complexity of the stimulus is in some sense matched by the complexity of the response, and in this way both are concealed. Nature exemplifies the maxim *"Ars est celare artem";* the workings on both sides cancel out, and we are left with an experience which is phenomenologically simple.

At this point there are to be distinguished two senses of simplicity and two different senses of complexity. We have on one hand a simple idea produced by a simple experience (or, what amounts to the same thing, a simple predicate describing a simple experience), and on the other a complex natural event, matched by a complexity in the apparatus which we use to detect the event. All these may be spoken of as kinds of complexity. In the case of ideas or predicates we have *logical* complexity; the logical complexity of theory is the kind of thing that has received most attention in previous studies of simplicity. In experience, we have *phenomenological* complexity, and for nature, *physical* complexity; these require no further clarification. Finally the terminology for the complexity of the sensory neural receptor may need some explanation; it will be called *mechanical* complexity, partly in view of recent work on the analogies between brains and machines, partly because our range of perception may be extended by means of instruments without altering the nature of the problem, and it is convenient to have a name which is obviously applicable to this wider case. Mechanical complexity is simply the complexity required in the sensory apparatus if information about the original event is to be received at all. For the neurophysiologist it is clearly a kind of physical complexity, when observed in other people, and in fact this is how we come to know about it; but even for him the physical complexity of the patient's brain has to be matched by a mechanical complexity in his own.

Just as a simple perception was seen to depend on a matching of mechanical complexity on the part of the organism with the physical complexity of the event giving rise to the perception, so in scientific observation and calculation there will be a need for some parity of complexity between the event under consideration and its representation in theory. The situations are not quite parallel; in the case of perception learning is automatic, and if *awareness* enters the picture it is only as an addition which can remain simple and is eliminable in the manner of T. H. Huxley and the behaviorists, whereas most of us would feel that science is more conscious of itself and that the logical complexity of the scientists' concepts becomes an important factor. In neither case do we have direct access to physical complexity, but learn only indirectly whether we have been successful in matching the complexity of our responses to that of the world; as long as the organism survives, its reaction must be succeeding in this task, and in the case of the scientist it is a matter of checking his predictions. In the latter case a further complication appears; not only must the theory be complex enough to handle the events, but it must also be simple enough to permit calculations to be made and predictions stated in less time than it takes the physical state of affairs to move from the event perceived to the event predicted. It is here that the principle of economy enters once more. It may turn out to be a waste of time to do a calculation in the simplest terms.

There would therefore appear to be an *optimum* level of complexity in scientific theory if it is to be successful. The development of science may be regarded as progressing in two ways: on one hand there is an increase in logical complexity, as simple ideas are combined, calculi worked out, and higher-level constructs introduced, and on the other hand there is a decrease in the complexity of the world the theory is trying to explain. The world of naive experience is complex in the highest degree; it is the business of science to find units in terms of which this complexity may be rationally explained. In so doing it reduces the complexity of the world as understood by us (which is different from the world as experienced by us, and different again from the theory in terms of which we understand it). The optimum will occur when these two processes —the increase in complexity of ideas, and the decrease in complexity of the world which confronts us—meet each other, and the logical complexity is of the same order as the physical complexity it is to explain. This physical complexity is, of course, relative to the units into which the world is analyzed; a forest regarded as composed of trees is a far less complex event than the same forest regarded as composed of plant cells, and the theoretical complexity of plant ecology need not therefore be as great, to deal with the forest adequately, as the theoretical complexity of cytology would have to be. In practice of course the latter would be prohibitive, so that cytologists do not deal with forests, any more than physicists deal with international relations.

Between a given pair of theories, then, the 'better' is the one which most nearly approaches the optimum level of complexity, in which there are neither too many variables nor too few, in which the unit of description is fitted to the unit of experience, and so on.

This *appropriateness* of theory to the abilities of those who use it and to the intricacy of the world with which it deals forms a better basis than formal simplicity alone for the choice between alternatives. In the end we might still be tempted to sum up all these qualities by saying that the better theory is the simpler, and according to a certain ordinary and intuitive use of 'simple' that would be accurate enough. But it is hard to be precise about ordinary usage, and with respect to simplicity Whitehead's caution deserves to be listened to: "The guiding motto in the life of every natural philosopher," he said, "should be, Seek simplicity and distrust it." [3]

REFERENCES

1. K. Popper, "Some Comments on Truth and the Growth of Knowledge," in Nagel, Suppes, and Tarski (eds.), *Logic, Methodology, and Philosophy of Science* (Stanford, 1962), pp. 286-288.
2. A. Einstein, B. Podolsky, and N. Rosen, "Can Quantum-Mechanical Description of Physical Reality Be Considered Complete?" *Physical Review*, 47 (1935), pp. 777-780.
3. A. N. Whitehead, *The Concept of Nature* (Cambridge, Eng., 1930), p. 163.

Chapter 32

THE LOGIC OF DISCOVERY

In our discussion so far 'induction' has been used, very generally, to mean any sort of inference which is non-demonstrative. This use, as was pointed out earlier, is somewhat less exact than some traditional uses (such as Mill's) in which the term is restricted to arguments from particulars to generalizations; but what it loses in exactness it gains in appropriateness, since induction is generally taken to be the characteristic logic of science. If a more precise term should be required, the term 'reduction', applied by Łukasiewicz to arguments whose general form is that of *modus tollens*,[1] may be suitable. We come now, however, in the psychological problem of induction, to a kind of transition from premises to a conclusion which hardly qualifies as logical at all. It certainly covers the same ground as logical processes of induction; but whereas inductive processes as we have so far considered them *follow* deductive ones —the very definitions of 'empirical generalization' and 'hypothesis' having been explicitly devised in terms of their deductive relationships to protocol sentences—the transition with which we now have to deal *precedes* deduction. It is in fact the transition which is made when an empirical generalization or hypothesis is first formulated —when its status as an empirical generalization or hypothesis is not yet conclusively known, since deduction has then to be carried out before the defining relationships spoken of above can be seen to hold. This is the process of discovery; and to claim that it hardly qualifies as logical is already to take sides in a current debate on the question whether there is or is not such a thing as a 'logic of discovery'.

Recent tradition in the philosophy of science has made genius

the stock answer to the question of how new hypotheses or generalizations are acquired. This is really an exaggeration as far as
generalizations are concerned, since all learning consists of a kind
of automatic generalizing, but for hypotheses it is accurate enough.
Unfortunately, the concept of genius does not lead to a testable explanation, since (at least in science) people are not commonly
recognized as geniuses until they have already made a significant
number of discoveries. One might, of course—on the assumption
that the genius, in earning his title, performs certain characteristic
actions of which a rational account can be given—ask the scientists
who have made discoveries how they did it, but those who have
followed this course have not had much better luck with the scientists than Socrates had with the poets. Kekulé discovered the ring
formula for benzene by dreaming of a snake which swallowed its
tail; "If we learn to dream, gentlemen," he said, "then we shall perhaps find truth." [2] Sir William Beveridge, a serious-minded inquirer
into such matters, remarks that

> . . . light occupations requiring no mental effort, such as walk
> ing in the country, bathing, shaving, travelling to and from work,
> are said by some to be when intuitions most often appear, prob
> ably because under these circumstances there is freedom from
> distraction or interruption and the conscious mind is not so oc
> cupied as to suppress anything interesting arising in the sub
> conscious. Others find lying in bed most favorable and some
> people deliberately go over the problem before going to sleep and
> others before rising in the morning. Some find that music has a
> helpful influence but it is notable that only very few consider
> that they get any assistance from tobacco, coffee, or alcohol. A
> hopeful attitude of mind may help.[3]

These do not look like promising avenues for the elucidation of
philosophical principles. But any adequate account of the process of
discovery must take note of this apparently random and inconsequential element in it.

Another striking fact of which such a theory must be able to give
a rational account is the frequency of *multiple* discoveries. The
most celebrated case of this phenomenon is the almost simultaneous
introduction of the calculus by Newton and by Leibniz. It may be
thought that this was a case of invention, and not of discovery, but
the distinction between the two has been very much overempha

sized—a discovery is just an invention which turns out to be empirically true. (We are not concerned here with discoveries in observation, such as the discovery of a new planet as a visual object. There is nothing of great intrinsic interest in seeing something which nobody has seen before. Such novelties become discoveries in our sense only when they are seen as exemplifying some new theoretical insight, for example when Neptune was seen as embodying the causal origin of anomalies in the motion of Uranus. Discoveries in this sense can be associated with quite commonplace observations.) It is often said that the calculus, and other principles invented or discovered by more than one person at the same time, was "in the air"—an explanation which is less illuminating, if anything, than the attribution of genius. What is meant, presumably, is that two scholars well versed in the accepted learning of their time, and thus starting out from very similar positions, are not unlikely to arrive at the same novelty, and this of course is true; but it does not explain how either of them actually arrived at the novelty.

What is more remarkable than a simple coincidence of this sort is the fact, which has recently been documented by Merton,[4] that a really great scientist may make a large number of discoveries *many* of which are duplicated by one or another of his contemporaries. For every genuine discovery, of course, there is a great number of unsuccessful attempts at discovery, and it is almost as if there were a constant relationship between the number of attempts and the number of discoveries. Let us suppose for the sake of simplicity that among every ten novel scientific ideas there is one discovery. A man who has ten novel ideas is then morally certain to make a discovery, while the man who has only one such idea has one chance in ten of doing so; but if someone actually makes a discovery there is no way of telling, without further investigation, whether he has earned the right to it by having ten ideas, or whether he is just the lucky one among the ten who had one idea each. Ordinarily, as Merton shows, the great scientist is so full of novel ideas that a considerable number of them turn out to be discoveries, while the fortunate one-idea man may never even make another interesting suggestion. Reputations have been built on this kind of good luck, but in general there is no difficulty in telling who the really creative scientists are.

Although it is true that hard work plays a crucial part in this whole question of discovery, it is also true that it is not, in general, difficult for the genius to be what he is. If one approach fails, he has a new one ready to hand, or even stumbles upon it while shaving. This is not a matter of logic. One of the misleading things about most discussions of the logic of discovery is that they hold out some hope of a *method* of discovery, as though every man could be his own genius if only he followed the rules. There are, unfortunately, some people who would never get a single worthwhile idea even if they shaved three times a day. It is, of course, true that quite dull people may get surprisingly large numbers of good ideas if they keep doggedly worrying about their problems for long enough periods, and in this fact lies the truth of the old saying that genius is a capacity for taking pains. But unless this stern application is accompanied by at least a measure of intellectual spontaneity it will lead to nothing. This is the essential ingredient in what Peirce called *retroduction,* the intuitive jump from observed facts to hypotheses about them which constitutes the genuine advance of science, every step of which, in Peirce's own words, depends on "the spontaneous conjectures of instinctive reason." [5]

It is not comforting to be told that if one does not have ideas already there is nothing to be done, but I believe that something very close to this is the truth. An awareness of this truth is implicit even in the inductive method of Francis Bacon[6]—a method which has been very widely misunderstood. It is true that Bacon believed, sincerely, that his method could be applied by anybody, but his only mistake in this was over-optimism; he wrongly supposed that all other men had imaginations as fertile as his own. It is worth looking more closely at Bacon's method, not only because of its intrinsic interest but also because of the light it throws on this question of discovery. What he is after is "a true and perfect rule of operation," namely, one which will "be certain, free, and disposing or leading to action"; this rule has commonly been represented as simpleminded enumerative induction, but that is only a very small part of the story. In the investigation of any phenomenon the first step is an orderly "Presentation of Instances to the Understanding," but this process has a highly organized internal structure. First of all there is to be constructed a Table of Essence and Presence, an enumeration of cases in which the phenomenon in question is observed; this is to be followed by a Table of Deviation, or of Absence in Proximity, this time enumerating cases in which, although by analogy with cases in the first table the phenomenon might be expected, it is not in fact found; and the last element of this first stage of the method is the construction of a Table of Degrees, or Table of Comparison, introducing quantitative considerations in those cases from the earlier tables where these are possible. In all these activities the judgment is suspended, and the scientist plays the role of a pure observer. And this comparatively uncritical attitude is preserved through the next stage, the "Exclusion, or Rejection of Natures," which consists in the elimination from among the instances presented to the understanding of those which, from considerations of internal consistency, are obviously not genuine cases of the phenomenon under investigation. "In the process of Exclusion," says Bacon, "are laid the foundations of true Induction, which however is not completed until it arrives at an Affirmative." At this point theoreticians of discovery are likely to be thrown into confusion—for how, out of all these instances, can one possibly arrive at an Affirmative? But Bacon sees no difficulty; on the contrary, the understanding by this time has an Affirmative ready, and is impatient to try it out. The next stage of the matter is introduced, therefore, with the remark:

> . . . I think it expedient that the understanding should have permission, after the three Tables of First Presentation (such as I have exhibited) have been made and weighed, to make an essay of the Interpretation of Nature in the Affirmative way; on the strength both of the instances given in the tables, and of any others it may meet with elsewhere. Which kind of essay I call the *indulgence of the understanding,* or the *commencement of interpretation,* or the *First Vintage.*

There is no struggle here to arrive at a hypothesis—in fact, the suggestion is that after all the instances the understanding can no longer be restrained from putting one forward. The emergence of a hypothesis no more calls for explanation than the tendency of newborn babies to make unintelligible noises.

Of course both these things do call for explanation, on a different level, and the analogy is quite exact. The behavior of scientists, like the behavior of babies, is a product of long evolutionary development; both are examples of the spontaneous proliferation of novelty which is made possible, ultimately, by the fact that both occur in a privileged environment. We live in one of the few places and at one of the few times in the history of the universe (the term 'few' is used relatively) at which the existence of an environment which receives more energy than it gives out makes possible a reversal of the cosmic trend toward disorganization. In these circumstances natural selection comes into play, and the process of discovery proceeds by *natural selection among hypotheses*. The problem is not really how to get ideas, but what to do with all the ideas which are constantly springing up—which to take seriously, which to discard out of hand. The logic of discovery turns out to be the logic, if it can be called that, of the evolutionary process.

In order for natural selection to take place two things are required: there must be novelty, and there must be serious competition for survival. The principal difference between the scientific case and the natural one is that in the former the competition may be replaced by a more rigorous kind of test. Among organisms, as long as the environment remains reasonably hospitable, some species will gain the ascendance over the others and survive whether or not they meet an ideal criterion of what an animal or plant species ought to be; in science, on the other hand, theories have not merely to compete with one another but also to submit to test individually, according to an independent specification of adequacy and accuracy. The scientist, in his theoretical moods, would rather have no theory at all than one which is in serious conflict with observation. This attitude, it is true, is of fairly recent origin, but it has entrenched itself firmly in contemporary scientific thought. Accordingly, while a temporary cessation in the production of biological novelty would not leave the world unpopulated, a suspension of scientific originality would leave the field clear for charlatanism and superstition as long as there were unfilled gaps in our theoretical understanding of the world.

It would therefore be useful to know how the production of novelty might be stimulated. Here again the biological analogy is helpful. There is in fact very little danger that biological mutations will cease, in view of the continual exposure of organisms to natural and artificial radiation, and we can therefore expect new diseases, new deformities, and so on. Occasionally there may even be a positively useful effect, but these are very rare. If such a thing were to occur it would have very little chance of establishing itself unless it could be protected from accidents, parasites, predators, and all the other hazards of the biological environment. There are two lessons here for scientific creativity: first there must be kept up and if possible increased a flow of random stimulation; second, factors which might inhibit the recognition and development of novelty must if possible be removed. Specialization and professionalism in the various branches of science militate against the first of these desiderata, and prejudice, vested interest, and lack of imagination, on the part of scientific administrators as well as of individual scientists, militate against the second. One of the lessons of the history of science is that a kind of conceptual momentum builds up which works against the acceptance of new points of view. A certain amount of this is, of course, a good thing; too much inertia is frustrating, but too little means time wasted on false scents. Evolution is a delicate business, and one has to be very careful how one interferes with it. If the competitive element is artificially removed, and an environment created in which species can proliferate which, in the ordinary course of events, would be kept small or extinguished, there may be a serious falling off in the strength and ability to resist adversity of the individual organisms. T. H. Huxley used to think of human society as a garden[7]—the paradigm of such a privileged enclosure, in contrast to the primordial evolutionary situation in which nature is wild and undomesticated. It may be that academic science, in some of its aspects, is in danger of becoming too much like a garden; not that we should wish all scientific work to be done in circumstances of adversity and competition, but rather that originality and excellence flourish in the presence of controversy and criticism.

An adequate account of the nature of and conditions for scientific discovery has yet to be given. The situation is complicated by the fact that there is more than one *kind* of discovery. There are, on the one hand, discoveries which occur *within* some scientific tradition—under the aegis of a 'paradigm' in Kuhn's sense, as a part of what he calls 'normal science'[8]—and these show considerable promise for logical analysis, as Hanson's work on Kepler has shown.[9] But there are, on the other hand, discoveries which involve a major *change* of scientific tradition—which lead, in Kuhn's language, to 'revolutions'—and in this case patterns are much harder to discern. This topic is one whose adequate treatment requires collaboration between the philosopher and the historian of science, and on which much further work remains to be done.

REFERENCES

1. See I. M. Bochenski (tr. Caws), *The Methods of Contemporary Thought* (Dordrecht, forthcoming), Ch. IV.
2. Quoted in W. I. B. Beveridge, *The Art of Scientific Investigation* (New York, Modern Library paperbacks), p. 76.
3. *Ibid.*, p. 103.
4. R. K. Merton, "The Role of Genius in Scientific Advance," *New Scientist*, 12 (1961), p. 308.
5. C. S. Peirce, "A Neglected Argument for the Existence of God," *Hibbert Journal*, 7 (1908), p. 102.
6. F. Bacon, *Novum Organum*, Aphorisms, Book II.
7. T. H. Huxley, *Evolution and Ethics* (New York, 1897), pp. 1-45.
8. Thomas Kuhn, *The Structure of Scientific Revolutions* (Chicago, 1962), *passim*.
9. Norwood Russell Hanson, *Patterns of Discovery* (Cambridge, Eng., 1958), esp. Ch. IV.

CHAPTER 33

HUME'S PROBLEM

The metaphysical problem of induction has to do with the possibility of our knowing whether or not the world is constructed in such a way as to justify our inductive inferences—whether, in other words, the vectorial tendencies spoken of at the beginning of this part can be trusted as a basis for extrapolation. The problem presents itself in two acute forms: the first has to do with the stability of the laws of nature in time, and the second with their uniform applicability in space. If the problem is posed in terms of knowledge, however, the latter of these two reduces to the former, since observations made elsewhere are automatically future observations. This applies even if the observations have already been made, as long as their results are not yet known to us; by a similar argument any observation of distant events whose results are known is automatically a past observation.

The metaphysical problem was posed for modern philosophy by Hume, and his formulation of it is just as challenging now as it was when he first made it public in the eighteenth century. His conclusion was a thoroughly skeptical one, as far as the establishment of the principle of induction on rational grounds was concerned; his "case against induction," according to Keynes, "has never been improved upon." [1] Hume's point of departure is in the division of the possible objects of knowledge into two classes, called, respectively, *matters of fact* and *relations of ideas*. This division anticipates that of the positivists and the logical empiricists; it draws the line sharply between the synthetic and the empirical on one hand and the analytic and logical on the other, and consigns to the realm of nonsense anything that does not fall

248

clearly into one of these two categories. Hume's own use of this principle of division and exclusion is best understood from a celebrated passage in his *Enquiry Concerning Human Understanding*:

> When we run over libraries, persuaded of these principles, what havoc must we make? If we take in our hand any volume; of divinity or school metaphysics, for instance; let us ask, *Does it contain any abstract reasoning concerning quantity or number?* No. *Does it contain any experimental reasoning concerning matter of fact and existence?* No. Commit it then to the flames: for it can contain nothing but sophistry and illusion.[2]

Such iconoclastic sentiments apart, it must be admitted that, at least as far as scientific knowledge is concerned, this analysis is perfectly fair. The logical and analytic truths or relations of ideas— Hume's abstract reasoning concerning quantity or number—can be known certainly; due attention being paid to the rules and definitions of the system, the deductive consequences of any true set of premises are true without qualification. Empirical truths about matters of fact, on the other hand, are in a much weaker position. "All reasonings concerning matter of fact seem," says Hume, "to be founded on the relation of *Cause and Effect*." [3] We judge that the appearance of the table indicates the factual presence of the table on the grounds that that presence causes the appearance, and we judge that the table is there (if in fact it is) as a result of earlier causes, such as the growth of a tree and the action of a carpenter. To know matters of fact, then, involves the necessity of knowing the causal relation which links them to our perceptions, or which links one event to another. But when we look for this causal relation among the events which we perceive we find no trace of it. There are events, and then there are more events; and while the pattern of events has a certain regularity we are never able to detect a *relation* between events—certainly not a causal relation. We may observe that one event follows another, that one event is linked with another through a series of intermediate events, that one event never seems to occur except just before or just after another; but they are all *events*. The best Hume can do by way of characterizing the causal relation is to say that it has three elements—contiguity, succession, and constant conjunction—these relations themselves being defined by means of pairs of events, both of which must be observed if the relation is to be known to hold. But this kind of relation is clearly useless in establishing truths about matters of fact, since we would have to have the matters of fact as well as the perceptions of them in order to see that the former caused the latter. Unfortunately we can never get directly at the matters of fact, only at the perceptions; and therefore all empirical knowledge is fallible, resting as it does on totally unprovable conjectures about the causes of what appears. The same argument applies in a slightly different way to the attempt to make predictions about the future on the basis of past observations. In the former case, we have a conclusion but no premise or implication; in the latter, we have a premise but no implication or conclusion.

The analysis of causality into contiguity, succession, and constant conjunction has been a center of controversy ever since. Many philosophers have felt that the internal necessity which compels one state of affairs to give way to another is in fact open to rational, if not empirical, scrutiny, and they have dismissed Hume's skeptical conclusion as an unworthy loss of faith in philosophy. But the alternative analyses which have been offered have shown that in a good many cases Hume's intentions were misunderstood. Hume does not deny that our idea of causality is derived from regularities in experience, nor does he deny that we have a strong tendency to expect such regularity in future experiences; he denies only that we can have any knowledge—other than the experience of regularity itself—on which to base these expectations, which are thus shown to be philosophically groundless. Other philosophers seem to have felt that logical connections, in the realms of thought and of language, were so clear that they *must* indicate real connections in the world of perception and the natural world. Hume admits the plausibility of this argument to the extent of defining causality, in the end, as the tendency of the mind to produce the idea of what we call the effect when the idea of what we call the cause is presented to it. But the fundamental problem of epistemology is exactly to discover on what grounds we may assume that connections and tendencies in the mind are accurate reflections of connections and tendencies in the world. No theory of causality has yet succeeded in doing this. From Aristotle's four causes—material, efficient, formal, and final (the terms are almost self-explanatory)—to Mill's inductive methods of determining which element of some antecedent situation is to be matched with which element of some consequent situation as cause to effect, this parallel between real relations and ideal relations has been assumed. Some extravagant theories, like that of Hegel, have, it is true, identified them, but even this is of no help whatever, since it leaves us with the question whether our understanding of the amalgam of what is actual with what is thought gives us an accurate representation of it.

Mill's methods, it is true, are an elegant recipe for detecting the constant conjunctions of which Hume speaks.[4] There are four of them: the method of agreement, the method of differences, the method of residues, and the method of concomitant variation. The first three deal with sets of antecedents and consequents. Suppose we are looking for the cause of some consequent C, and suppose a number of sets of antecedents $\{A_i\}$ after each of which C is observed; the method of *agreements* directs us to look for the cause of C among those antecedents which are members of *all* the sets. Alternatively, suppose the consequent C to follow after only one of these sets of antecedents; the method of *differences* instructs us to look for the cause among those members of that set which it does *not* share with any of the other sets which failed to produce C. The method of *residues* instructs us to discard from the set of antecedents any elements whose effects are known to be different from the consequent in question, and to look for its cause among those that are left after this operation has been carried out. And finally the method of *concomitant variation* instructs us to look for the cause of any phenomenon whose intensity varies with time among other phenomena whose simultaneous or slightly prior intensity varies in some simple way with respect to the intensity of the first. But all these, given the rule of constant conjunction, are obvious, and give no help at all in solving Hume's problem.

It has been frequently observed, by critics of Hume, that although he threw up such formidable skeptical obstacles to the possibility of any knowledge about the future or distant course of events, or for that matter about the most ordinary daily matters of fact, that did not prevent him from behaving, in everyday affairs, in much the same way as men do who have a naive confidence in induction and the uniformity of nature; and this fact was often taken as in some way a deepening of the scandal. It was as if nobody who was prepared to question the eternal validity of some principle was entitled to share the benefit of its practical operation (one finds the same attitude taken up today with respect to concepts like democracy). Hume, however, had anticipated these criticisms, and in the *Enquiry* he says: "My practice, you say, refutes my doubts. But you mistake the purport of my question. As an agent, I am quite satisfied in the point; but as a philosopher, who has some share of curiosity, I will not say skepticism, I am anxious to learn the foundation of this inference." [5] There may or may not be any internal necessity linking states of affairs in the world, and we cannot know whether there is or not, but it is only reasonable to behave as if there were.

This conclusion of Hume's is a perfectly sane and plausible one, which ought to be acceptable to intelligent beings conscious of their own limitations. One moment succeeds another, and the state of the world at the later moment bears a discoverable relation to its state at the earlier moment—this is a matter for simple observation. Knowing both states, we are able to *call* this relationship causal, and to suppose that the present state of the world will bear a causal relation to its future states analogous to the relation which its past states bear to its present one. What drives the world on from one state to another we cannot expect to know. The Greeks thought of it as Fate and the medieval philosophers as God; the nearest modern equivalent is probably the notion of time as an independent variable. Now consciousness, tied as it is to physiological mechanisms, keeps up with and in a sense measures the pace of this procession of states; the whole thing might stop and start up again, without our being aware of it any more than the characters on the screen would be aware of the fact that the projector had been stopped and started again. This is a fanciful but illuminating analogy. Suppose there were beings who existed as images on the screen, and who were aware of the stepwise succession of one frame to another: they would be able to devise causal laws exactly similar to those known to us, but as long as they remained restricted to the screen there would be no possibility whatever of their finding out about the mechanism of the projector which caused these states to succeed one another. They would be phenomenalists with a vengeance, and Humean skeptics to a man. The danger with the analogy is, of course, that naive persons may pursue it too far, and suppose that if we are, as it were, images on a cosmic screen, there must be a Cosmic Projector which accounts for our being. Some such causal argument has formed the basis for the greater part of traditional demonstrations of the existence of God. But every exportation of one terminus of the causal relation outside the domain in which that relation is discovered at work commits a fallacy. Causes and effects are members of the same class, the class of events; and while it is not inconceivable that there may be events which are unknown to us causing what we perceive—some such assumption underlies the *natura naturans-natura naturata* argument—these events would have to be of the same general character as more familiar ones; they would have to consist of objects with properties, arranged in configurations, enduring through or changing in time, exhibiting sequences, and so on. In the analogy they would still be events on the screen, although perhaps taking place at a different and inaccessible part of it.

The only excuse for stepping outside this phenomenal framework lies in the experience which we all occasionally have of deciding to do something which effects a real change in the world—for example, walking across a room, lighting a match, killing an insect —and then actually doing it. The decision *seems* to be a cause of the action; and although other causes could easily be found by restricting attention to muscular effort, reflex action (like aversion to insects), and so forth, success in this does not weaken the conviction that something which is *not* an event in the ordinary phenomenal sense has contributed to the causal determination of something which *is*. In Schopenhauer the non-phenomenal aspect is elevated to the point where it stands alongside the phenomenal as an alternative view of the world as a whole; we know the world as *idea* or *representation*, but we know it also as *will*.[6] While this may be true, it does nothing to simplify the philosophical problem of causality—quite the contrary. It suggests, however, that there need be no mystery in principle about the driving force behind the progression of the world from one state to another, and that this may be something of which we have an inkling in our own subjective experience of volition. As far as science is concerned, the nature of this mechanism is a matter of total indifference; as long as the succession of states is observed, and standard movements (like those of clocks), standard lengths, standard masses, and the like are available, the work of science can proceed uninterrupted. That it will continue to do so cannot be known with certainty, but it would be unreasonable to expect such knowledge.

For what, after all, would an answer to this question of causality amount to? The law of the uniformity of nature, phrased in causal language, says that similar causes are always followed by similar effects, and enables us to use the relation *past-present* as an analogy for the relation *present-future*. But suppose it were suddenly to be revealed to us that this law was about to break down, and that starting in a week's time similar causes would not have similar effects. Unless we were told in advance what the differences were going to be, we would have to wait for the change in order to be able to base new kinds of prediction on new kinds of observation —but this activity itself would presuppose the same regularity of causal connection to which the change was offered as a counter-example. A genuine failure of the principle would involve complete chaos, but we would be prevented from knowing about it by the fact that this chaos would extend to perception and thought themselves. If all that is argued for is the *occasional* fallibility of the causal principle, then this argument does not hold and once again we are driven into a skeptical impasse. The solution to all this lies, not in trying to establish the truth of the principle, but rather (by an exercise of will) in asserting it. By this, however, I do not mean that it is to be taken on faith. This is a standard outcry against irreligious scientists—that they make little of other people's faith in the creation of the world, the immortality of the soul, and so on, but that all the time their own work rests on just as large an assumption about the invariability of causal relations or the uniformity of nature. The assertion of the principle of causality, however, is made not on the level of belief but on the level of action, and it conveys, not a confidence in the truth of the principle, but a resolve not to abandon it in practice. The scientist, if he knows what he is doing, does not have a faith in the order of nature, Whitehead to the contrary notwithstanding, but a determination to discover whatever order there may be in nature, which is a very different matter. The introduction of the term 'faith' only clouds the issue. The causal principle, which is now seen to lie at the root of the problem of induction, cannot of course be applied simple-mindedly. In any particular test the cause and the effect have to be abstracted from a more or less complex setting which we may call the background; and a better formulation of the principle would be: Similar causes lead to similar effects if the backgrounds are similar. This condition can be summed up in the phrase *ceteris paribus,* 'other things being equal'—a phrase which is implicitly scattered all through every scientific work. Other things being equal, we are resolved to proceed on the assumption that the causal principle holds, but, at the same time, to treat with courteous skepticism any claim to have finally established it.

REFERENCES

1. J. M. Keynes, *Treatise on Probability,* p. 272.
2. David Hume, *An Enquiry Concerning Human Understanding* (London, 1777), p. 165.
3. *Ibid.,* p. 26.
4. J. S. Mill, *System of Logic,* Book III, ch. VIII.
5. Hume, *op. cit.,* p. 38.
6. Arthur Schopenhauer (trs. Haldane and Kemp), *The World as Will and Idea* (London, 1907), vol. I, pp. 141 ff.

CHAPTER 34

THE PARADOX OF INDUCTION

Most attempts to solve the problem of induction end in one of two ways: either they fail, or they succeed in solving a problem, but not the problem of induction. The latter process is known as 'transformation'. The problem of induction has been transformed into the problem of developing a rational theory of probability, into the problem of statistical inference, and so on. Transformation, in fact, is such a satisfactory way of getting rid of the feelings of discomfort engendered by our inability to justify our actions that hardly anybody can be found who is still rash enough to tackle the problem in its original form. But there has been one notable attempt in recent years, which, although in the end it joins the ranks of failures, comes closer to giving a rational account than any previous attempt. It therefore deserves separate consideration.

This proposed solution, which is due to Sir Roy Harrod,[1] has all the simplicity and obviousness (after it has been explained) of the principles known as 'self-evident'. Harrod does not demand uniformity in his universe, although he does demand something a little better than chaos; he supposes simply that there are *some* continuities in natural processes. Such a continuity might be the regular succession of night to day over a period of time, or a similar limited stretch of any law-like behavior. Let such a continuity be represented by a straight horizontal line of finite length, and let our experience of it be represented by the uniform movement from left to right of a point on the line. We may use our standard example (of A's being B's) and suppose that, at any point on the line, all A's so far observed have been B's. Once the observer moves off the right-hand end of the line the A's may cease to be B's, but the limited assumption of continuity guarantees that until then the retrospective generalization will hold true. Let the whole length of the line be s, and suppose that at some juncture the observer has moved a distance x along the line from its left-hand end. He wishes to make a prediction about conditions in the next segment of the line, and for convenience we assume that he always makes his predictions in a standard form: he chooses some arbitrary number n (once chosen, it is the same number in all predictions) and predicts that the regularity already observed will continue to hold for a distance along the line $\frac{1}{n}x$. The simplest assumption is, of course, that s and x are measures of *time*, but this is not necessary. Harrod's contention is that *whenever* an observer makes predictions in this form the probability of his being right is $\frac{n}{n+1}$, as long as he happens to be on a continuity. The argument for this contention has a simple arithmetical conclusiveness. If we divide the line into $(n+1)$ segments each of length $\frac{s}{n+1}$, then if the point which the observer has reached lies in any segment except the last, x will have a value such that $\frac{1}{n}x$ is less than the length of one segment; and since until this segment is reached there is always one more to be traversed all predictions made in standard form must be true at every point except those in the last segment. By taking n large enough we can get the probability of the prediction as near to 1 as we please.

To put it differently, Harrod's thesis amounts to this: If there are continuities, and if we traverse them uniformly, then we are always more likely to be somewhere in the beginning or middle regions than very near the end of any one of them. And this is obviously true. The reason why this solution too ends in failure is that such a consideration is of no comfort to somebody who happens to be near the end. There are short continuities and long continuities, and to the observer who is actually traversing one they look just the same. Some of them may go on indefinitely, and practically we treat them all as if this were the case—if we knew, in fact, that any particular continuity was finite, we would know also that every step took us nearer its end, and would grow progressively more nervous accordingly. While, therefore, it is true that looking back over past continuities, or taking a privileged and timeless view of a universe containing such continuities, Harrod's analysis applies, it cannot be known to apply usefully to the situation of anybody who actually needs assurance that a given prediction has a chance of being true. And yet he is the only person who has the slightest use for a solution to the problem of induction. Unfortunately, he is also the one person to whom a solution of the problem is systematically denied, and an inductive argument can be constructed to show that this must always be the case.

To attempt to show the insolubility of the problem of induction by means of an inductive argument, since it involves self-reference, is to tread on dangerous ground, self-reference in philosophy having very frequently led to paradoxical conclusions (as is the case, for example, in Epimenedes' paradox of the Cretan). But paradoxes are not in themselves such bad things, and they sometimes indicate profound truths; Unamuno once defined a paradox as "a proposition which is at least as evident as the syllogism, only not as boring." The conditions necessary for the generation of paradoxes always include a negation; for example, in Grelling's paradox of heterological terms, it is only when a term is not descriptive of itself that difficulties arise. Similarly, in this case the paradox rests on the assumption that the principle of induction has not been successfully proven. It has often been remarked that induction cannot be relied upon for a proof of itself; but if other proofs had been successful, the continued reliability of inductive inferences would only serve to confirm the principle more fully. If other proofs are not successful, the continued reliability of inductive inferences is, in a sense, an embarrassment. I shall assume that the latter is the case. The difficulty is expressed in the following passage from Hume:

> These two propositions are far from being the same, *I have found that such an object has always been attended with such an effect,* and *I foresee, that other objects, which are, in appearance, similar, will be attended with similar effects.* I shall allow, if you please, that the one proposition may justly be inferred from the other; I know, in fact, that it always is inferred. But if you insist that the inference is made by a chain of reasoning, I desire you to produce that reasoning.[2]

And again:

> Let the course of things be allowed hitherto ever so regular; that
> alone, without some new argument or inference, proves not that,
> for the future, it will continue so. In vain do you pretend to have
> learned the nature of bodies from your past experience. Their
> secret nature, and consequently all their effects and influence,
> may change, without any change in their sensible qualities. This
> happens sometimes, and with regard to some objects: Why may
> it not happen always, and with regard to all objects? What logic,
> what process of argument secures you against this supposition? [3]

To this challenge Hume found no answer, and this fact is responsible for his reputation as the worst pessimist in the history of induction. Nevertheless, as we saw earlier, he himself had the greatest
confidence in the principle. There is an interesting passage in the
Enquiry where he actually does apply an inductive procedure to
the problem of induction: "This negative argument," he says, "must
certainly, in process of time, become altogether convincing, if many
penetrating and able philosophers shall turn their enquiries this
way and no one be ever able to discover any connecting proposition
or intermediate step, which supports the understanding in this conclusion." [4] But there are obviously two sides to this question, and a
little later he appears to have changed to the other:

> I must confess that a man is guilty of unpardonable arrogance
> who concludes, because an argument has escaped his own in-
> vestigation, that therefore it does not really exist. I must also
> confess that, though all the learned, for several ages, should
> have employed themselves in fruitless search on any subject,
> it may still, perhaps, be rash to conclude positively that the
> subject must, therefore, pass all human comprehension. [5]

This is exactly the situation in which we find ourselves. "Many
penetrating and able philosophers," at least, if not "all the learned,"
have attempted to discover logical grounds on which a demonstration of the certainty of inductive inferences could rest; many more,
since the abandonment of the search for certainty, have tried to
do the same for its probability.

But it must be conceded that all attempts to solve the problem
of induction have so far been unsuccessful. Let the ith attempt at

solution be called A_i; then (overlooking the considerable difficulties involved in identifying the A's) we might exhibit a series

$$A_1, A_2, \ldots\ldots\ldots A_n,$$

to which the methods of induction could be applied. If we let U stand for the predicate 'unsuccessful', the state of affairs may be described by the sentence 'All A's so far observed are U'. This can clearly serve as the premise of an inductive inference, the conclusion of which will be 'All A's are U', or 'Probably all A's are U', or 'At least 99 per cent (or some other figure, depending on the theory adhered to) of A's are U'. The making of such an inference depends, of course, on the reliability of the principle of induction. The assumption of the reliability of the principle leads, therefore, to the conclusion that it is probably indemonstrable. Conversely, if somebody were at last to produce a convincing argument for its validity, that would in effect justify us in saying that what he had done was impossible, or at least highly improbable, since it provided a counter-example of a generalization of a type whose soundness had just been demonstrated.

The longer we go on using the principle of induction, then, the less likely we are to find a justification for it. This is what I have called the 'paradox of induction'. It is not a rigidly formalized paradox—the introduction of probability prevents that—but whatever variety of inductive theory is employed, conclusions which are, at least to a degree, paradoxical result. For example, if one uses Harrod's formulation, the hopes for success of a new solution can be dampened by pointing out that one is always likely *not* to be on the verge of a great philosophical discovery.

One objection springs to mind immediately. Nobody considers it paradoxical, for instance, that after years of research a solution should be found to some scientific problem, although it had eluded previous generations; why then should it be so for a philosophical problem? The answer to this is, of course, that the scientific problem yields to new evidence, but that in the philosophical case no new evidence is available. In principle, the fact that different animals require different groups of proteins is just as mysterious as the fact, which intrigued Hume so, that bread is nourishing for men but not for lions and tigers. The causal relation, objectively speaking, is as ineffable as it ever was. It is not inconceivable, I suppose, that new evidence might be forthcoming, and this would be the only way in which a theory of induction could escape the paradox; but it is difficult to imagine what might constitute new evidence in this sense. Williams remarks that "the solution of the problem of induction must be at bottom as banal and monolithic as the process of induction itself. Philosophers and logicians have walked around and over our principle for centuries . . .";[6] and it is to be supposed that they have seen most of what there is to be seen.

What really convinced Hume of the hopelessness of the situation with regard to induction was the inaccessibility of future data. In his discussion of causality he suggests that there are three elements in a prediction—an observed event, a predicted event, and a causal mechanism, corresponding on the logical side to a premise, a conclusion, and an inductive principle, respectively—two of which are needed for the determination of the third (as two sides of a triangle are needed for the determination of the third). If the observed and predicted events are both available, they may be taken as defining the causal relation, and this is the way in which the word 'cause' is generally used. In the logical case, if premise and conclusion are both known, some probability relation may be established between them, and this may serve as the paradigm of an inductive inference. But where the predicted event has not yet been observed, where the conclusion is not known, the situation is like that of trying to guess where the rest of a triangle lies, if one is given one side. Without further information the task is impossible, and the only way to get further information is to wait. In the absence of any other principle we use, of course, the relation defined by previous sequences of observations; but that the new case will conform to the pattern cannot be known until it has already done so.

Science constructs theories which are designed to fit as closely as possible evidence that is already in, and relies on them, as it is bound to do, when it is necessary to speculate as to future states of affairs. The theories present a more or less finished appearance, and as conceptual structures may be explored again and again without revealing any flaws; they may even be rigorously axiomatized and exhibited as logical systems. This in itself does not compel the world to behave as they say it will, and if it behaves differently changes are made in the theories. If physicists had resolved to cling tenaciously to apparently reasonable principles—principles of symmetry or of conservation, for instance—to the extent of demonstrating their logical necessity, there would have been more difficulty than in fact there has been in adjusting to recent developments. The same considerations apply to the principle of induction, which is simply the most general and inclusive theory we possess. I am not suggesting that a disproof of the inductive principle is likely—if it is not verifiable it would not seem to be falsifiable either. Verifiability and falsifiability, as methodological tools, are not as different as they are sometimes thought to be; whenever a crucial test arises, the principle of double negation turns the one into the other. But the principle of induction needs logical foundations as little as the conservation principles needed them; and if they are not needed it hardly seems worth a great deal of effort to supply them.

It is claimed, however, that logical foundations are needed—that their absence is a "scandal" which is likely to have dire consequences for civilization.[7] This kind of language betrays a concern which is more than philosophical. We do in fact rely on the principle; it has in fact worked, up to this point. We are shocked at our inability to justify our actions logically. We are in the position of people who, as Pascal says, have been acting on an uncertainty without knowing why: *"Rem viderunt, causam non viderunt."* [8]

Pascal was the first to use a mathematical theory of probability as a justification for action on uncertainties, although in a rather unlikely context:

> If we must not act save on a certainty, we ought not to act on religion, for it is not certain. But how many things we do on an uncertainty, sea voyages, battles! . . . Now when we work for tomorrow, and do so on an uncertainty, we act reasonably; for we ought to work for an uncertainty according to the doctrine of chance. . . . St. Augustine has seen that we work for an uncertainty, on sea, in battle, etc. But he has not seen the doctrine of chance which proves that we should do so. . . .[9]

It is quite possible to agree with him that acting on chances is acting 'reasonably' in the broad sense of the term (which does not mean 'logically') without following to the conclusion of his argument, which is the existence of God—for this passage is taken from the section of the *Pensées* entitled "The Necessity of the Wager."

Similarly, it is quite possible to agree with writers on induction who say, as Williams does, "It remains none the less reasonable to wager our lives and fortunes where our chances are best," [10] without following to the conclusion, reached by some in a manner strikingly similar to Pascal's, that a wager can justify induction as a metaphysical principle. This, however, seems to be the logical outcome of some recent proposals.

The two writers in whose treatments of induction the parallel with Pascal is most striking are Reichenbach and J. O. Wisdom. Both authors agree that the problem does not admit of a straightforward solution, either affirmative or negative, just as Pascal admitted that neither of the two propositions "God is, or He is not," could be defended according to reason. And just as Pascal presented two alternative modes of action—to believe or not to believe—so in the case of induction there is a choice: to trust inductively confirmed statements or not to trust them. Nature may or may not be such as to vindicate our trust—in Reichenbach's language the world may or may not be "predictable," [11] in Wisdom's the universe may be "favourable" or "unfavourable." [12] We are, in effect, invited to wager on the former possibility, since the odds are heaviest on that side. Although neither of these authors believes himself to have solved the problem exactly as Hume set it—both, in fact, agree with Hume's main criticisms—nevertheless, each claims to have removed the problematic elements from it. Reichenbach speaks straightforwardly of "the justification of induction which Hume thought impossible," while Wisdom solves the problem only after "transformation." In both cases their conclusions penetrate beneath immediate strategic necessity to a more fundamental level.

There is a distinction to be made here between recommendations as to strategy—the maximizing of the chances, assuming a regular universe in which we know less than we would like, as practiced in the theory of games—and conclusions as to principle. Many authors stand behind the theory of probability as the best tool we have for guiding our practical decisions, and in this case the wager remains unchallenged—it is what we actually use. But this is not the point at issue. As far as practical affairs were concerned, as was pointed out earlier, Hume too knew and used the principle of induction, and would no doubt have been happy to learn and use also modern methods of probability. What is at stake is its justification, which has been taken to lie in a metaphysical principle—the Principle of the Uniformity of Nature, the Principle of Sufficient Reason, or the like. Such principles can be used to justify anything; happily, this kind of metaphysics is increasingly in disrepute. The principle needed is metaphysical, however, in Collingwood's sense,[13] in that some form of it, however restricted, is an absolute presupposition of scientific activity. It appears to me unfortunate to suppose that a wager can be properly used to justify such a principle. If we ask ourselves what is the status of a concept which is made the subject of an intellectual wager—what, for instance, the existence of God meant to Pascal—we have to answer that it is that of something to which there is passionate attachment. Pascal already believed in God; the wager was a rationalization of his belief for the benefit of his worldly friends. Similarly, when Reichenbach says: "It is better to try even in uncertainty than not to try and be certain of getting nothing," [14] or Wisdom: "We must not, however, slur over . . . the possibility that the universe is favourable," [15] one is not impressed with a conviction of genuine uncertainty, of genuine doubt as to the nature of things; these devices are merely the best that can be done to provide visible support for a belief which is already stronger than any such devices could possibly make it.

Today we are not, most of us, moved by Pascal's argument. If the arguments of Reichenbach and Wisdom appear more compelling, that is because of our historical perspective. The conflict between religion and the world is more or less quiescent; science, together with the philosophy of science, occupies an area of active concern. Induction has an importance to us now that the existence of God has not; we are therefore more sympathetic to proposals for providing it with a logical foundation. But the truth or falsity of the principle of induction is not affected by our efforts, any more than the truth or falsity of the existence of God is. Electing one side or the other, *as a result of logical calculation,* is in any case futile. A regular world, viewed *sub specie aeternitatis,* is a fantastic improbability; an irregular world, viewed from our temporal standpoint, is an equally fantastic improbability. "It is incomprehensible," says Pascal, "that God should exist, and it is incomprehensible that He should not exist." [16] In our niche of space and time it seems foolish not to trust the principle of induction; in Pascal's, it seemed foolish to question God's existence. I do not doubt that in his circumstances he was right, and I do not doubt that in our circumstances we are right, but that gives us no reason for claiming the philosophical immutability of the principles to which we subscribe. Wagers are appropriate to limited objectives, not to ultimate metaphysical commitments. Neither Reichenbach nor Wisdom, perhaps, intends to give the impression that an ultimate metaphysical commitment is in mind, but by bringing in the notion of the world in which series converge to limits coincident with "best posits," the universe in which regularly unfalsified hypotheses remain unfalsified, they have moved into metaphysical territory, where gambling is out of place.

In any case there is very little point in gambling on the principle of induction; the best attitude to it, as in the earlier cases of causality and simplicity, is to make it the subject of a resolve: in the absence of any better guide to future behavior, we shall use the lessons of past experience. It would be absurd to pretend that we need reassurances about the course of events in the distant future, just as it would be absurd to pretend that we know anything about the course of events in the distant past. Scientific observations have been made with some accuracy for perhaps 5,000 years; they have been made in quantity and variety only for about 500 years, if as long. An extrapolation (on inductive grounds) into the past suggests that these periods represent an almost infinitesimal fraction of the whole life of the universe. Further, all these observations have been made within a very thin spherical shell surrounding one planet of a small star. It may be that an animal species thus restricted in time and space has, in fact, succeeded in discovering the principles according to which the cosmos operates, but if it were not for the fact that we ourselves are members of this species, we should find the *a priori* probability of this rather small. What success we can claim lies in the construction of a theoretical account of a hypothetical universe which, if it existed, would be like our universe in those places and at those times where the latter has been observed; and we expect that, in limited predictions, the fit of the theoretical universe to the real one will still be fairly close. It would be presumptuous to say more.

REFERENCES

1. R. Harrod, *Foundations of Inductive Logic* (London, 1956).
2. David Hume, *Enquiry*, Section IV, Part II, p. 34.
3. *Ibid.*, p. 38.
4. *Ibid.*, p. 34.
5. *Ibid.*
6. Donald Williams, *The Ground of Induction* (Cambridge, Mass., 1947), p. 21.
7. *Ibid.*, ch. I, *passim*.
8. Blaise Pascal (tr. Trotter), *Pensées* (New York, 1941), p. 84, no. 235.
9. *Ibid.*, no. 234.
10. Donald Williams, *loc. cit.*
11. Hans Reichenbach, *Experience and Prediction* (Chicago, 1938), p. 350.
12. J. O. Wisdom, *Foundations of Inference in Natural Science* (London, 1952), p. 226.
13. R. G. Collingwood, *An Essay on Metaphysics* (Oxford, 1940), p. 41.
14. Hans Reichenbach, *op. cit.*, p. 363.
15. J. O. Wisdom, *op. cit.*, p. 229.
16. Blaise Pascal, *op. cit.*, p. 79, no. 230.

CHAPTER 35

SCIENTIFIC METHOD

This book has been concerned so far with questions of logic and epistemology; it will proceed in the last part to more general philosophical questions, verging on the ontological, and enough will be said about value to show why, in the philosophy of science, it is comparatively neglected. All four branches of philosophy mentioned in Chapter 2 are therefore either included or honorably omitted; and in a sense the last part is a luxury, the essentials of the subject lying in epistemology and logic. But to these two, in discussions of the philosophy of science, is often added a third division known as *methodology,* and some account must now be taken of this subject and its relevance or irrelevance to the rest.

The scientific method, like the Abominable Snowman, has been the object of an enthusiastic but on the whole unsuccessful search on the part of many well-intentioned people, who have felt that if captured it could be persuaded to act as a sure-footed guide to those austere but rewarding heights of intellectual endeavor which the layman faintly discerns looming through a scientific mist of formulas and diagrams. The search has yielded up a number of somewhat bewildered scientists; but these, after some personal anecdotes and hesitant generalizations, have gone off again leaping from crag to crag, leaving the searchers no more enlightened than before. The trouble is that the scientific method means three different things. One of them has already been implicitly dealt with; the other two, in a book of this sort, cannot properly be dealt with at all, the first because it is too complex, the second because it is too uninteresting.

Plato used to say that nobody, having come to know the better,

267

could voluntarily choose the worse, by which he meant that good theory leads automatically to good practice. The application of this maxim in the present case is simple: if it is understood what the structure of scientific theory is, how it is linked to observation, what steps are necessary in order to confirm a given theory, and so on, then the method of science will lie in working toward that structure, establishing those links, and taking those steps. In the present case this will amount to following the pattern of hypothesis, deduction, and test. It is rather as though one knew the geographical relationships between two towns—what roads led from one to the other, what rivers or mountains had to be crossed, what dangers might be encountered—and were then to ask, But what method is there for getting from one to the other? This is the sense in which the question, How does one go from A to B? may be answered by producing a map of the region. Theories are like maps; the analogy has been overworked, but here it is useful.

But of course there is another sense in which the question of how to get from one place to another, or of what method exists for doing so, may be understood, a sense in which the answer may be "take the bus" or "I'll lend you my bicycle." These are practical matters, and scientific method in this sense cannot be dealt with by the philosophy of science. This does not mean that it is not an object of legitimate interest to the philosophy of science, but that (at least so far) nobody has successfully extracted from it any reproducible pattern. This aspect of scientific method consists of an expertise which follows no prescription but is best learned by working in the laboratory alongside some experienced scientist who already possesses it. Here again I do not mean to say that it defies rational description, but that such a description would be so complicated as to be practically useless. There are some complexities of understanding and experience whose rendering in language is unenlightening to anybody who has not directly participated in them; and the practice of science falls into this category. Every discipline whatever has this component, however, so that it is not something of which the scientist can be especially proud.

The third aspect appears when some technique has become a matter of routine; having been devised by a method of the second kind (presumably guided in its general conception by one of the first kind) it is now to be applied unimaginatively by unimaginative people, who get from A to B along a well-worn trail by putting one foot before the other and following the signposts. This kind of activity is only by courtesy called scientific at all, but quite often when 'scientific method' is referred to something *methodical* of this kind is meant. The conventions and techniques of protocol discussed in Chapter 11 belong to scientific method in this sense; they are certainly important, but it would be better to think of them as elements of good scientific *practice*.

In spite of these disclaimers it must be admitted that there is such a thing as methodology. One might prefer its partition between the theory and practice of science in the way I have indicated above, but since this is not universally accepted its independent status must be reckoned with. The trouble is that scientists themselves have often tended to couch their epistemological insights in methodological terms. This was true, for example, of the great seventeenth-century trio, Bacon, Galileo, and Descartes. Bacon, as we have seen, propounded an inductive method to establish what we would consider epistemological links between hypotheses and instances; Descartes' best known work is his *Discourse on the Method of Rightly Conducting the Reason and of Finding Truth in the Sciences;* Galileo (the best scientist of the three) comes closest to the contemporary concept of method in specifying the three steps through which a theory has to pass. Galileo's method, as a matter of fact, has a surprisingly modern ring: his three steps are intuition, demonstration, and experiment, which can be translated almost exactly into our terminology, once again as hypothesis, deduction, and test. The greatest advantage of methodological formulations is that they make quite clear the relative importance of the various steps in the epistemological process, regarded as the emergence of a more or less accurate theory from primitive observation and conjecture.

The historical examination of this process of emergence is itself sometimes thought of as an exercise in methodology, although it would probably be better to use J. B. Conant's phrase "the tactics and strategy of science." [1] The best example is provided by the development of celestial mechanics. The primitive observations were those of the early calendar makers; the primitive conjecture that of Aristarchus, who, as early as the fourth century B.C., hit upon the idea that the earth might possibly go around the sun. This case history gives, in fact, illustrations of much more than methodological development, for the next stage is of course the complete neglect of Aristarchus' hypothesis in the centuries of Ptolemaic astronomy—a striking example of what may happen to novelty in competition with what is more attractive on traditional grounds. The hypothesis was resurrected by Copernicus, not, however, in the disinterested search for scientific truth as much as in the hope of saving the circular motion of the planets, and of producing an aesthetically more satisfying theory than the Ptolemaic. But Copernicus worked with inadequate data, and it was only after further observations had been made by Brahe that Kepler was able to arrive at his three laws of planetary motion—laws which in the scheme developed earlier would have the status of generalizations. It was left for Newton to axiomatize all this into a system of mechanics in which the particular behavior of the heavenly bodies was only a special case of something completely general. The interest of this story lies in the fact that each of the men mentioned was responsible for one important stage in the development of the theory: Aristarchus and Copernicus jointly for the hypothesis, Brahe for the observation basis, Kepler for the stage of inductive generalization, and Newton for the axiomatic and deductive organization of the finished theory.

Now this historical order is not quite the order in which theory has been represented as establishing itself in the earlier parts of this book, and other histories could be quoted to show that other orders may lead just as successfully to a conclusion. There is no 'method' of creating history. The whole of Newtonian mechanics might have begun with Halley's famous question, Newton's reply to which required the *Principia* by way of clarification. The question was simply what path a body would follow if it moved in such a way as to be constantly attracted toward some other body along the line joining them with a force inversely proportional to the square of the distance between them; Newton's answer was that of course the body would move in an ellipse. Given that starting point, Newtonian mechanics *might* have developed even if Aristarchus, Copernicus, Brahe, and Kepler had never existed. Historically it would have been unlikely—indeed if it had not been for the work of these earlier scientists the question would probably not have been posed

—but such contingent details apart it would have been as good a way of developing theory as any other.

The details of every such history, in fact, exhibit a different method. The end is a fully developed scientific theory; the means are almost infinitely various. Newton himself, had he been asked to give an account of the method he used in making his many contributions, would probably not have done much better than the scientists mentioned at the beginning of the chapter, although he might have referred the inquirer to his "Rules of Reasoning in Philosophy," which occur near the end of Book II of the *Principia:*

> Rule I: We are to admit no more causes of natural things than such as are both true and sufficient to explain their appearances.
>
> Rule II: Therefore to the same natural effects we must, as far as possible, assign the same causes.
>
> Rule III: The qualities of bodies, which admit neither intension nor remission of degrees, and which are found to belong to all bodies within the reach of our experiments, are to be esteemed the universal qualities of all bodies whatsoever.
>
> Rule IV: In experimental philosophy we are to look upon propositions collected by general induction from phaenomena as accurately or very nearly true, notwithstanding any contrary hypotheses that may be imagined, till such time as other phaenomena occur, by which they may either be made more accurate or liable to exceptions.

These four rules form a compendious summary of almost everything which is of central importance for modern science, but they do not so much specify a scientific method as suggest certain restrictions which must be observed if mistakes are to be avoided. Rule I is obviously the principle of economy, which restricts the number of explanatory categories; rule II is the principle of induction, which restricts variety in these categories; rule III is the principle of extrapolation, which together with rule IV restricts scientific fantasy; while rule IV, if allowance is made for the Newtonian language, will be recognized as the fundamental principle of empiricism. Newton's apparent aversion to hypotheses (found also in his famous phrase *"hypotheses non fingo"* [2]) is explained by the fact that he understands by the term hypothesis a *merely* speculative account. In the sense in which we have used the term a hypothesis can form a perfectly respectable element of a thoroughly empiricist system, and can even be regarded loosely as a "proposition collected by general induction from phaenomena," since Newton, like Bacon, frequently made imaginative jumps to explanatory hypotheses as though this were a perfectly natural thing to do, and without being explicitly aware of his own unusual powers in this respect. Very few people have the scientific imagination of Newton, but as we saw in the chapter on discovery nobody can do creative work in science if he does not have at least some measure of it. Without that, the rules of reasoning are useless as rules, except in the negative sense of showing that some popularly accepted explanations are inadequate.

Newton's rules may serve, in fact, as an epitome of the value, and at the same time of the inadequacy, of 'method' as a category in the philosophy of science. From them, together with some considerations from earlier chapters, may be distilled four *methodological resolves*, namely: (1) treat the results of observation as sacred; (2) look for causal laws to explain those results; (3) formulate those laws as simply as possible; and (4) in the absence of a better strategy, use simple laws which explain previous observations as the basis for further action. But in scientific practice these maxims are honored as much in the breach as in the observance. Anomalous observations are unhesitatingly thrown out as due to extraneous interference, defects in the apparatus, and so on; it might be that following them up would lead to startling new discoveries, but more often than not this would just be a waste of time. (If thousands of oysters are clogging an important channel, there is not time to open them one by one looking for pearls.) Statistical correlations between observations may be just as useful as causal laws, and complex formulations, as long as they work, may as we have seen be just as convenient as, and even hamper the search for, simpler ones. The fourth resolve *would* be generally adhered to if it were known what simple laws, explaining previous observations, were available. Of course there grows up, out of the aggregate experience of scientists over comparatively long periods, a canon of such laws, and these are relied on by engineers. But, once they are established, the scientist's interest in them falls sharply until exceptions begin to appear. *His* 'further action' is after all devoted either to testing and refining old laws or discovering new ones.

In conclusion, it is worth distinguishing again between two senses in which 'method' may be understood—as referring to the *methodical* application of standard results, which is the way in which science as an effective body of knowledge enters into the lives of ordinary men, or as referring to *methodological* inquiry about the adequacy and reliability of explanations, which is part of philosophical criticism of science as an intellectual activity. The latter sense was intended when it was said, at the beginning of this part, that the validation of theory is a *method* for the tying down of abstract logical systems to empirical contents.

REFERENCES

1. J. B. Conant, *On Understanding Science* (New Haven, 1947), *passim*.
2. I. Newton, *Principia*, Scholium generale.

PART IV

THE SPECTRUM OF THEORY

PROLOGUE

The fourth part begins from a point where the work of theory-construction is already completed. Theory is given as a logical structure, having a conceptual interpretation and resting, as surely as certain philosophical limitations will allow, on empirical foundations. It serves for the description, classification, and explanation of observed events as well as for the prediction of future ones by assigning to them various degrees of probability. The task of this part is to inquire what philosophical views about the world as a whole, and about the nature of science itself, have been supposed to follow from the successful fulfillment of these functions, and whether those views are justified.

CHAPTER 36

SCIENTIFIC THEORIES

Although it has occasionally been useful to draw examples from particular sciences, the first three parts of this book have as far as possible maintained complete generality. The subject of discussion has been scientific *theory* without qualification—how such a thing emerges from ordinary experience; what are the principles of its internal organization; what criteria it must meet to qualify as relevant, true (or highly confirmed), and genuinely scientific. The only answer so far given to the question of what theory *is* involves isomorphic conceptual schemes held by individual scientists, and while that is an appropriate answer it may be objected that it does not do justice to the obvious fact that scientific theory is also physics and chemistry and zoology and the like. On the whole, however, it is better to reserve the term *theory* for the general concept, and to say of these divisions that they are distinct scientific *theories* or simply *sciences*, that is, *examples* of theory. (What are popularly called theories are certain memorable parts of these sciences: the theory of evolution, Mendel's genetic theory, the quantum theory, the theory of relativity, and so on.)

If we assume that nothing exists except the world, then theory is part of the world, a part which stands in some way for the whole; and a comprehensive theory, in dealing with the world, would have to deal also with itself *as* part of the world, just as the map of a country drawn somewhere in that country would have, if its scale were large enough, to contain a very much reduced replica of itself. But for any particular theory a better analogy would be a map which showed only roads, or one which showed only railways. Such a map, wherever it was drawn, would not have to worry about including itself—that would not be one of its functions. Scientific theories are selective, any one science dealing with only a fraction of what there is to be observed, namely the fraction constituting its observation basis. For that matter, all the sciences taken together still give a very incomplete account of the world we know, just as the superimposition of all the specialized maps—the road map, the railway map, the map showing the distribution of population, the map showing water resources and land use—would still leave indefinitely many concrete facts about the country unexpressed.

The different sciences are distinguished from one another not only by means of the different parts of the world of experience which they explain, but also by means of the different ways in which they explain the same parts. The familiar distinction between the physical, biological, and social sciences rests principally on the former kind of difference, but there is associated with it a difference of the latter kind which has to do with the stage of development which each group of sciences happens to have reached. Our previous classification of the sentences of science suggests three stages, which may be called *descriptive, nomological,* and *hypothetical,* respectively. The first is the stage at which explanation proceeds mainly by classification and correlation, and at which generalizations and hypotheses, if formulated at all, have comparatively low degrees of confirmation; the second is the stage at which classification and correlation have been completed to the point where well-confirmed generalizations (that is, empirical laws—'nomological' is from the Greek *'nomos',* 'law') emerge, but at which as yet the lines of a fully developed and axiomatized theory are not firmly laid down; and the third is the final stage of development at which the resources of mathematics and logic are drawn upon in the construction of a complete theory. The association of these stages with the three kinds of science mentioned above is not by any means a tight one. For one thing, the fact that a given stage is reached does not mean that activity ceases at earlier stages; physics still has its descriptive and nomological problems. For another, there are certain very well-confirmed hypotheses in the biological sciences, of which the principles of genetics are the best example. But some developments on the hypothetical level in biology (such as the theories of the vitalists), and on the nomological level in the social sciences, have stood in the way of progress because of premature acceptance and the subsequent necessity of reconsideration. This has been principally due to unresolved problems remaining on the nomological and descriptive levels, respectively. This sketchy treatment, however, needs to be supplemented by a more detailed examination of each of the three stages.

Historically, the first concrete achievement of science—as distinguished from empty theorizing—was a *description* of the phenomenal world, resting on observations which were as far as possible accurate and systematic, if partial. The key term is 'partial'. Not only does the experience of a single individual cover an infinitesimally small part of the universe, but also the elements of the individual's experience which are attended to carefully enough to be accurately describable constitute only a very small part of that, and among them only a fraction qualify for description in the observational vocabulary of any one of the special sciences. The descriptive sciences therefore yield skeleton outlines of fragments of the world. The usefulness of this stage is in providing a *record*, and the past exists for us exactly as a series of such skeletal remains in more or less detail, none of them, however, being more than a shadow of the full and vivid world of present experience, which is itself merely a fragmentary perspective of the whole. History, whose status as a science is still a matter of controversy, has to deal with these remains in the aggregate; the other sciences pay attention to special collections chosen according to particular criteria. Sometimes the term 'collection' is literally appropriate; the great scientific expeditions have been devoted to *acquiring* the material whose description is to form the foundation of theoretical work. And all scientific observation is acquisitive in this sense, the observer appropriating only those parts of what presents itself to him which he expects to find useful. The world of science is to that extent artificial. There would be no point in observing everything that could be seen, even supposing this to be possible. Popper once dramatized this point by challenging his students, who had too readily accepted the notion that one of the fundamental tasks of science is description, to *observe*.[1] The students, of course, were at a complete loss; they wanted to be told what kind of thing to observe—that is, what descriptions were called for—and such instructions can only be given if it is known what kind of theory one

wishes to refute or justify. Description as merely a kind of catalogue
of things in the world is a necessary forerunner of scientific activity,
as Bacon realized when he made natural history the first stage in
his great *Instauration*, but it is only a forerunner. It is therefore
not surprising to find it a prominent feature of *popular* science;
for many years before the full impact of technology had been felt,
the naturalist with his magnifying glass and butterfly net was in
the minds of many people the paradigm of the scientist. But description viewed as a struggle to render specific contents of observation in terms suitable for the eventual construction of theories is a
genuinely scientific task.

	Objects	Aggregates	Organisms	Persons
Objects	Physics	Chemistry	Biology	Psychology
Aggregates		Geology	Ecology	Sociology
Organisms			Anthropology	Economics, Political Science etc.

Fig. 36.1.

Figure 36.1 shows in tabular form a possible classification of the
sciences according to the nature of the entities whose observation
provides their starting point. The underlying presupposition of this
arrangement is that the ultimate nature of matter is atomic, although the disproof of this hypothesis would not disrupt the relative positions of the sciences in the table, but simply add a more
fundamental category. Physics deals with objects which retain their
unitary character throughout the events in which they participate;
chemistry, with aggregates whose character changes by the addition
or subtraction or substitution of parts; biology, with organized
aggregates, which again preserve a unitary character in spite of an
exchange of parts; and psychology, with organisms whose behavior
is no longer easily explicable in terms of the parts, but exhibits an
apparently self-conscious ability to direct itself. Geology, ecology,
and sociology represent a complication of chemistry, biology, and

psychology analogous to the transition from objects to aggregates; and anthropology and the various other social sciences represent a complication of ecology and sociology analogous to the transition from aggregates to organisms. Of course, there are boundary problems in every case, but these need not at this point be taken too seriously; the division of the field of science into these elements is based on the grossest and most obvious distinctions between the objects which they study, and is not intended to convey the impression of territorial rights. The viruses, for example, would have been considered purely chemical entities if biology had not got there first. What is much more important is the possibility, to be discussed in a later chapter, that by a process of reduction one of these sciences, namely physics, might be extended in principle to cover the whole field, the divisions then becoming merely convenient ways of separating problems of different complexities from one another.

Such a reductionist program could not, however, be conceived before each of the sciences involved had reached the second stage, which consists in the discovery of regularities in the observable world and the enunciation of empirical laws to account for such observed regularities. This calls for the clarification of concepts and logical relations, the rendering of our theoretical apparatus satisfactory for explanatory purposes. In one sense, of course, empirical laws are only generalized descriptions, and the explanations made possible by them nothing more than the reiteration of observed regularity. It was remarked earlier that the stage of generalization is often rapidly passed over in highly developed sciences, and the importance of this stage lies principally in its being a convenient stopping place in the logical ascent from particulars to hypotheses. It is nevertheless true that by far the greater proportion of scientific activity has in the past been concentrated at this stage, and there are two principal reasons for this. First, the practical benefits of science lie mainly in the possession of information about regularities in the world, even if those regularities cannot be explained in terms of unobservable entities, so that—to take a short-sighted view—it might be claimed that the ascent beyond generalizations was superfluous. Second, it may be a very long time, even when many generalizations are established, before a hypothesis which accounts for more than a few of them occurs to anybody. The really great scientific theories contain very powerful hypotheses, or (to use the language of an earlier chapter) very strong ones, from which large numbers of generalizations follow. Such hypotheses emerge rarely—a quite short list would exhaust the principal cases. The day-to-day work of the great majority of experimental scientists consists, then, of discovering new but minor regularities in fields whose total extent is known in principle even though large parts may as yet be unexplored in detail, and of checking and refining the accuracy of our knowledge of such regularities. Similarly, the work of theoretical scientists consists of following out logical relationships between established hypotheses and the detailed generalizations of the experimenter, and of adjusting and redefining the concepts which enter into those generalizations.

The third stage is reached with the establishment of hypotheses, which, taken together, constitute a theoretical system having complete internal coherence, yet resting on empirical foundations. The provision of such a working replica of the real world is the goal of theory. And yet the claim that it is a replica of the *real* world is, as we have seen, always presumptuous. In the development of theoretical science there comes a point, which has so far been reached only in theoretical physics, when this no longer matters. Physics provides a rationally coherent account of *a* world, and the *practical* objectives of physics will of course only be realized to the extent that this turns out to be like the real world. But the theoretical physicist may not care as much about that as about the autonomous nature and the intrinsic value of *his* world, namely the world in which his theories are fully true. In this sense, theory is invulnerable to possible destruction by counter-examples. We profess to be ready to discard theories if they turn out to be false with respect to the observable world, and undoubtedly in the long run such theories are eliminated. But there is a stage in the growth of theories when the internal development is so exciting that for the time being the necessity of later test is forgotten. What is important is not the wrongness or rightness of the theory in its applicability to the world, but the theory itself as a speculative construction. The *usefulness* of any theory is an empirical matter; its status as a created and autonomous entity is not.

This view may seem heretical, and in some philosophical senses it is, but I believe it to be close to scientific orthodoxy. The question raises fundamental issues about the nature of science. Whitehead used to complain that the world described by modern physics was a bleak and cheerless place, unsuitable as a habitation for ordinary men, and he summed up his objection in a famous passage: "Nature is a dull affair, soundless, scentless, colourless; merely the hurrying of material, endlessly, meaninglessly. However you disguise it, this is the practical outcome of the characteristic scientific philosophy which closed the seventeenth century." [2] The implied criticism is that the scientific philosophy which closed the seventeenth century is still rampant in the twentieth, and that it introduces a systematic distortion into the understanding of the contemporary world.

The trouble lay, according to Whitehead, in the fact that scientists had been careless in abstracting their fundamental categories from observed fact—that indeed these categories had often been acquired by mere postulation and invention. There ought, he felt, to be a continuous gradation from the warm, colorful contents of sense experience to the abstractions of science, which would preserve the qualitative appropriateness of the latter to the former; instead of which he found a cavalier adoption of materialistic and mechanistic categories, which were then read back into the world as real and present entities alongside chairs and tables. His complaint was in large part legitimate; scientists were constantly committing (and still constantly commit) the *fallacy of misplaced concreteness*, which makes the mistake of placing theoretical entities in the same world as observable ones. If they are there at all, they are by definition there *invisibly,* which is certainly odd in a world whose claim to existence lies in its being observed. But there is nothing wrong with the invention of theoretical entities as long as they are not thought of as belonging in the observable world. All sorts of possible worlds, with all sorts of imaginary constituents, behaving in all sorts of bizarre ways, may be constructed by science, and nobody will have any right to criticize until the scientist tries to force the conclusions derived in his hypothetical world upon actions to be carried out in the observable world.

This is the moment of truth for science in a pragmatic sense, and the utilitarian justification for the expenditure of public funds on scientific activity will in the long run rest on this kind of applicability. But there is no reason why the pure scientist, like the pure mathematician, should not explore theoretical possibilities, not (as in the case of mathematics) in a merely formal sense, but with hypothetical *content* also, far beyond the boundaries of any immediate prospect of applicability. There is indeed every reason to suppose that only if this is done will science continue to advance.

Among the speculative theories produced by scientists, some will be agreed upon (by virtue of the agreement of their consequences with observation) as representing the nearest available approximation to the truth about the world. These will constitute the network of constructs with which natural reality is considered to be isomorphic. But although in the discussion of Chapter 10 the expression 'natural reality' was used as if it had a perfectly clear meaning, it is evident—in the light of the preceding discussion—that the concept requires further clarification. Whitehead sometimes expressed his objection to the dominant philosophical outlook of modern science by saying it *bifurcated* nature into what he called, respectively, *causal* nature and *apparent* nature, the former corresponding roughly to *natura naturans* and the latter to *natura naturata*. This he thought was a mistake, his clear preference being for the latter as the sole meaning of the term. The following chapters will be devoted to a clarification of the relation between the conclusions which science has traditionally drawn about nature and the obvious common sense facts of everyday experience.

REFERENCES

1. K. R. Popper, *Conjectures and Refutations* (London, 1963), p. 46.
2. A. N. Whitehead, *Science and the Modern World* (London, 1925), p. 80.

CHAPTER 37

NATURE AND REALITY

Science is the explanation of nature in its own terms, but there is an ambiguity in the concept of nature. The force of the phrase 'in its own terms' is to rule out the supernatural and the occult as scientifically acceptable categories—"so that" in Newton's words, "the argument of induction be not evaded by hypotheses" [1]—but if nature is to be taken in Whitehead's sense as what *appears* only, then explanations in terms of theoretical entities will be judged to be occult and accordingly excluded. This is obviously too stringent, so that if the definition of science is to be retained the meaning of the term 'nature' must be extended. The lines along which such an extension can be carried out are already laid down in the recursive criterion of significance given in Chapter 25, which may offer a satisfactory solution to Whitehead's problem of linking the rough world of experience with the smooth world of theory without necessitating an exclusive reliance upon abstractive (as against inventive) entities. 'The explanation of nature in its own terms' is guaranteed by limiting the contents of nature to the elements of acceptable explanations, while allowing it to contain far more than what is directly observable.

Only in the last few centuries has anybody doubted the assumption that nature so defined is in fact identical with the real world. The Greek term for nature was *'phusis'*, meaning the root or origin of things, and was derived from a verb which meant 'to engender'; its use to refer to things brought into being by the operation of such original principles—that is, to the observed world—was derivative, but the double meaning referred to in the previous paragraph has a long history. The writers of ancient texts on physics (many of

which were entitled '*Peri phusis*', 'on nature') certainly intended
their accounts to be taken as true of the real world and not merely
as sets of explanatory hypotheses. These scientific accounts did not,
at first, diverge very much from realistic common-sense beliefs
about the world; it was only gradually that the bifurcation spoken
of in the last chapter took place, and in fact the link between the
rough and smooth worlds may be fully exhibited in a genetic account of scientific realism.

Like most philosophical terms, 'realism' has many meanings (one
of its traditional uses being to designate what we would now ordinarily consider a version of idealism, namely the theory, held by
Plato among others, that universals have a *real* existence in some
privileged realm), but it is usually accepted as indicating the belief
that the world exists independently of its being perceived by any
observer. (This might be called *epistemological* realism as distinct
from the *metaphysical* realism of the Platonists.) The real world
may of course be perceived, although it *need* not be. In the simple
version of this view known as *naive realism,* the real world is assumed to have just those properties it appears to have. This is the
attitude naturally taken up by unreflective men, and there is a
good reason for it. The successful survival of man as a species has
been due to his ability to escape danger, overcome obstacles, and
so on; and this ability is principally achieved through his natural
tendency to project a three-dimensional world containing objects to
be avoided and manipulated. Naive realism makes possible the
straightforward and unreflective apprehension of complex perceptual relationships, and it is to be doubted whether a creature which
lived in a purely phenomenal world (as Santayana suspects some
animals do),[2] not giving body and duration to the objects it encountered, would have been able to achieve as much. We may bring
ourselves to see that strictly speaking the world of naive realism
is an illegitimate extrapolation from the world of appearance,
without on that account ceasing to live in it. In a similar way the
successful advancement of science, in the last few hundred years,
has been largely due to the tendency of scientists to think in realistic terms (perhaps a little less naive); and it would only be a
hindrance in most cases if philosophical caution were insisted upon.

Scientific realism in its more sophisticated form begins with
Descartes' dualism of thought and extension. The problem is to dis-

cover the objectively real world as opposed to the subjective world
of appearance, and Descartes' answer to it, arrived at in his *Meditations*[3] from a consideration of the relation between the thinking
subject and the world known to him, was his distinction of the *res
extensa* from the *res cogitans,* a realm of extended but unthinking
matter from the thinking but unextended mind by which it is
known. This contrast was given its more familiar form in Locke,[4]
who distinguished between *primary qualities,* qualities known to
belong to the external world because of their invariance under different conditions of perception (for example, extension, duration,
and number), and *secondary qualities,* which do vary with different
conditions of perception and are consequently assumed to belong
at least in part to the private experience of the individual (for
example, colors and sounds). Objects are thought of as possessing
just the properties necessary to account for their observed behavior; and since the precisely ascertainable forms of that behavior
can usually be characterized quantitatively, the objective world
easily acquires a somewhat arid mathematical flavor.

The upshot of Locke's analysis of perception was that material
objects could not be known as such ('material substance' being as
we saw in Chapter 3, a "something I know not what") but only as
sets of qualities some of which could be shown to be inauthentic.
The authenticity of *primary* qualities was clung to as the key to
nature, and it seemed that if secondary qualities could only be
expressed in terms of primary ones human knowledge would be
complete. A good deal of progress has in fact been made toward
this goal, by rendering light and sound as wave motions, heat as
random molecular motion, and so on, but even before these achievements the confidence that the ideal could be realized had led to a
general acceptance of a special *kind* of realism, namely, materialism, which reached its highest form in the eighteenth century in
France.

Everything, according to the materialist, is matter in motion, and
there is nothing else in the world; man is an automaton, and all
secondary qualities are illusory. There are two main criticisms
which can be brought against this account. The first is that it is pre-
posterously inadequate to all our intuitive understanding of our
situation in the world. The quotation from Whitehead in the previous chapter embodies this criticism. We inhabit a world of sounds

and scents and colors, and they are *not* "the hurrying of material."
It may very well be that the hurrying of material is a necessary
condition of the existence of such a world; eyes and ears are material objects, and they are indispensable to the ordinary perception
of colors and sounds. But that does not make colors and sounds
material objects. Primary qualities are always accompanied in perception by secondary ones—extended bodies are colored, surfaces
are cold or warm—which are certainly not identical with them. Of
course in a way this misses the point, which is to construct a world
as it might be when not perceived. Realism after all claims that
there is such a world. But it must be *perceptible*, and arrangements
for perception must be made internally, to avoid ruling out psychology, sociology, and anthropology from the sciences and making
consciousness something transcendent or occult, and these arrangements cannot be made with the assumptions of materialism.

The other criticism of materialism was adumbrated by Berkeley
and has already been referred to in Chapter 3. To say that everything is matter in motion is not enlightening if the nature of matter is not known. Motion is all right, since it can genuinely be
expressed in terms of primary qualities, but matter has no standing in a materialistic universe except as a dogmatic first principle.
The assertion that there is an external world has some philosophical
content, but the assertion that this world is a material one adds
nothing whatever. Matter, etymologically, is just 'stuff', and as
long as the world is made of anything (ideas, emanations, and so
on) it is material in a minimal sense. It is of course unobjectionable
to talk about 'matter' if no more is meant than this. The special
sense attached to the word was presumably intended as a rejection of idealism; but in fact the problems of the two schools, where
the relation between the observer and what he observes is concerned, are identical. A material world and the idea of it are no
more distinct from one another than an ideal world and the idea of
it, the idea which *is* the world and the idea *of* the world being opposite terms of a two-termed relation.

The crisis in contemporary physics which arises when the observation of an event destroys or modifies the event itself, so that
this sharp distinction between observer and observed seems to
break down, has led some scientists to a quasi-idealist point of view
which claims that the things science talks about are really only

constructions of the mind. The position adopted in this book might seem to be akin to that, in view of its reference to concepts, constructs, and so on. But we must never forget that constructs and concepts arise out of the perceptual world, and that the perceptual world is by definition taken as an indication of a hypothetical external world. Although we handle science conceptually, the conceptual scheme is always meant, in the end, to refer to such an external world. The use of theoretical constructs is not a gesture toward idealism, but simply a recognition of the fact that, since everything in the world is not given in perception, those elements of it which are concealed have to be represented in theory by inventions whose adequacy can only be tested indirectly.

The distinction between the world and its representation in theory on the one hand and that between the observer and what he observes on the other are not quite parallel; in fact, the observer himself can be represented in theory in cases where his interaction with the world is crucial. But here there is an ambiguity in the notion of the 'observer'. The scientific observer who interacts with what he observes does so as a physical system interacting with another physical system, and a theory can be devised which deals with these two systems as parts of a larger system. But the metascientific or philosophical observer, reading a theoretical account of this comprehensive system, remains outside it. These two observers may be one person, who in his capacity as a scientific observer gets the data and in his capacity as a metascientific observer understands their theoretical significance. As a realist, he realizes that his body is part of the external world, independent of his observation of it in his second capacity. He *might* be an automaton.

The conclusion that men are not automata rests on arguments which would be out of place here and which are in any case irrelevant to the point at issue. Science *requires* a kind of hypothetical realism in order for theory, which is conceptual and propositional, to have a referent which is perceptual and factual. If it were to turn out that the real world did not exist (how we could possibly come to know this is a puzzle, but it may be supposed for the sake of argument), then the hypothesis would be seen to be false. That, of course, is the risk that every hypothesis runs. It could never turn out that the metascientific observer, who made the hypothesis, did not exist, but scientifically speaking he is of little use by himself;

he needs the hypothesis. For that matter, scientifically speaking, it is better for him to forget his existence as a metascientific observer, and even to entertain the idea that he might, as a scientific observer, be an automaton, than to become preoccupied with the philosophical question at the expense of his scientific work.

Realism, then, remains the natural standpoint of the scientist. While philosophically this may be naive, pragmatically it is a very good thing, because such a presupposition leaves the scientist free to do what he really can do well, that is, to make observations, and theories to account for them. It is more difficult to keep oneself involved, more difficult to feel, as a scientist, that one is really getting something done, if one has a sneaking suspicion that the whole thing is subjective.

REFERENCES

1. Isaac Newton (tr. Motte, rev. Cajori), *Mathematical Principles* (Berkeley, Calif., 1947), p. 400.
2. G. Santayana, *Scepticism and Animal Faith* (New York, 1923), p. 17.
3. R. Descartes (tr. J. Veitch), *Meditations* (London, 1887), p. 101.
4. John Locke, *An Essay Concerning Human Understanding*, Book II, ch. 8, Sections 9-10.

CHAPTER 38

SPACE, TIME, AND MATTER

The metaphysical realism which was said in the previous chapter to be the characteristic philosophical outlook of working scientists places the observer in a world which is thoroughly familiar to every educated man in our epoch, although it would have looked strange to some earlier generations. It is a world of objects participating in events, these events being *located* in the world so that to each of them may be assigned a date and an address. Its address locates an event in space, a vast receptacle immovably attached to some unshakable foundation, and incapable of rupture or distortion. Its date locates the event in time, which proceeds inexorably from past to future from an unimaginable beginning to an inevitable end. This view of the world prevailed in scientific circles from the sixteenth century to the end of the nineteenth, and its plausibility today in nonscientific circles testifies to the pervasive influence of scientific theory on popular belief. Although the notion of an all-encompassing space and a steadily flowing time go back to Plato and beyond,[1] the rigid, infinitely extended, three-dimensional framework in which events succeed one another eternally in a measured and orderly way did not really become established until Descartes' introduction of analytic geometry and Galileo's observations on isochronism in the cathedral at Pisa. Space, in this view, endures through time, but the three dimensions of the former have no intimate relation with the one dimension of the latter.

The classical view of space and time has lost the status it enjoyed in early modern science. As a matter of fact, to call *this* view 'classical' at all is to yield to a common scientific prejudice. The receptacle theory has had challengers for a very long time, the most important among them in the modern period being Leibniz, who maintained, as one element in a rather complex metaphysical doctrine, the view that space and time were nothing apart from the events which occurred in them.[2] Space and time, according to this view, are properties of the whole collection of events which constitute nature. Space is the set of relationships between contemporary events, and time is the successive relationship between instantaneous spaces. But since space is defined in terms of contemporary events, while time is defined in terms of events happening at the same place, their definitions will be circular unless some decision is made as to which takes priority. Since each of us views the universe from a unique perspective, any two events in which the same observer can participate must be separated in time, although they need not be separated in space; and this suggests that the foundation for the whole rational system must lie in our experience of time. Time is directional, and moves from future to past: events are first future, then present, then past. We know the meaning of 'before' and 'after', not through any theoretical apprehension of the laws of motion, but through a purely subjective apprehension of the succession of events, and this makes plausible the definition of space as the relationship between contemporary events. Time is prior to space, in this analysis, but the events which succeed one another are prior to both.

There is, then, an ontological conflict. Are space and time prior to events, or are events prior to space and time? Do events take place *in* space and time or are space and time merely relations between events which take place independently? Einstein once made a remark which would lead one to think that he believed the relational view to be correct. When asked by reporters to sum up the theory of relativity in a sentence he replied that before the theory of relativity, if one took away events, space and time would remain; after the theory of relativity, if one took away events, nothing would remain. But even in the theory of relativity space and time are not made secondary to events—the receptacle, in fact, reappears not now as space enduring through time, but as space-time. This amalgam is associated with the name of Minkowski, who declared: "Henceforth space by itself, and time by itself, are doomed to fade away into mere shadows, and only a kind of union of the two will preserve an independent reality." [3] This new entity has taken on the role of absolute existence, and scientists have remained realists; the space-time continuum has become in some expositions of the subject the only real thing there is, and attempts have been made to show that events are merely local geometrical distortions of it.

To do them justice, reflective scientists have sometimes adopted the more cautious view that space is what is measured with rods, and time what is measured with clocks, space-time being characterized simply by a metric. (For any two points separated by a distance ds, the metric is an expression which gives ds in terms of dx, dy, dz, dt, and so on.) This is a question of the choice of a geometry, and is to be distinguished from the ontological question of what space and time are; according to this view, it is enough for science to know that they can be measured in certain ways. But on the whole there has not been such a great change of heart on the part of scientists since the time of Descartes, and the tendency still is to think of the world of science as objectively real, in spite of the fact that this new, more positivistic, operational point of view has been endorsed by some great scientists in their redefinition of certain old ideas—for example, Einstein's redefinition of distant simultaneity of local events.[4] For Einstein two distant events are simultaneous if light signals sent out from each reach a point midway between them at the same time. One has to judge *that* simultaneity in local terms which are unanalyzable further, and this avoids any commitment as to the over-all nature of space and time.

The question remains of how we can describe the world in such an over-all way, starting with such local characteristics. Figure 38.1, which is adapted from Eddington,[5] takes account of the unique position of each observer and shows what kind of world can be constructed if the only fixed point is here and now. The vertical axis represents time, the horizontal axis a generalized space; the observer's here and now is located at the origin. What is seen now lies on the surface of a cone, the lower of the two in the diagram, the events on which are further back in time the further away they are in space, since light travels with a finite velocity. In a Euclidean world, it would be possible to construct a contemporary spread of events in space in a plane orthogonal to the time-axis (called 'constructed now' in the diagram). What distinguishes the relativistic case from the Euclidean is that in the former this constructed

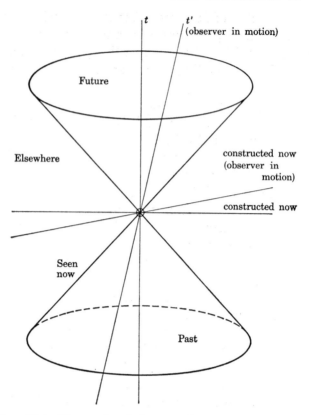

FIG. 38.1. *The angle of the cone is much exaggerated.*

simultaneity is unique to each observer; no observer moving with respect to the one at the origin would arrive at quite the same set of contemporary events, and in fact (depending on the velocity of the second observer) any event in the space between the two cones might qualify as contemporary with the origin. The whole point of the theory of relativity has been to construct a formulation of the laws of nature which shall be indifferent to the observer, that is, a formulation which might be objectively true. And this can be seen as an attempt to get back once more to the certainty of realism.

The two components of the real world of the seventeenth century were extension on the one hand and matter on the other, motion being the link between the two. Motion is the history of matter in space and time. The view of Plato and that of Descartes was that space was somehow *identical* with matter. There is an extended arena which is at the same time the raw material of the world, not only formally but also materially. There is no vacuum, that is, no space that is not occupied by matter. Matter and space are then in some sense synonymous. Aristotle, on the other hand, regarded matter as the *substratum* for qualities. Matter is no longer identical with any property of the world of the senses, but it is the substratum for all such properties. It is not that matter is *extension,* but that matter is *extended;* it is the universal featureless substratum of a world which has features. Before the time of Plato there had already been a school which maintained neither that matter is identical with extension nor that matter is the universal substratum for extension and all other properties, but that matter occurs only in some places; it is the substratum for the properties of all *things,* but not for the properties of space itself. Space is not substantial. This is the view of Democritus and the atomists, who said that there are atoms and the void, the atoms being material and substantial, and the void merely empty.

It has often been remarked that the pre-Socratic outlook on the world was much more like the outlook of modern science than anything which intervened between them, and among the early atomists it was already understood that the identification of space and matter could not be consistently carried through. This conclusion was forced by the critics of atomism, notably Zeno, who (as we saw in Chapter 20) showed the absurdity of trying to construct a geometrical interval out of discrete units. If the units are of finite size, then the interval will not be infinitely divisible, which is a condition for the success of geometry; if they have no size, then even infinitely many of them will not suffice to produce the interval. A consistent atomism therefore requires the separation of the material properties of bodies from their geometrical properties.

Atomism was revived in the eighteenth century, hardly changed since the time of Democritus, and with the accepted theories of space and time it completed the mechanistic world-picture which prevailed until the turn of the present century. The universe is like a box with particles in it—the box represents the space-time framework, and the particles represent the matter. The problem that has arisen in the twentieth century is that it has become harder and harder to identify the particles. It was easy when the box contained discrete particles which weighed a fixed amount and reacted with each other in a Newtonian way; but what happens when the particles begin to disintegrate, when one can no longer count on their individuality? In modern physics there is a well-known relationship between mass and energy; what before would have been considered an unchanging property of a massive particle under all circumstances becomes in part a function of its state of motion. And recent work has suggested the possibility of deriving particle properties from field properties, which might look like a return to a Platonic or Cartesian view of the identity of extension and matter. Starting from such a view, there were historically two stages in sophistication: first the separation of matter from space and time and then the separation of time from space. But we have come to the conclusion that it is not so easy to separate space from time; and now the spatio-temporal characteristics of matter are seen to be not merely locations in a framework, but also modifications of the properties of the framework itself, which becomes a scalar field in which the properties of a thing are a function of where it is. There is an intimate relation between materiality and spatio-temporality which confuses the traditional mind. Yet even this last difficulty in the details of scientific realism has not destroyed the possibility that in its general features such a realism may be retained.

Let me recapitulate. Naive realism says: there is the world, and it is as it appears to be. Science says that this is *too* naive; if we say that 'now' means what we see, then the fact that signals travel with a finite speed introduces paradoxes, and so on. Therefore we reconstruct the world and say that it consists of space enduring through time, and is known to us by signals which take a finite time to travel. So we have given up one kind of realism, but we have given it up for another, for we are now hypostatizing a framework of space enduring through time, where before what had been real was the naive world of perception. Now Minkowski objects: one cannot separate time and space like that, one can only have space-time. So once again we give up a form of realism, but again we replace it by a new form, in which we have a space-time framework. This space-time framework may be considered to contain particles of matter; we find, however, that it makes a difference in our understanding of the particles of matter what their state of motion is, or where they are with relation to other particles of matter, or even to the space-time framework itself. The realism which represents the world as a box with particles of matter in it has therefore in turn to be given up, and gives way to yet another, a new version of the old substratum theory, in which there is a universal underlying reality which modifies itself in various ways to give us the impression of there being particles and space and time. What we always want is a unitary theory. Einstein used to look forward to such a theory, and Heisenberg has recently tried without much success to develop one, in which we have, instead of a number of different factors brought fortuitously together, one fundamental underlying field, all appearances, all massive bodies and space-time relationships, being functions of conditions imposed on this field in what we hope will turn out to be a purely geometrical way. One might then be able to say that particles are standing waves in the field, which keep the same pattern over a period of time; what used to look like a collection of solid particles would turn out to be a state of the field, and the disappearance of such particles a change in its state. But the field itself, in an important sense, would still be taken to be real.

REFERENCES

1. Plato's view of these matters is found in the *Timaeus*.
2. H. G. Alexander, *The Leibniz-Clarke Correspondence* (Manchester, 1956), p. 25.
3. H. Minkowski, "Space and Time," in Einstein *et al.*, *The Principle of Relativity* (London, 1923), p. 75.
4. A. Einstein, "On the Electrodynamics of Moving Bodies," in Einstein *et al.*, *op. cit.*, p. 38.
5. A. S. Eddington, *The Nature of the Physical World* (London, Everyman ed., 1935), p. 54.

CHAPTER 39

CAUSALITY AND DETERMINISM

So far we have agreed that scientific realism requires, first of all, a framework; secondly, things in the framework; thirdly, modifications of and interactions between the things in the framework. We have seen how the space-time framework and the concept of matter have been modified historically, and we now turn to the question of determinism and its historical modification, beginning with the famous statement of Laplace:

> We must thus envisage the present state of the universe as the effect of its previous state, and as the cause of that which will follow. An intelligence that could know, at a given instant, all the forces governing the natural world, and the respective positions of the entities which compose it, if in addition it was great enough to analyze all this information, would be able to embrace in a single formula the movements of the largest bodies in the universe and those of the lightest atom: nothing would be uncertain for it, and the future, like the past, would be directly present to its observation.[1]

This intelligence has been called 'Laplace's demon', and it has become the patron saint of determinism.

There are two requirements for the demonstration of determinism: (1) a precise knowledge of the state of affairs now, and (2) a precise knowledge of the causal relationships between different states of affairs. By 'causal relationship' I mean an effectively productive relationship between antecedent conditions and subsequent results. Hume, as we saw earlier, could discover no such relationship; he merely saw the antecedent conditions and then the subsequent results. The scientific realism of the eighteenth and nineteenth centuries maintained the possibility in principle of knowing, if not the nature of the relationship, at least the *precise* correlation of antecedent conditions and subsequent results. That kind of realism has had again to be given up in the light of developments in the twentieth century; but by now we may expect the old realistic faith to emerge again, as it did in the case of space and time and matter. Two difficulties stand in the way of this re-emergence. One is the *precision* of the determination of the state, and the second is the *universality* of the correlation between states.

The impossibility of resolving these difficulties has become the central doctrine of the Copenhagen school of quantum physicists, on the basis of Heisenberg's discovery that on the submicroscopic level there are pairs of parameters which are mutually vague, as it were, so that one cannot determine them both simultaneously with perfect accuracy. One cannot, for example, determine the momentum *and* the position of a particle, and one cannot determine the energy in an interaction *and* the exact time of the interaction, with more than limited precision. It looks, therefore, as though we have to give up the ideal of causality as a perfectly universal and precisely specified correlation between perfectly determinate and precisely specified states. What the Copenhagen view offers as a kind of weak compensation for this sacrifice is the principle of complementarity. According to this principle, we can have *either* a precise geometrical account, *or* a precise energetic account. The first gives a kinematic system (as opposed to a dynamic one) in which spatio-temporal coordinates can be assigned exactly but in which the nature of the processes taking place at these locations is imperfectly known; the second gives a system of energy exchanges of unlimited precision, in which it cannot be known where these exchanges are taking place or where anything is going. Now there are two Laplace's demons; one of them views the world kinematically, the other views the world energetically. But they can never compare notes, and consequently neither of them is able to predict the future in detail; each lacks some of the essential data for the complete specification of an actual state of the world.

These limitations have a negligible effect on the situation with respect to what can actually be predicted on the basis of information actually available. The failure of a given microscopic event to take place at a given time is generally compensated for by the occurrence of another similar event; this nucleus did not disintegrate, but that one did, and the statistical picture remains the same. In human affairs single events, such as a statistically predictable heart attack, may of course have far-reaching consequences in the private lives of those concerned, but they have no effect on the life insurance company, which remains impervious to such details. The events dealt with by classical physics are analogous to the trends studied by the insurance company's actuaries rather than to the experiences of its policy-holders. The claim that there is an inherent indeterminism in nature at the quantum level is not incompatible with the claim that macroscopic relations can be regarded as determinate within quite narrow limits.

But even if the problem of quantum indeterminacy were settled against the Copenhagen interpretation it would not be possible to make fully accurate determinations on the macroscopic level, and this can be seen from everyday considerations.[2] Heavy stones thrown hard at thin windows will certainly break them; small pebbles thrown gently at thick ones will certainly not do so. If these conditions are varied continuously there will, however, be a range of indeterminacy in which it cannot be told whether the window will break or not. But while this adds a statistical fringe, as it were, to the concept of causal determination, and while operations on this fringe may suffer from gross uncertainties as far as long-range predictions are concerned, this does not in any way impair the usefulness of the concept in areas remote from the fringe. Causal chains behave deterministically if they can be kept near the middle of the effective range and insulated against random interference; the function of the engineer is to design such chains and insulating devices. But even well-designed machines go wrong; and the world itself is not, in that sense, a machine at all.

Just as materialism was seen to be an unnecessarily strong form of the general doctrine of realism, so determinism is an unnecessarily strong form of the general doctrine of causality. Science requires causal laws, but these laws may express one-many relationships between causes and effects, by the incorporation of probabilities, whereas one-one relationships would be required if determinism were to be maintained successfully. (Some workers are still holding out for a fully deterministic account, in the hope that a new formulation of physics will show that what appears on one level as a probability may on another level be accounted for in terms of determinate events.)[3] Scientific realism, then, and the associated doctrine of causality, die hard; whenever something seems to be wrong or strange about the view that the world is independent of us and can be described in terms which do not involve subjectivity, a new approach is found which makes it possible to preserve the realistic attitude, differently in detail but with essentially the same philosophical perspective. Science remains unregenerate from this point of view, and this is entirely proper.

The only caution necessary at this point is to beware of allowing *scientific* realism to turn into *philosophical* realism, and of concluding that now science has told us what the world is like. Science has abstracted, as Whitehead would say, from the world; an abstraction is simply the omission of something, and Whitehead's test of a good abstraction is whether what is left is or is not vitiated by this omission. There is no reason why the scientist should not cling to his realism; in fact what can be learned from the short and moral history which I have been recounting is that science progresses by reformulations of realism on successively higher levels. The warning is simply against the danger of extending this habit beyond the confines of science itself.

There is, however, one problem which remains intractable, namely the problem of individual freedom. An enormous amount of confusion clouds the issue between freedom and determinism. This is not the place to rehearse old arguments, but it is clear that one cannot avoid bringing this question down to the level of individual human beings if their behavior (singly or collectively) is to be explained at all. If sociology, political science, history, and so on are to be sciences, then there must be laws of these disciplines which are determinate within suitable limits. We must be able to make generalizations under which cases can be subsumed, and consequently the behavior of the individual must be subject to laws— at least to statistical laws. We know that that is the case; very accurate predictions can be made about the responses of customers, about the suicide rate, and so on. It seems, then, that there are two levels which do not fit together—the requirements of individual action do not seem to be consistent with the requirements of group action. The gross over-all situation is determined, but the precise individual situation is not determined. It has often been pointed out that there is a parallel situation in physics, for example, in connection with the disintegration of radioactive nuclei. There are statistical laws which govern the half-life of radioactive substances; we know that after a certain time only half a given mass will be in its original chemical form, and that the other half will have transmuted into something else by the emission of particles. Another similar case is that of excited atoms which are emitting radiation: the time it takes for an electron to return to its ground state is not given, although one knows perfectly well that after a short period of time nearly all the electrons will have returned to their ground state.

Two ways of approaching this problem, and of preserving the doctrine of causality, present themselves. First of all, as we saw in an earlier chapter, the metaphysical principle of causality can be replaced by a methodological resolve, to the effect that we will never stop looking for causal influences. This means that although the individual appears to be free, and although in society, whether the individual is free or not, we cannot help behaving as if he were, still the resolve of psychology is to look for causal influences for *all* actions. This is not to say that we shall always *find* causal influences, merely that we are resolved to look for them. The same is true in physics. There is no reason why we should not continue to look for determinate accounts of apparently statistical behavior, speculating about the fine structure of subatomic configurations, and putting forward possible theories of determinate micro-micro events which on the higher level appear as random. The point may be illustrated by a hypothetical case from political science in which the two levels can be clearly seen. Suppose a theory to be constructed about the likelihood or unlikelihood of Republicans or Democrats winning elections in states which are predominantly agricultural or predominantly industrial. The theory will be a statistical one, in which people occur only as probable Republicans or probable Democrats. But for any particular election it might be possible in principle to show that each voter had made what he considered a rational decision, and that his vote had therefore been determined. This is an example of a process which is determinate on the individual level, although on the gross level it is only statistical, and it establishes the possibility in principle of such a relationship between levels. It enables the proponents of the new micro-microphysics to answer the traditionalists who maintain that statistical regularities on the gross level are the product of spontaneous or free transitions on the individual level; they may be so, but there is at least a viable alternative.

The other way of preserving the causal doctrine in these cases, which was hinted at in Chapter 33, is to invoke a *non-phenomenal* causality. While this will not do for quantum theory—it would be absurd to look for intelligence at work in the behavior of fundamental particles—it is plausible, in dealing with human decisions, to locate some elements of determination elsewhere than in the physical world. Men, after all, are *beings*, in the existential sense; they are also *agents*. But science must remain silent on this issue. Science, and for that matter the philosophy of science, are among the pursuits the agent can choose to follow. The activities of investigation and speculation are consequent upon that choice, and while other choices may be examined from a scientific point of view there are always some antecedent choices out of the reach of such examination. Modern physics has often been thought to throw light on this question of choice, but it does not. After Heisenberg it was claimed that everybody was free; but of course it is absurd to pretend that my freedom depends on my manipulation of submicroscopic particles within the range of non-commuting variables p and q in such a way that $\Delta p \Delta q \geqslant h$. These values are much too small for my conscious endeavors to make the slightest difference to them. Nevertheless, analogies between the apparent breakdown of causality in physics and its apparent breakdown in human action are illuminating, as long as it is realized that the relation is *only* analogical. They do not, however, constitute a good reason for abandoning the empiricist's view, which is that science can at least *try* to solve all these problems, not necessarily that it will succeed in doing so.

REFERENCES

1. P. S. Laplace, *Essai Philosophique sur les Probabilités* (Paris, Gauthier-Villars ed., 1921), p. 3.
2. A. Landé, *From Dualism to Unity in Quantum Physics* (Cambridge, Eng., 1960), *passim*.

3. The leader of this attempt has been De Broglie, who has never been happy about the Copenhagen view; the best known current work is being done by Bohm and Vigier. For an earlier reference to the Paris-Copenhagen controversy, see ch. 29.

CHAPTER 40

EMERGENCE AND PURPOSE

The world described in the foregoing chapters is a mechanistic one, built out of separate parts and operating according to the laws which govern the behavior of those parts in a framework of space and time. (The relativistic view of space-time does not change the situation—it simply calls for somewhat more sophistication in the formulation of the laws.) There is no reason whatever why this world view should be abandoned, especially since it is so useful over so wide a range, but there do seem to be large classes of phenomena whose explanation in mechanistic terms presents special difficulty.

'Mechanism' is used here simply as a convenient label for the realistic and causal doctrine outlined above, and this use is in agreement with the interpretation suggested by Dijksterhuis when he defines 'mechanistic' as " 'with the aid of the concepts of mechanics' . . . in the sense of the doctrine of the motions of material bodies in accordance with Newton's system." [1] The difficulty of maintaining the mechanistic position arises when one admits into science areas other than physics, chemistry, and so on. The phenomena dealt with by the biological and social sciences seem far too complex to admit of analysis in terms of matter in motion, and the causality which they exhibit seems often to be less a relationship between a prior cause and its subsequent effects than one between prior effects and their subsequent cause—in other words, a *teleological* relationship. (Teleology, in the Aristotelian system, is a kind of causality, but 'teleological' and 'causal' are now usually taken as antithetical.) Theories capable of handling such relationships cannot, it might seem, be reduced to mechanistic theories.

We say that one science can be *reduced* to another if every term belonging to the former can be defined by means of terms belonging to the latter (which entails the translatability of sentences of the former into sentences of the latter) and if every law of the former can be derived from laws of the latter. The reduction of psychology to physiology would make psychology a special branch of physiology, enabling us, from the state of a man's brain, to predict among other things what sort of psychological disturbance he would exhibit under various conditions of stress. The reduction goes in that direction because physiology employs principles which are wider in application than the principles of psychology. Physiology deals with muscles and tissues as well as the brain, but it in turn might be reducible to chemistry, which is again a wider science because it deals with inanimate things. If every empirically confirmed relationship in physiology could be derived from empirically confirmed relationships in chemistry we would be able to describe bodily functions in purely chemical terms, without introducing any special physiological terms, that is, terms not having a translation into chemical terms. Then again chemistry would be reducible to physics if for every chemical term, and so forth, there were terms of physics into which it could be fully translated. Everything might be reducible in the end to the study of fundamental particles, the lowest (that is, the most basic) in a hierarchy of disciplines each of which is reducible to the next below it.

The reductionist program has not, as yet, been fully carried out for any pair of sciences, the closest to realization being the reduction of chemistry to physics. This failure might be simply a function of the complexity of the task, or it might on the other hand indicate an obstacle in principle. Adherents of the latter view sometimes appeal to the idea of emergence as the inverse of reduction. We say that one science is *emergent* with respect to another if there is some event described and explained by the former, whose parts are described and explained by the latter, such that no combination of the explanations of the parts as described by the latter can be made to yield an acceptable explanation of the whole as described by the former. Psychology would, according to this criterion, be emergent with respect to physiology if no set of explanations of brain states could be made to yield an acceptable explanation of, for example, some exhibition of problem-solving behavior.

Similar cases could easily be constructed for physiology and chemistry, chemistry and physics, and so on. It is perhaps somewhat artificial to insist that the unit in this process of emergence should be the step from one science to another (for that matter there was a similar artificiality in the foregoing account of reduction); the same relationship may occur within a science—for example, in chemistry the properties of molecules may be emergent with respect to the properties of their constituent atoms.

It might still seem that the limitation on reducibility which makes the concept of emergence applicable is a matter of ignorance ("can be made to yield an acceptable explanation"). But the defender of emergence would claim that there is something about the whole event as described in the emergent science to which the concepts of the science from which it is emergent are not even relevant. The whole, he would say, is greater than the sum of its parts, just as a musical work is more than just notes strung together, a great novel more than just black marks on white paper. The use of such analogies is, however, unfortunate, since the idea of a value attached to the whole inevitably enters the picture and puts the question outside the scope of this book. There are of course different sciences dealing with events of different levels of complexity, and it is at every level an empirical question what the features of such events may be, so that if we knew only how fundamental particles behaved when participating in simple events it would be unreasonable to demand a full prediction of their behavior when participating in more complex ones. Once that was empirically known, however, the new knowledge could be added to the description of the particles, and at the same time the complex event would acquire an acceptable mechanistic explanation.

Now it seemed for many years that the problem of species was emergent with respect to biological science, or more precisely that ecology was emergent with respect to zoology—the distribution of species with respect to what is known of individuals of those species. However, the general principles of the theory of evolution —variety, and selection under competition—give us a solution to that particular problem of emergence. They show us that there is nothing mysterious about higher levels of organization; emergence is merely the result of selection among random possibilities. One can devise a mechanism for it, although still not one which yields

exact predictions. The mechanism calls, not for a few objects behaving causally in lawlike ways, but rather for very large numbers
of objects behaving in apparently random ways. Out of these
random interactions certain configurations arise which could not
by any ordinary methods have been predicted. It can be shown that
with a sufficiently long span of time stable and self-reproducing
configurations are bound to emerge,[2] unstable or non-reproducing
ones having naturally been eliminated.

We have to contend, however, not only with the contingent
emergence of novelty but also at times with the deliberate and conscious production of novelty, that is, with what we ordinarily call
purposive or *goal-seeking* behavior. This kind of behavior is generally considered to be a special function of living organisms, and
especially of rational organisms. It is the ability to make intelligent choices and to seek goals that distinguishes living and rational
beings from non-living and non-rational beings. Some early thinkers, it is true, believed that it was possible to regard the behavior
of non-living things as exhibiting purpose in a general sense; there
is a well-known passage in which Aristotle outlines a theory of
natural selection remarkably similar to Darwin's, and then rejects
it on the grounds that nature is one of the things that works
'toward an end'.[3] In Aristotle, as a matter of fact, final causes, that
is to say the ends toward which operations lead, are more important
than the other kinds of cause (material, formal, and efficient)
which are those we ordinarily deal with in science. And this tendency to think of everything as somehow working toward an end,
especially living organisms working toward deliberate ends, has led
to a series of explanatory hypotheses designed to supply what is
lacking in the mechanistic account. Among such explanatory hypotheses, the strongest is the idea of God. God sets the universe
on its way; things are happening because he planned it so. One
finds this in recent works of apparently respectable people, such as
Teilhard de Chardin[4]—theories about the point to which the universe is tending, supposedly backed up by geological, palaeonto-
logical, and biological evidence. Teilhard de Chardin has a point
'omega' toward which everything is going; what happens when the
universe gets there is obscure, but it is apparently something
rather splendid. Others have been content with something less
than God; for example, one of the better known theories is Berg-

son's theory of creative evolution,[5] in which he speaks of an *élan vital,* or life force, which compels novelty to emerge in a certain vectorial sense, directed toward something or other. Bergson cannot say what that is either. The most serious attempt to make all this into a scientific account is that of Hans Driesch,[6] who introduces 'entelechies', teleological factors which accompany the physical and physiological properties of the organism. These do not actually produce any concrete result but they have the function of suspending certain natural processes until it is the right time for them to take place, so that things do not grow in the wrong places. The entelechy directs in a negative way, and prevents eyes from growing in embryos where elbows ought to be, and so on.

All this is very pleasant, and gives one a great sense of explaining away mysterious problems. But actually these are not *scientific* explanations at all, because they take no predictive risks. One cannot use God to calculate what the universe is going to do, nor can one use the *élan vital* to find out what direction evolution is going to take, nor can one use an entelechy to predict that an organ will develop in a freakish way or that a mutation is going to occur. They are all purely retrospective, and explanatory only in the logical sense that if one gives objects these properties then according to the definition of the properties the objects must behave as they in fact do behave. If there were a certain entelechy, then such and such an ontogenetic change would take place; it does take place, therefore there is such an entelechy. But we know how fallacious that form of argument is, and, as we have seen, it is only when scientific theories take risks and make predictions which are antecedently improbable that the confirmation of these predictions lends any strength to the theory.

We have to leave the problems of the will and of deliberate, purposive choice, with the remark that from the scientific point of view these are problems which still await solution. In doing so we reject teleological explanations of the kind described above, on the grounds that they are not genuinely scientific explanations, none so far put forward having been of the least use in prediction. We can reasonably ask, however, whether there are any such genuine explanations accounting for apparently purposive behavior. The answer is that there are. They occur in a comparatively new science called *cybernetics* (a term derived by Norbert Wiener from the

Greek word meaning 'steersman'), which is concerned with the control of processes of all sorts—mainly, in its contemporary development, the control of automatic processes in manufacturing, but in general the control of any processes, even natural ones. The fundamental notion of cybernetics is *feedback*. Feedback is information given to the source of a change to tell it what kind of change it has produced. The most usual variety is *negative* feedback, because feedback is in general corrective, and works *against* the source. Suppose, for example, a room the temperature of which is controlled by a thermostat. The source of energy is the furnace. The state of affairs which is to be controlled is the temperature of the room, and the negative feedback is from the thermostat to the furnace. The furnace just burns, and is perfectly unintelligent; if left to itself, given sufficient fuel, and so on, it would be quite content to burn down the house. The thermostat notices when the temperature gets to a certain point, and restrains the furnace by cutting it off; and then it notices again when the temperature drops below a certain level, and encourages the furnace by turning it on. The thermostat, as it were, is the master of the furnace; it is the steersman; it is the device which makes the arrangement apparently purposive, the purpose being to keep the room at an equable temperature.

In this case, the goal is known antecedently to the construction of the mechanism, and the techniques for arriving at it are fairly obvious. But known goals may be arrived at even when no technique is obvious, and sometimes the goal itself may emerge from an originally nonpurposive activity. The procedure for arriving at a known goal in the total absence of technique is to act at random and look to see what effect the action has had. If the goal seems further away than ever, or if no advance seems to have been made, *that* line of action is abandoned and another tried; on the other hand, if the results look promising (which would be a case of *positive* feedback), the same action will be repeated. This is not, it must be admitted, a quick or economical way of getting results, but it is an effective way, given enough time. "Enough time," in this context, may of course mean some millions of years, so that the effectiveness of the method is an effectiveness in principle rather than in practice. It is hardly necessary to add that the goal must be physically possible for this approach to work, but there is a further restriction which may not be quite so obvious, namely that the world should be finite and not increasing in size or complexity in such a way as to allow the number of unexplored possibilities to grow with time. Usually, of course, we are not *completely* in the dark about techniques, so that trial-and-error methods of this sort do produce useful results. Cybernetics is simply the programming of mechanical devices to perform the trials and detect the errors, in this way creating an illusion of purposeful activity, as, for example, in missiles which seek out and destroy aircraft.

The most obvious case in which a goal has emerged from nonpurposive activity is that of evolutionary development; the goal is the survival of the species. It is not a consciously apprehended goal—most of the mutations which occur are in fact harmful. But once the self-reproduction of chemical systems began to occur the stage was set for competition and the elimination of alternatives; and naturally the species which survived were those whose structure and behavior, in the period between birth and reproduction, were such as to respond 'correctly' to opportunities and challenges—that is, in such a way as to insure the survival of the succeeding generation. The instinct for self-preservation which man shares with the animals is simply his badge of membership in the class of viable species.

The issue between emergence and reduction is not settled by these considerations. The complexity of nature prevents the successful completion of the reductionist program, and will no doubt continue to do so indefinitely; but the persistence of science in seeking realistic and causal explanations, and the failure of any theory of emergence to make even a plausible case, keeps that program alive. It should by now be clear that science has no alternative. This does not mean, however, that the explanation of complex events explains away the values we may invest in them. To judge the worth of anything according to its causal antecedents is to commit the *genetic fallacy*—a fallacy which the Victorians committed *en masse* when they supposed that descent from apelike creatures lowered the status of man. Reduction does not involve itself in such questions; it is, like explanation, a logical rather than a psychological matter.

REFERENCES

1. E. J. Dijksterhuis (tr. Dikshoorn), *The Mechanization of the World Picture* (Oxford, 1961), p. 498.
2. W. R. Ashby, *Design for a Brain* (New York, 1960), p. 233.
3. Aristotle, *Physics* 198b.
4. P. Teilhard de Chardin (tr. Wall), *The Phenomenon of Man* (New York, 1959).
5. H. Bergson (tr. Mitchell), *Creative Evolution* (New York, 1911).
6. Hans Driesch, *The Science and Philosophy of the Organism* (London, 1908), vol. 1, p. 143.

CHAPTER 41

METAPHYSICS AND POSITIVISM

The outcome of the preceding discussion is that the mechanistic view does not have to be abandoned even in dealing with highly developed forms of life engaged in apparently purposive activities. But the feeling that the resulting *explanations* of emergence, of purpose, and of freedom are unsatisfactory at least offers an invitation to a new kind of metaphysical approach. There are relations between objects in the world, for example, geometrical relations between particles, to the analysis of which mechanistic philosophy is especially suitable. But there are also other relations, and the most important of these is the relation between the observer and what he observes, between a conscious subject and the world of which he is conscious. Certain difficulties are encountered in the attempt to build up from the former kind of relation to the latter kind, among which two stand out; the first arises in the transition from the inorganic to the organic, and the second in the transition from the organic to the conscious or rational. We may claim to have solved the problem of the nature of life, with the aid of genetics, the theory of metabolic exchanges and cyclic chemical processes, and so on. But the nature of consciousness remains an intractable problem. It seems out of the question to build up, from a *mechanistic* relationship between particles, a *cognitive* relationship between an observer and what he observes.

This perplexity suggested to Whitehead that it might be possible to invert the argument from mechanism to cognition, and, taking the latter as primordial, show how mechanism might arise from it. Although most scientists are not prepared to raise fundamental questions as to the *reasons* for things happening in the way they do—scientific explanation, as we have seen, consisting not so much in giving reasons as in locating the event to be explained in a logical framework—there is something intriguing about the fact that events influence one another: effects are *effected by* causes, which suggests a sort of communication between them. In *Science and the Modern World*, Whitehead quotes a passage from Bacon's *Silva Silvarum* in which the germ of this idea is to be found:

> It is certain that all bodies whatsoever, though they have no sense, yet they have perception; for when one body is applied to another, there is a kind of election to embrace that which is agreeable, and to exclude or expel that which is ingrate; and whether the body be alterant or altered, evermore a perception precedeth operation; for else all bodies would be like to one another.[1]

This is no mere correlation, and in the absence of Hume's skeptical analysis of causality it might never have been thought so. The suggestion that our immediate experience of volition might throw some light on causality is taken seriously by Whitehead. Even more dramatic than cases which fall under Hume's categories of contiguity, succession, and constant conjunction is the problem of action at a distance. The planets move round the sun, and the moon round the earth, in just such a way as to balance gravitational and centrifugal forces—or, to be exact, we say that these forces are balanced because the planets and the moon move as they do. But nobody has ever explained how the planets know where the sun is, so as to keep falling toward it. An acceptable scientific explanation would refer to the gravitational field, and so on, but we have to admit that this throws no light on the qualitative aspects of the relation between planet and sun.

To speak of the planets' 'knowing where the sun is' is of course to commit an anthropomorphic fallacy. But it dramatizes Whitehead's suggestion that the relationship between physical bodies may be merely a lower-level form of the paradigmatic relationship between minds and what they know, or that the relationship between one man and another may be a higher-level and conscious form of the qualitatively identical relationship between the planet and the sun. This calls for a solution of the problem of rendering point events (particles interacting and so on) in terms of experiences, not experiences in terms of point events. Experience becomes primordial, but it is always experience of the whole world. My attention may be focused on a particular enduring object, and I may therefore consider myself to have the same experience more than once. But there never is in fact a repetition of the same experience, because the world is different the second time. Whitehead therefore says that although of course there are striking *similarities* between natural events, there are really never two natural events which are identical with one another. The lines of development may be so closely similar in two cases that the difference is infinitesimal; what a particular electron does in an electron tube is likely to be practically identical with what a previous electron did in the same electron tube. Nevertheless, when an electron gets into a metal, for example, it is in a different environment and perhaps will behave in a different way; when it gets into a brain cell the environment is again different, and it may behave in a still different way.

The participation of any object in any event whatever is a function of the immediate previous history of the world, and in a certain sense, although of course not in very useful detail, a function of the whole previous history of the world. The relationship between events Whitehead calls *prehension,* a lower-level version of conscious apprehension; and the *actual occasion* prehends *all* previous actual occasions which are available to it causally. It cannot prehend actual occasions which are contemporary with it—which lie on the right- and left-hand sides of the light cone (see Fig. 38.1). An actual occasion at 0 is therefore the outcome of all the actual occasions contained in the bottom segment of the cone; it contributes something to each of the actual occasions which are going to lie in the top segment of the cone, and it is causally independent of all the actual occasions which lie on the right and left sides of the cone.

The problems of emergence and of purpose and of freedom are now solved in a new way, by changing one set of ultimate presuppositions for another. Instead of having material particles in space and time, we have actual occasions, which Whitehead calls *nexus* of causal relations, each one unique, and yet occurring in families the members of which are so nearly identical as to make no difference to the practical purposes of science. Now this is meta-

physics, at least in the sense that the English philosopher Collingwood used to regard metaphysics,[2] that is, as the study of the
fundamental presuppositions of any philosophical point of view.
The fundamental presupposition of Whitehead's point of view is
that there are such things as actual occasions which have a relation
of prehension to other actual occasions. The fundamental presupposition of the mechanistic point of view is that there is a space-
time framework with particles or waves in it. The question that
has to be posed and answered is "Is one presupposition preferable
to the other?" As far as the history of science is concerned, nearly
all the successes have been scored with the latter, but there are
some problems which are quite out of reach to a mechanistic
philosophy although they can be dealt with, if not solved, by an
organismic theory such as Whitehead's. Such a problem, as we
have seen, is the problem of uncoerced free individual action (if
there is such a thing).

The thoughtful reader might reasonably ask at this point
whether it is necessary to have any metaphysics at all—why one
should adopt either of these points of view. There is a well-estab-
lished tendency, which began in the eighteenth century with
D'Alembert and continued in the nineteenth century with Comte,
to say that we might as well restrict ourselves to what we can
know positively, and not make any speculations whatever about
the nature of the world apart from our observation. What we can
know positively is the content of our sense experience. We are not
acquainted with the external world, and we should therefore take
up an agnostic position with respect to it, saying neither that it
exists nor that it does not exist. Observations exist, and if we stick
to those we shall be safe, never falling into contradictions. Comte's
celebrated 'law of the three stages' [3] makes positivism the apotheosis
of the philosophy of science. Primitive explanations are *theological*,
calling on God and demons and so on; they are followed by *metaphysical* explanations, calling on forces, prehensions, actual occasions, electrons, space and time, and things of that sort; but mature
scientific explanation is *positive*—it calls on one set of observations
to explain another set, but never goes outside the observational
framework. If it uses theoretical terms, they are merely devices of
calculation which help one to get from one set of observations to
another.

The ground of the positivist hope is that there cannot be any contradiction in observation. (We might recall in this connection the test for the consistency of axioms by giving them interpretations in some actual domain, which rests on the same assumption.) This metaphysical view, albeit disguised as a logical truism, is required in order to make the positivist outlook plausible. That is only the beginning of the trouble, because then it can be pointed out that contradictions do not in any case occur in *things;* they occur only in *statements*. What must be assumed is the impossibility of deriving contradictory statements from observation, and that depends on *how* one derives statements from observation. It is by no means certain that the positivist can describe what he observes without introducing a potentiality for contradiction that did not exist in the observations themselves. We need therefore a precise language of observation, and positivism sees in this requirement the future development of the philosophy of science. The function of *science* is merely the correlation of observations; the function of the *philosophy* of science is the clarification of the language in which this correlation is described.

Positivism nevertheless admits the analytic-synthetic distinction, which can be briefly summed up as follows: What is certain is not factual, what is factual is not certain. Analytic statements, which do not refer to the world, can be known to be true absolutely, but only by definition or according to logical principles. Synthetic statements, which do say something about the world, cannot be known to be true for certain. The claim of positivism, therefore, is not that certain knowledge is attainable, but that gross errors can be avoided by using the reliable techniques of logic on the least unreliable empirical basis. The positivist would concede that, given a suitably rectified language, we can be *virtually* certain of some factual statements, namely those statements—protocol sentences— which report immediate experience. If one never makes any general assertions, but only particular inferences from one set of observations to another, then one cannot go wrong, at least retrospectively. But this leaves unresolved the status of unfulfilled predictions, generalizations, and statements about non-observable entities; it allows no substantial knowledge of the world, but only what looks like a disappointingly superficial summary of collective experience. According to tough-minded thinkers like Pearson that ought to be quite enough; as early as 1911 he thought anything else out of date: "Nobody believes now that science *explains* anything; we all look upon it as a shorthand description, as an economy of thought." [4] And there are still plenty of people who agree with Carnap that there are two uses of language, assertive and expressive; the assertive use describes phenomena and also to some extent logical relations, while the expressive use merely betrays emotions, which really do not belong to the world at all, but only to the subject, and it is just this undesirable element which positivism omits. No other use of language is possible, and the desire for substantial knowledge of the world is idle.

But such a desire dies hard. James may have been right when he suggested that temperament decides what is acceptable as a philosophical account of the world. [5] And a substantial, although rather thin, world may be achieved by taking a short, simple, and obvious metaphysical step away from positivism. In itself positivism claims not to be metaphysical; it does have metaphysical presuppositions having to do with the consistency of experience, but it does not assert anything about the world as a whole. The very closely related position *phenomenalism* is prepared to go further and make the ontological claim that phenomena *are* the world—that the world of appearance is the only world there is. This position accounts for theoretical terms, not merely as calculating devices inserted between descriptions, but as logical constructions out of sense-data (an electron is a logical construction out of certain sorts of sense-datum, namely, bubble-chamber tracks, scintillations, and so on). It enables one to talk about objects not merely when they are present but also when they are not, as sets of aspects or perspectives. Objects *are* phenomena, actual and potential. One can also talk about unobserved facts, which go *conditionally* beyond the world as we experience it: *if* one had the requisite sensory apparatus one *could* see such things. This is consistent, but it is bizarre. To say that the world is made of phenomena means, as Berkeley pointed out long ago, [6] that it does not really exist when nobody is looking at it; therefore potential fires warm real rooms, potential electrons activate real electron tubes, and other such strange and perplexing processes take place.

Some phenomenalists, to avoid such ontological extremes, have turned to linguistic considerations. The fundamental linguistic tenet of phenomenalism is that every significant statement in science, or for that matter in philosophy, must be *translatable* into a statement about sense-data. This is known as the 'translatability thesis'; in itself it involves no ontological commitment, but it still makes a stronger claim than positivism. While positivism ruled out as meaningless certain non-observational sentences, it nevertheless permitted the use of empty symbols as steps from one observational sentence to another. Linguistic phenomenalism denies this privilege unless the intermediate sentences can be translated into sentences about sense-data. But in practice this is a prohibitive demand. Such a translation for every statement of physics, for example, would be extremely tedious even if it were possible, which is doubtful. Sentences about alpha-particles can be translated, after a fashion, into sentences about sense-data, but then it is hard to recognize them as being about alpha-particles. Also there may be alternative sentences about sense-data, translatable into the same sentence about alpha-particles, and that makes the principle of identity merely an arbitrary correlation.

Phenomenalism is in turn not very satisfactory; either it brings back some of the metaphysical elements that the positivists wish to avoid, or it outdoes positivism in excluding useful linguistic forms. There is another formulation of positivism, however, which has become very popular in the twentieth century. This has already been referred to in connection with measurement; here its general philosophical implications are in question. In view of the positivist's difficulty of insuring that his observational language is not a source of ambiguity and error, the suggestion was made that one might restrict scientific discourse to sentences about operations of measurement done in laboratories by scientists. This was the view put forward by Bridgman in his book *The Logic of Modern Physics,* which achieved considerable popularity after its publication in 1927. Bridgman, however, never intended this as a metaphysic. He simply noticed that the conceptual revolution which accompanied the theory of relativity had disturbed the structure of physics in a very radical way, and in a way he thought could have been avoided if only physicists had been more careful about committing themselves to categories like absolute motion and absolute simultaneity.

Operationism maintains, not that there is nothing in the world of science except operations, but rather that if we refuse to give cognitive status to anything except operations, then we shall not make mistakes. So at least Bridgman thought. He defined the concept 'length', for example, as the set of operations which we use to measure the length of something. Now this turns out to be an extreme version of the testability criterion. Not only does one have to know in principle how to test for something, one has also to be able to *perform* the operation in order for the concept to enter into theory. There are again difficulties with concepts whose values can be measured in different ways. We can measure length by reflecting light beams, or by laying down meter sticks, or by echo-sounding devices. There must be three concepts corresponding to these three sorts of operation: how do we know that they are all *lengths?* Of course, they are not really the same at all, they are all different— they occur in different circumstances; but if we want to formulate a theory which will be applicable to *various* circumstances, then we must be able to show that the three are cases of the same concept. It was not possible for Bridgman to do this, and yet he knew perfectly well that such theories are the aim of science, and that the identification would be made in any case. So he had to make rather lame excuses, and say that we may *assert* the identity. But once that is done we have really got rid of the characteristically *operational* viewpoint.

Operational meaning is all right, but it is a minimum meaning, and it is not especially useful in any science, such as physics, where one wishes to go beyond the observations. Operationism applies itself to the task of eliminating certain kinds of metaphysical danger, and, by the time Bridgman's work appeared, thoughtful physicists had either been sufficiently warned of these dangers to be able to avoid them or had concluded that they represented risks which had to be run if science was not to become moribund. In psychology, on the other hand, following the work of Watson, operationism was enthusiastically received. Watson, basing his approach on Pavlov's theory of conditioning, undertook to provide a foundation for psychology in the behavior of the organism, eliminating such metaphysical concepts as that of mind. Psychologists of the behavioristic school were glad to adopt Bridgman's new device, and operationism became a much more important movement in psychology than in physics. But the price which has to be paid for the metaphysical purification offered by operationism is very high indeed. It is in fact the almost complete sterilization of science. Operations can only be known retrospectively. This means, it is true, that they can be known with some degree of confidence, and Bridgman therefore claimed that science could be sure of not landing in the wrong places if the operational technique was used. But the problem is that it may not be able to land anywhere, except perhaps just where it started from; there is no openness in operational formulations, no way of going beyond the given set of operations. What is now known as operationism is, in fact, a rather weakened version of the original doctrine. Bridgman was compelled to bring in what he called "pencil-and-paper operations," [7] and once he had done that operationism was finished, as far as the strong form of the theory was concerned. Obviously, there have to be operations, trivially speaking, when one makes measurements, but it seems to me that what is now called 'operational meaning' is not much more than what I would call simply 'empirical meaning'.

REFERENCES

1. A. N. Whitehead, *Science and the Modern World* (New York, Mentor ed., 1948), p. 42.
2. See note 13, ch. 34.
3. A. Comte (tr. Bridges), *A General View of Positivism* (London, 1908), ch. I.
4. Karl Pearson, *The Grammar of Science* (London, 3rd ed., 1911), p. 35.
5. W. James, *Pragmatism* (New York, Meridian Books ed., 1955), p. 19.
6. G. Berkeley (eds. Luce and Jessop), *The Works of George Berkeley* (London, 1949), v. II, p. 200.
7. P. W. Bridgman, *Reflections of a Physicist* (New York, 1950), p. 15.

Chapter 42

CONVENTIONALISM

There are sentences which are indispensable for science but which cannot be translated into sentences about sense-data. One can trace, in most cases, a genetic path from one to the other, showing how the theoretical sentences *arise* out of sense-datum sentences in the context of a suitable theory, but by the time the theoretical sentences are reached there is much more there than could ever be represented in terms of sense-data. Furthermore, a certain open texture is required in scientific theory, which is spoiled by an insistence on translatability criteria, since theory, if it is to be of any use, is bound to move ahead of the observations which support it. This criticism of phenomenalism applies also to operationism. One cannot maintain that the concept is a set of operations, because sometimes a situation arises in which one has a perfectly clear concept, and is trying to discover an operation whereby to measure its values; there are as yet no operations, although there certainly is a concept. Both these views, then, can be shown to be inadequate. This leads to interesting reflections about the status of theories in general. Theory is not something which can be summed up in terms of observations, operations, or the positive content of our empirical knowledge; there must be more to theory than there is to the world of appearance, and theory must therefore in some sense be autonomous. But if this is the case we need never abandon a theory, or at least there are some parts of theory which, if we very badly want them, can be preserved in the face of all opposition. The technique of preserving a preferred part of a theory has been called by Popper a 'conventionalist stratagem'.[1]

By conventionalism is meant the view, held by Duhem,[2] Poincaré,[3] and others, that no scientific hypothesis is conclusively justifiable, and that therefore it is a matter of choice which hypotheses we assert and defend. Duhem's argument for this view runs roughly as follows: No hypothesis stands alone as the explanation of a given state of affairs—it must always be supplemented by other generalizations or hypotheses, statements of boundary conditions, and so on. Let us call the hypothesis in question h and the ancillary statements which accompany it collectively $\{a\}$, and let the state of affairs be described by a protocol sentence p. The traditional view regarded the explanation of p by h as resting on the simple inference

$$h \supset p$$

so that in the event of a contrary instance $\sim p$, h would be refuted by *modus tollens*. Duhem points out, however, that with the set $\{a\}$ of supplementary assumptions the situation is really

$$h \cdot \{a\} \supset p$$

and in this case the occurrence of $\sim p$ leads, not to $\sim h$, but to $\sim(h \cdot \{a\})$, which by De Morgan is seen to be equivalent to $\sim h \lor \sim \{a\}$. We can always choose the second disjunct of this pair, and by abandoning $\{a\}$ preserve the truth of h. This leaves us, of course, without an explanation for the state of affairs $\sim p$; but if we can find a new set of assumptions $\{a'\}$ such that

$$h \cdot \{a'\} \supset \sim p$$

we have a theory just as good as the previous one which still incorporates the hypothesis h. Our convention is to retain h, and we have succeeded in doing so in the face of apparently contrary evidence.

It is to be observed that there are two distinct parts to the conventionalist claim. The first is that contrary evidence cannot force us to give up a chosen hypothesis, and this is clearly justified. We could preserve the phlogiston theory, if we wished, by making some rather odd supplementary assumptions and rules of correspondence. The second is that this hypothesis, if supplemented by a suitable set of assumptions, is still useful in explaining the evidence even when it is contrary—that it can in fact be made to explain any evidence whatever, and is thus *merely* conventional. The hypothesis together with some assumption predicts p; we get $\sim p$, and the conventionalist now claims to explain why we did not get *p,* by altering the assumptions or the rules of correspondence. But this quite clearly is a trick, and the claim is not really justified; it could only be justified if the alterations were made before the observation, in which case of course the prediction would have come out differently. Conventionalism, therefore, is at once right and wrong—right in claiming that no hypothesis ever stands by itself, but always requires supplementary sentences such as basic assumptions or rules of correspondence; wrong in attaching as much importance as it does to the hypothesis in the absence of these supplementary sentences. Without them the hypothesis can neither explain nor predict, just as a law cannot be applied unless the conditions of its application are specified.

Some hypotheses, however, have historical or customary usefulness in their own right, and it might be worth adopting certain stratagems to preserve *them.* The clearest examples of conventionalism in this sense occur in geometry. There are two senses in which conventionalism enters into geometry. The first has to do with the equality of space-time intervals which are not coincident. There is no way of comparing the lengths of two meter sticks, separated from one another by a finite distance, which does not involve the transport of one or the other of them or of some third object, and there is no way of being sure that such transport does not alter the length. Even less is it possible to compare the length of one second with that of a subsequent second, even the next one. We therefore adopt the kind of convention referred to in the discussion of rules of correspondence (Chapter 17). An associated case is the definition, by Einstein, of distant simultaneity in terms of light signals. The constant value of the velocity of light is itself a convention—for current theories an indispensable one.

The second sense of conventionalism is, in this context, more interesting. It concerns the claim that any space may be considered to be Euclidean (or Lobachewskian or Riemannian) as long as forces are introduced to account for distortions that occur in the shapes or the paths of objects moving in the space. For example, the measurements made at the eclipse of 1919, which confirmed Einstein's prediction about the bending of light-rays near the sun (he calculated a deflection double that which was to be expected due to the gravitational field of the sun, and a series of famous observations by Eddington proved him right), are usually taken to mean that there is a non-Euclidean curvature of space in the vicinity of massive bodies. But they could be interpreted equally well as meaning that there is a 'massive-body force' to be added to Newtonian gravitation, negligible in terrestrial experiments but significant sufficiently near the sun. This is a perfect case of Duhem's argument; the hypothesis that space is Euclidean, apparently refuted by the anomalous curvature, is saved by the additional assumption of the massive-body force.

Reichenbach points out that here there is a whole family of possibilities.[4] There are various sorts of geometry, and one can use any of them as long as one introduces the right supplementary forces. There will, according to Reichenbach, be a *normal* geometry, that is, one in which *no* supplementary forces are necessary. But is it *better* to use a very complicated non-Eucliden geometry with no supplementary forces, even if it is 'normal', than to use a very simple Euclidean geometry with some supplementary forces, such as we have become accustomed to? The answer to that question depends, of course, on what kind of thing one wants to do with the geometry, and how complicated the forces are going to get if one preserves the Euclidean view. But at least the conventionalist has something on his side when he says that it is possible for him, by making manipulations in other parts of the system, to retain certain aspects of a favored theory, and Euclidean geometry may certainly be considered a favored theory of the relationships of objects in space. We have then a certain amount of leeway, in fact three kinds: either we can change the hypothesis, or we can change the supplementary assumptions, or we can change the rules of correspondence. The conventionalist point is that nobody can claim to know which is the right formulation. One might maintain that certain relationships must be fulfilled in order for a given formulation to be *one* of the right ones. But within the family of possible theories the aesthetic choice has to be made as to whether one wants to have, for example, Euclidean space *with* forces or non-Euclidean space *without*.

From the conventionalist view that it is possible to preserve any one of a number of alternative theories, depending on where one puts the emphasis, one might move on rather simply to the view that the world that we are trying to describe is itself a product of the structure of the reason which seeks to make theories about it. I think that in some sciences, notably psychoanalysis, for example, one finds that what is described turns out to be an *interpretation* of the state of affairs in the light of the theory. In other words, the form of the theory imposes itself on the world that is being described. There are quite clearly Kantian elements in this view.[5] Kant's position was that the phenomenal world (and this is the world to which theory refers) is the joint product of a real world that we cannot know, and reason, the faculty through which we acquire knowledge. We have to apprehend things phenomenally, according to Kant, because that is the condition of their intelligibility. We have, for example, to treat the world under the category of causality if we are to make scientific sense of it, and to locate objects in space, and events in time. When we conclude that space-time is three-dimensional and Euclidean, it is not that we have *chosen* to regard the world in this way, but that this is the way in which, being constituted as we are, we cannot help but regard it. There is no ultimate set of three mutually orthogonal axes anywhere, but we can only conceive of three dimensions according to the external form of our understanding. Time we apprehend as linear, and moving in a certain direction, because there is an internal form of the understanding which orders events with respect to one another along a dimension of 'before' and 'after', just as the external form arranges objects with respect to one another in terms of 'in front of', 'behind', 'to the left of', 'to the right of', 'below', and 'above'. This accounts also for the radical separation of space and time which we find in classical physics. Time is something utterly different from space; it is as different, Kant would say, as the inside is from the outside. Time has a way of ordering things internally; space has a way of ordering them externally. According to this view, since events in the world fall under the categories of reason, a similarity of structure between a theory and the world it describes is not to be wondered at. The danger of this view is that its adherents may come to regard experimental test as unnecessary, on the grounds that the similarity between reason and experience may be known *a priori*. The later work of Eddington[6] shows that he succumbed to this danger, and believed himself to have access to truth about the world on purely rational grounds. There can of course be no doubt that the nature and scope of our everyday experience is influenced and limited by our finite intellect and imperfect sensory apparatus; the challenge to science, however, is to devise theories, grounded in that experience, which are not themselves subject to such limitations.

We may conclude the argument of the preceding chapters by reverting to Whitehead's concern over the bifurcation of nature. The world in which we live, and in which science is discovered at work, is apparent nature; the world which science describes is a creation of the human intellect which, while it may bear some resemblance to causal nature, is not identical with it. Neither of these taken by itself is adequate to be considered in the role of the nature which is referred to in the definition of science. Science, while it is the explanation of nature in its own terms, is not the explanation of apparent nature simply. What is explained is of course discovered *within* apparent nature—if it were not we could have no access to it—but in order to be explained it is rendered, even at the descriptive level, in characteristically scientific terms, and to that extent given entry into a new realm. Explanation, being a logical relationship, lies entirely within the fields of thought and language. The nature which is explained is given in perception, but rendered in conceptual and linguistic terms; the nature in whose terms the explanation is provided, on the other hand, is not given at all, but conjectured. There are, no doubt, events and processes to which, for one reason or another, we cannot have access. These constitute causal nature, and they have a directly *productive* relationship with apparent nature. We render causal nature in conceptual and linguistic terms by means of our hypotheses, and the deductive relationship between these hypotheses and our protocol sentences mirrors the productive relation between causal and apparent nature. The correctness of our rendering of causal nature is testified to by the success of theory, when submitted to the boundary conditions imposed by the concrete situation of some observer, in yielding an adequate account of his observations.

The root of the bifurcation is thus seen to lie in each individual. Apparent nature presents itself to him, and he forms a conception of causal nature—a conception which can, it is true, be learned from and shared with others, but whose relation to what is perceived is a thoroughly individual matter. And only the individual can decide which elements of nature as given he chooses to render in the observation language of science, and thus to constitute as candidates for scientific explanation. The public and shared aspects of science and of the philosophy of science are the collective outcome of individual decisions of this sort, and not the other way round.

REFERENCES

1. K. R. Popper, "The Philosophy of Science, A Personal Report," in Mace (ed.), *British Philosophy at Midcentury* (London, 1956), p. 160.
2. P. Duhem (tr. Wiener), *The Aim and Structure of Physical Theory* (Princeton, 1953), *passim.*
3. Henri Poincaré (tr. Halstead), *The Value of Science* (New York, 1907), pp. 112 ff.
4. Hans Reichenbach, *The Rise of Scientific Philosophy* (Berkeley and Los Angeles, 1951), p. 134.
5. I. Kant, *Critique of Pure Reason*, pp. 65-66.
6. See, e.g., A. S. Eddington, *The Philosophy of Physical Science* (Ann Arbor ed., 1958), pp. 170 *et seq.*

CHAPTER 43

THE UNITY AND DIVERSITY OF SCIENCE

It is instructive to regard the development of science as a continuing dialectical process. This implies no commitment to the Hegelian dialectic, or any other special version; it simply takes account of the fact that what is required for the advancement of science is a continuing interplay between its logical frontiers and its experimental frontiers. The logical aspect is embodied in the doctrine which has generally been known as rationalism; it proceeds from the rational investigation of connections between concepts, without special regard to the adequacy of those concepts to experience, developing formal structures in a free and creative fashion. The experimental aspect is embodied in the doctrine which has generally been known as empiricism; it proceeds from the empirical investigation of connections between events, without special regard to the significance of those events in any total scheme of things, accumulating factual information in a disciplined and receptive fashion. Both of these aspects are absolutely essential, and scientific progress may be regarded as a dialectical process of mutual feedback between them. If empirical investigations outrun logical construction, science is at a loss; logical construction has to catch up before we can put the new empirical findings in their place. If logical construction outruns empirical investigation, that is not so serious, because there is always time for something to come up on the empirical side which will fill the new branch of logical development, and provide an interpretation for part of the calculus which was not interpreted before, but until it does so the construction remains a mere exercise of intellectual ingenuity.

The principle which governs the logical and rational construc-

tion is once again Ockham's razor. This we saw in Chapter 31 to be
a principle of economy rather than of simplicity; its consistent application makes of theory a sparing and tightly woven account of
the world, and explains in large measure the aesthetic satisfaction
which scientific understanding can provide. It hardly needs to be
repeated that the ideal austerity suggested here is very rarely
achieved; scientific theories tend all too often to the baroque. The
application of the principle is, in fact, more a matter of style than
anything else, and it is fully consistent with the kind of imaginative construction referred to earlier, as long as that construction is
carried out in an economical way. The principle which governs the
empirical and practical inquiry, on the other hand, is the Demo-
critean maxim 'save the appearances', that is, be faithful to the
data at all costs. If the calculus, on interpretation, turns out to dis-
tort the data, it has to be discarded as far as that branch of science
is concerned, and another calculus devised. In the synthesis of the
two aspects the maxim 'save the appearances' always takes precedence over the maxim 'economize on categories' in the long run. It
does not always in the short run; obviously there are times when
we are prepared to overlook certain details in order to achieve
simplicity, as in popular accounts of science, for example. But when
it is a question of a full scientific account of the world, then we will
always say that theory must be changed and not the results of observation, provided the results of observation have been suitably
safeguarded by the selection of a proper language, by attention to
definition, classification, and so on.

The complexity of scientific theory is something which science
always tries to keep to a minimum, but allows to grow whenever
this kind of empirical necessity presents itself. I call the shift from
a simple to a complex theory in the face of accumulating evidence
a 'Van der Waals shift', from the paradigm case (referred to in
Chapter 22) in which the gas law, although simple, proved to be
wrong for many gases over a wide range of pressures and had to be
modified by the introduction of additional terms. In principle one
keeps the logical apparatus simple until it turns out to be inadequate to empirical discovery; then and only then does one com-
plicate it. The precedence that 'save the appearances' takes over
Ockham's razor reflects the fact that science, apart from its purely
speculative development (which in Chapter 36 was called 'pure

science') adopts characteristically an empiricist attitude. One must always be prepared, when it comes to a question of saying what the world is like, to give up any elegance in theory in favor of accuracy in the face of observation.

The dialectical interplay between the rational and the empirical is reflected also in the debate over the ultimate function of science. On the rational side that function appears as *understanding;* on the empirical side it appears as *control.* These correspond roughly, again, to explanation and prediction. In the logical treatment of Part II, explanation and prediction were said to be different aspects of the same deductive relationship, distinguished from one another on the grounds that in the former case the analysis looked back to a relation already established in fact, while in the latter it looked forward to something as yet unrealized. As far as the logical account of theory given there was concerned that was true, since (in the language of this chapter) the concern there was entirely on the rational side. As a purely practical matter, however, prediction means only knowing what will happen in advance, without regard to the means by which this knowledge is arrived at; and it may be that methods can be found of producing predictions with high degrees of probability over numbers of cases, which will not depend on going analytically through the logical steps of Part II. The usefulness of theory, it was said earlier, depends on its being able to produce deductive consequences before the events to which they refer take place—which is just the condition for a deduction's being a prediction. As the problems which science tackles become more and more complex there frequently arise cases in which logical and mathematical calculations of the old kind are too cumbersome to produce useful predictions, if indeed they can reach any conclusion at all in the time at our disposal. Means have been found, however, with the aid of computers, to speed up the process and make it possible once more to anticipate events.

This asymmetry between explanation and prediction is, as a result, accompanied by a divergence of purpose between the activities of science which offer, respectively, an understanding of nature and control over nature. According to the former view knowledge is an end in itself, and the chief function of science is the satisfaction of man's intellectual curiosity. According to the latter view knowledge is power, and the chief function of science is the satisfaction of man's material needs. The divergence is not as yet very serious, but with the present rapid advance of technology, especially toward the increased automation not only of physical tasks but also of intellectual ones, it may become so. The control of nature is a simple and intelligible objective, and we are rapidly approaching it, but understanding is an elusive value whose defense is much more difficult. If it is not maintained *as* a value, however, the control of nature may turn out to be a hollow victory.

This is not a suitable place for an inquiry into the nature of understanding, which would be protracted and would inevitably become involved in difficulties about the relationship between fact and value. Facts have to do with the way things are, values with the way we would like them to be, not only, however, with respect to the external distribution of property and power, but also with respect to the relation of the individual human being to his world. And the latter may take different forms for different people, who will consequently have different views of scientific understanding. Pascal [1] used to speak of two dominant characters among men, the *'esprit de géometrie'* and the *'esprit de finesse'*. Persons in whom the former predominates will be satisfied with the logical and quantitative understanding of Cartesian science and mathematics, while persons in whom the later predominates will put science alongside other ways of knowing the world in order to achieve a syncretic and intuitive, although perhaps less precise, view of the whole.

Value in science, in short, is again a matter of style—it involves a sense of proportion, and a feeling for the 'fit' of theory to the world. The danger in any dialectical development is that extreme formulations may be put forward before a final balanced view is arrived at, and the history of science is full of examples of this. Such excesses are still to be found, but the point may be illustrated by a case from a remote period. Roger Bacon, a late medieval English philosopher, was a skillful exponent of the science of his time who understood very well a great many qualitative relations; what was lacking at that time was information about and sensitivity to quantitative matters. Bacon knew, correctly, that the earth was spherical, from the observation of ships disappearing over the horizon; as a consequence of this knowledge he propounded seriously the view that it was better to store liquids in basements than on balconies. The argument was perfectly sound: the radius of the earth being smaller as measured from the basement, the curvature of liquid surfaces would be greater, and vessels would therefore hold more.[2] The point should be clear enough. It is very easy to get a one-sided view by concentrating on some aspect of science to the exclusion of others, and it is also easy to get such a view by concentrating on science to the exclusion of other ways of approaching the world.

A similar ambiguity occurs also in the concept of the unity of science, which may be taken formally, as referring to logical or methodological elements common to various sciences, or materially, as referring to a single description and explanation of the whole world. The latter would require the identification of a single observation basis and a single set of hypotheses, and would presuppose a solution to the problem of emergence and reduction (in favor of reduction). The single science would of necessity be the science of the simplest elements available, out of which more complex ones could be built up—in other words, it would, in the present state of our knowledge, be physics. 'Unity of science' has sometimes been understood in this way, but (for reasons already given) the program for *this* kind of unification has never been carried through. It has to be admitted that there are different observation bases, the contents of which are explained by different sets of hypotheses, and that these cannot conveniently be amalgamated. It is more profitable to concentrate on logical and methodological similarities between the resulting theories. The logical similarity between the sciences was implicitly assumed in the earlier parts of this book, where 'theory' was dealt with in the abstract, without regard to particular empirical contents. Methodological considerations might seem to lead to diversity rather than unity, since the operations which are actually carried out and the calculations which are actually made by workers in the various sciences seem to be insurmountably different. But it is easy to exaggerate such differences —for example, between the experimental situations of the physicist and the social scientist. Of course in obvious and gross ways the meter-readings of the former are nothing like the questionnaires of the latter, but the obvious and gross elements here are, as in so many cases, irrelevant to the situation. In fact, the physicist's experiment is very like an interview with his apparatus; he asks questions of it and writes down the answers, just as the psychologist does, only the questions are not verbal. The kinds of answer obtained by psychologists lack the rigorous repeatability of the physicists' answers, but we know this (apart from analogical consideration of our own experience) only because of an analysis of the results actually obtained. They might have been just as rigorous, and some behavioristically inclined psychologists would say that, correctly interpreted, they really are.

The differences between the various sciences, then, are not *essential* differences; there is a genuine logical and methodological unity underlying their apparent diversity. Whether or not this unity is of great practical value is another matter. The logic which provides each of the sciences with its articulate structure is one logic, although each theory makes use of a different part of it. There is certainly some overlap, which accounts for the possibility of using one theory as a model for another; and mathematics, viewed as a formal science with content and not merely as a ramified logic, since it overlaps with all the others, can provide models for them all. It is encouraging to find an increasing number of cases in which quite unexpected parallels between widely different theories prove illuminating in the solution of problems; the discipline which has come to be known as *general systems theory* was developed in an attempt to rationalize and exploit such apparently gratuitous similarities. It is in this direction, I think, that future progress in the 'unification of science' is to be looked for.

REFERENCES

1. B. Pascal, *Pensées* (Paris, ed. Louandre, 1876), p. 202.
2. R. Bacon (tr. Burke), *The Opus Majus* (Philadelphia, 1928).

CHAPTER 44

SCIENCE AND THE HUMANITIES

We have seen in Part I what science is and how it fits in with the rest of experience, in Part II how it is organized formally for maximum efficiency, in Part III what grounds we have for trusting it, and in Part IV what problems it helps to solve and what new problems it poses. It will be appropriate finally to reflect on the place which science occupies in the organization of contemporary intellectual life. A hundred and fifty years ago the humanities dominated the academic world; science as we know it was hardly taught in the universities, and the professors, most of them clergymen, would have been horrified if they could have foreseen its present position of dignity. A very brief consideration of the history of science among the other disciplines will help to put this in perspective.

For what follows it will be useful to bear in mind the triad:

philosophy—science—technology;

the historical relations between these terms are very illuminating. In ancient Greece the first two were almost synonymous ('science' comes, as was seen earlier, from the Latin; the Greek word was *'episteme'*, meaning, like the Latin root, 'knowledge'), the attainment of true science being regarded as the highest objective of philosophy. Technology (from *'techne'*, meaning 'art' or 'skill', the origin also of our word 'technique'), in so far as it existed at all, existed separately. Some famous men, such as Archimedes, united the theoretical and the practical; in these cases, however, the practice was something which even its most skillful practitioners held to be inferior to theory. It is sometimes said that the Greeks actually despised observation as a source of knowledge, but this is only partly true. It was considered better to have knowledge which was derived from universal principles, but at the same time the difficulties of finding such principles were understood, so that empirical knowledge, while of a less satisfactory kind, might in some cases be all that was available. Aristotle at least was fully aware of this: "In certitude and completeness," he says, "our knowledge of terrestrial things has the advantage. Moreover, their greater nearness and affinity to us balances somewhat the loftier interest of the heavenly things that are the objects of the higher philosophy." [1] His bow to the "heavenly things" is in part an acknowledgment of indebtedness to Plato, who influenced him in such a way that whenever he talks *about* science (for instance, in the *Posterior Analytics*) he imagines a deductive system descending from the highest principles, while as soon as he turns to his actual scientific work he begins to sound like a contemporary observer. Some of Aristotle's biological observations were not repeated until the nineteenth century, when most of them were found to be amazingly accurate (even as great a naturalist as Cuvier described mistakenly some things that Aristotle had described correctly more than two thousand years earlier).

What is important for us in all this is not the particular merit of the Aristotelian science and philosophy, but the fact that both were part of one system. The biological observations belonged to a different part of knowledge from the description, for instance, of political communities, but there was no suggestion that they were different *kinds* of knowledge, and no sense of incongruity in the same author's writing, in different places, on metaphysics, reproduction in animals, and the best organization of the tragic drama.

Something happened, however, to break up this promising combination of interests. The process had already begun in Plato, and there were probably two reasons for it. First, the distinctly scientific systems of the pre-Socratics did not seem to be getting anywhere. A number of great thinkers had constructed elegant and even plausible speculative theories, some of which (like the atomic theory of Democritus) were surprisingly close in their assumptions to modern science, but they could not be brought to any kind of empirical test, and so could not be defended against other equally plausible but incompatible theories. Second, plausible as these theories were where the physical world was concerned, they seemed to be deficient in their handling of human questions. It was hard to account for the presence of minds in a world governed by natural law, and they had to be taken care of by *ad hoc* additions to the theories, which rather spoiled the over-all effect. There is a famous passage in Plato's *Phaedo* where Socrates expresses his disappointment with the philosophy of Anaxagoras just because, in spite of mentioning 'Mind', it accounts for actual events in what we should now call a scientific way instead of by reference to human desires and intentions.[2]

We are hardly in a position to criticize the Greeks for failing to solve an extremely difficult problem—that of the place of reason in the natural world—which we have not begun to solve ourselves; it was achievement enough to have arrived at the conception of a natural world at all. In the circumstances, however, it was not surprising that the interest of philosophy turned away from scientific matters to questions of value, and to the nature, destiny, and proper conduct of man, a development which was given enormous impetus by the advent of Christianity. If some way had been found of joining up the descent from Platonic principles to the ascent from Aristotelian observations the story might have been different, but as it was very little of practical interest followed by deduction from the principles, and very little of theoretical interest followed by generalization from the observations.

The permanent contribution of Greek science lay in mathematics and astronomy, but the latter especially was complicated, as time went on, with theological additions which ruled out the possibility, hinted at by some Alexandrian astronomers, that the earth might be a heavenly body on a par with the other planets instead of a central habitation for man. The astronomy was mainly geometrical, since, without certain developments in physics which did not begin until the later Middle Ages and were not fully worked out until the seventeenth century, it was impossible to account for the regular motion of heavy objects freely suspended in space. The intellectual equipment of scholars from Hellenistic times until the end of the medieval period was therefore the philosophy of Plato and Aristotle (especially the logic of the latter), the geometry of Euclid, and the astronomy of Ptolemy. Even geometry and astronomy might be said to have been more philosophical than scientific; they were taught as intellectual, not practical, disciplines, and were numbered among the seven liberal arts (divided into the *trivium*, which consisted of logic, grammar, and rhetoric, and the more advanced *quadrivium,* including arithmetic, geometry, astronomy, and music). These were the things an educated man was supposed to know in the later Middle Ages, and, supplemented in the Renaissance by the rediscovered Greek classics, constituted the humanities—the body of 'polite learning'.

There was a sense in which the Italian Renaissance, for a short time, was really a rebirth of the Greek spirit, bringing together in outstanding individuals the whole range of human knowledge. But through the intervening centuries classical philosophy and science had crystallized into dogma as unyielding as that of Christian theology, and conflicts of interest arose which were settled, after a few spectacular episodes like the burning at the stake of Giordano Bruno in 1600, by a parting of the ways between the new science and the old philosophy. There were still people who combined both interests, and the dangers of such dual allegiances gradually decreased, because the Reformation, while it did not signal any great liberalization of religious belief, at least reduced the power of intimidation wielded by the churches. (If there is only one official belief heresy may seem a very serious matter, but if there are two one of them must be wrong, and if one is wrong then perhaps both are.) Science, however, having once cut itself loose from philosophy, was not soon to be distracted again by metaphysical controversy—not, in fact, until the twentieth-century crises of relativity and quantum theory. Instead, it contracted an alliance with technology which has lasted ever since, and entered on a period of instrumentation, experimentation, and discovery.

Philosophy itself was not static, and throughout the seventeenth and eighteenth centuries educated philosophers and scientists at least spoke each others' languages, although it was usually a matter of philosophers' taking an interest in science, rather than the other way round. Modern science was novel, and seemed at first to offer a set of new philosophical attitudes. With the nineteenth century, however, philosophy went off in search of the Absolute, and for a time the link was almost completely severed. The picture of the world which was emerging from the practical investigations of scientists and engineers was quite different from that preserved and cherished by the humanities, and serious scientific work was no longer the kind of thing that could successfully be done on much less than a full-time basis, although there were some exceptions to this rule. Science, furthermore, was closely allied with industry, and the academic man of the nineteenth century, while he did not much mind living on the profits of industry, was not anxious to become too closely acquainted with its practices. It was at this time very easy to look down on science as something intellectually inferior: Keble, the famous Anglican scholar, when Oxford conferred honorary degrees on Dalton and on Faraday, was heard to remark that the university had "truckled sadly to the spirit of the age." [3]

The tone of that remark, however, indicates an awareness that the humanities were fighting a losing battle, or at least that those who wished to be humanists in the reactionary sense were fighting one. The impact of science upon intellectual life could not be ignored; it was no longer a vision of future discovery, a program for philosophical revolution, but a going concern with apparently unlimited potentialities for the control of nature and the improvement of the condition of man. At the same time it made demands on intelligence and ingenuity equal to or greater than those made by classical studies, and demanded recognition alongside them as a serious contender for the interest of educated men. This recognition did not come at once, but under the influence of popular spokesmen like T. H. Huxley the public mind was made aware of these developments, and 'science' became a catchword for anything progressive, revolutionary, iconoclastic, or exciting. It seemed very different from anything that had gone before, and people began to search for the key to its success, so that the scientific method could be applied to everything. Indifferent to all this, science continued to score dramatic practical successes, climaxed by the development of atomic energy, and there grew up in some quarters a kind of snobbery in reverse, the scientist being looked up to as in some way more talented or more serious than the worker in the liberal arts. A well-known novelist who had formerly been a scientist dignified this situation by referring to it as the "crisis of the two cultures," [4] which made people who had never thought about the matter before believe that something esoteric was passing them by.

It would be wrong to say that all is well with the present organization of intellectual life, but it would, I think, be equally wrong to make a mystery out of those parts of it which are not widely familiar. There has always been fragmentation between specialties, and something *is* badly needed by way of a common human factor underlying the arts and the sciences through which specialists might communicate. The situation is serious now (and the 'two cultures' talk has in some ways helped to make people aware of it) partly because of what science has done in developing weapons, speeding up the movement of men and ideas, and so on, but only incidentally because the way in which scientists think is different from the way in which other men think.

Science is a human activity among others, and no intelligent person is incapable of mastering its principles. It may, in fact, be putting it too strongly to say that there is a difference in ways of thinking; certainly it is hard to specify what the difference is. Is science more precise? Nothing could be more precise than classical philology. Is it more concerned with truth? Nobody could be more concerned with truth than the biographer. Does it look more carefully at nature? Nobody looks more carefully at nature than the artist. Of course different activities induce different habits, and the longer and harder the course of study needed to acquire one set of habits, the more alien they are bound to seem to somebody who has been at equal pains to acquire a different set. It would be pointless, besides being impossible, to learn many such sets. The physicist does not need the skills involved in collating Old English manuscripts, nor does the drama critic need the manual dexterity involved in giving injections to albino mice; but there is no reason why the geneticist should not know in general the part that the theater has played in the growth of culture, or why the editor of *Beowulf* should not appreciate the way in which physics hangs together, and how its sometimes surprising statements about the world are related to observation.

George Sarton, the great historian of science, writing toward the end of his life, summed the matter up in the following words:

> Humanities are inseparable from human creations, whether these be philosophic, scientific, technical, or artistic and literary. . . . It would be very foolish to claim that a good poem or a beautiful statue is more humanistic or more inspiring than a scientific discovery; it all depends on the relation obtaining between them and you. Some people will be more deeply moved by poetry

than by astronomy; it all depends upon their own experience, mind, and sensibility.[5]

As to the enormous 'success' of science, that is due to a fortunate combination of method, accessibility of data (especially with the aid of instruments) and objectives, helped along by the fact that what science studies is so interesting that many talented people have been willing to work very hard at it. The world which it studies being always with us, and thus available for constant reference, the achievements of these people have been cumulative. There is nothing mysterious about that.

REFERENCES

1. Aristotle, *On the Parts of Animals*, 645a.
2. Plato, *Phaedo*, 97c *et seq.*
3. Quoted in W. O. Lester Smith, *Education in Great Britain* (London, 1949), p. 57.
4. C. P. Snow, *The Two Cultures and the Scientific Revolution* (Cambridge, 1959).
5. G. Sarton, *A History of Science: Hellenistic Science and Culture in the Last Three Centuries B.C.* (Cambridge, Mass., 1959), p. ix.

APPENDIX

Courses in the Philosophy of Science

One of the greatest, but unfortunately one of the most common, hindrances to the study of the philosophy of science is ignorance of science. Such ignorance is not confined to those who specialize in nonscientific subjects; it is fully compatible with a profound knowledge of physics or of biology or of psychology. This somewhat paradoxical assertion carries no criticism whatever of physicists or their colleagues in other scientific disciplines; every good scientist pursues an aim which is exceedingly narrow by comparison with the aim of science as put forward in this book, and most pursue one which is narrow even by comparison with the aim of their own discipline within the spectrum of science. "It is clear," says Wigner, in his acceptance speech for the Nobel prize,

> that . . . physics does not endeavour to explain nature. In fact, the great success of physics is due to a restriction of its objectives: it only endeavours to explain the regularities in the behavior of objects. This renunciation of the broader aim, and the specification of the domain for which an explanation can be sought, now appears to us an obvious necessity. In fact, the specification of the explainable may have been the greatest discovery of physics so far.[1]

Students of the special disciplines accept this limitation on the explainable at the outset of their training; not only is their attention restricted to regularities—and fairly obvious regularities—but also among these each science chooses a small class whose explanation has a certain theoretical unity. Furthermore, such regularities are observed under atypical conditions from the beginning. An experiment, it was said in Chapter 8, is "only an artificial device for putting the observer in a favorable position with respect to nature—a contrivance to have things happen where they can be seen"; the situation now is that scientists observe *only* such con-

[1] E. P. Wigner, "Events, Laws of Nature, and Invariance Principles," *Science*, 145, 3636, p. 995.

trived states of affairs, so that the relevance of science to ordinary events, such as the blueness of the sky or family resemblances between people, loses its force. The *adequate* explanation of such things, however—not a casual reference to diffusion or Mendel, but the full account which science is capable of providing—calls for great sophistication in a number of interrelated sciences and exhibits, as more precisely specified problems cannot, the resources of science as a whole.

It cannot be denied that knowledge of some particular science helps in grasping the philosophical principles governing scientific activity in general; each science provides a ready source of paradigms for the illustration of various parts of the theory of theories developed in the foregoing chapters. Ideally, though, the transition from observation to theory and to subsequent questions of organization and justification could begin at any arbitrarily chosen point in nature. The necessity, which would sooner or later arise, of separating out parts of the problem for treatment by different sciences would itself be a valuable lesson in the unity and diversity of science not easily taught to specialists for whom the limits of the observation basis are laid down in advance. And the necessity of experimental investigation, sometimes into auxiliary problems, would show what parts of science have to go into the laboratory and what can comfortably remain outside, again a difficult lesson for those brought up, scientifically speaking, in laboratories. Such an approach to science is not taught by any of the sciences, but the philosophy of science must be grounded on this kind of acquaintance with nature if it is to perform its task adequately.

If I were to venture one pedagogical recommendation in connection with this book it would be that, making a virtue of necessity, the philosophy of science should be used as a vehicle for teaching science in this generalized sense. For this task a laboratory is not needed; in fact, for reasons given above, it may be a hindrance to clear understanding. There is a widespread belief that science cannot be properly taught without a laboratory. This holds, however, only if by "science" is meant "what it is like to be a scientist in the modern world". According to this conception of education the teaching of literature would require acquaintance with rejection slips and proofreaders' marks. Of course there is a legitimate place for the teaching of scientific and literary practice, but for the purpose of general education it is far more important to convey an understanding of the finished product. Part of this understanding, in the case of science, involves an awareness of the historical indispensability of laboratory investigation, and of the difference of focus and perspective in man's view of the world which laboratories provide. However, this awareness is induced most effectively by a visit to a research laboratory where experimental work of a serious kind is going on. If laboratory classes showed clearly the intractability of nature, and how difficult it is to arrive at firm and precise conclusions, there would be some point in them, but this is exactly what simple prearranged experiments conceal, and there is not time for more. I do not intend to suggest, of course, that this kind of science should be taught entirely out of any empirical context, but rather that the empirical raw material can be drawn from everyday nature with a minimum of equipment. These remarks do not apply to introductory courses in physics, chemistry, etc., but I question the wisdom of arrangements which force students whose inclinations and aptitudes lie elsewhere to enroll in *such* courses.

This incidental function is complementary to each of the more usual objects of the philosophy of science course. These I take to be, on the one hand, for students of particular sciences, the elucidation and criticism of the structure and practices of their own discipline, and, on the other, for students of philosophy, the demonstration of the relevance to *their* discipline of an important segment of human intellectual activity, and the development of the critical techniques necessary for its adequate treatment. At advanced levels it is difficult to achieve both of these more technical ends at once; for the scientists the philosophy of science passes over into the philosophy of physics, etc., while for students of philosophy it passes over into the higher reaches of logic and epistemology. These considerations suggest that there is room for at least three different courses which might legitimately be called "philosophy of science":

(1) A general course for students who are not, or not yet, specialists either in science or philosophy;

(2) A course, taking various forms according to the special discipline involved, for students of the sciences;

(3) A course for students specializing in philosophy.

This book, suitably supplemented with illustrative material, might usefully serve as a basis for any one of these courses. (Such material has deliberately been kept to a minimum in the main text, where too many examples would obscure the course of the argument.) In the case of (1) it is useful, I think, for the instructor to decide on a small set of well-known, representative, and comparatively simple theories (i.e., such as can be presented in fairly simple outline and on the basis of fairly simple observations) to form the general-science nucleus of the course, from which illustrations can be drawn at appropriate points; such a set might include astronomical theory from Copernicus to Newton, Harvey's theory of the circulation of the blood, Hutton's theory of uniformitarianism in geology, Darwin's theory of natural selection and Mendel's of heredity, Dalton's atomic theory and its development as far as the Bohr-Rutherford atom, and Pavlov's theory of the conditioned reflex. Alternatives will readily suggest themselves. The identification of observation bases in these various examples, the discovery in the literature of typical protocols, etc., form useful exercises for students, who can be encouraged at least to look at technical journals and treatises even though most of what they find there is far beyond the level of their understanding—the parts in plain English between the technicalities often make surprisingly interesting reading and give invaluable glimpses into the workings of science. But at the same time the central body of material must be kept well within the student's, and particularly within the instructor's, competence. Too many good courses in the philosophy of science have been spoiled by gallant but fruitless attempts to explain the theory of relativity by means of stories about flashlights on the roofs of trains. It is true that the theory of relativity is an excellent example of a van der Waals shift, but van der Waals' law itself is just as good, and, starting with Boyle's, the gas laws make a much more manageable unit. In a high-level version of (1) for students having some acquaintance with science, relativity might play a part; it would of course be centrally important, along with quantum theory and thermodynamics, for the physicist's version of (2).

For the latter course each of the sciences has to choose, among its own theories, those which require philosophical clarification or exhibit most transparently the principles of the discipline; the function of such a course is after all to throw light on scientific questions rather than philosophical ones, and it would hardly be undertaken if it did not do this. I shall not presume to suggest what these theories ought to be in each case; for the same reason I would not undertake to teach a course of this kind in any science except physics. There is a difference between a broad understanding of the methods and results characteristic of some field, and a general appreciation of the adequacy of a philosophical theory to its analysis, on the one hand, and the professional competence necessary to assess its current problems and most recent insights, on the other. It may be worth remarking, however, that most fields provide one or two writers who are philosophically inclined, and whose works make useful supplementary reading: Eddington, de Broglie, Schrödinger, and others in physics; D'Arcy Wentworth Thompson, von Bertalanffy, Woodger, and others in biology; Spence, Skinner, Bruner, and others in psychology; Lazarsfeld, Merton, Parsons, and others in the social sciences. This list is no more than a hint at what is available.

From the point of view of (3), some of the early parts of the book, and the chapter on logic, can be safely passed over; they were included to make the whole philosophically self-contained, but will obviously have been anticipated, much more thoroughly, by other philosophy courses. As

far as illustrative material is concerned, the same recommendations as for
(1) can be repeated, but here some exemplary *wrong* theories might be
added as especially useful test cases—phlogiston theory, for example, or
the theory of spontaneous generation. It is also worth examining theories
like Newton's optics (was it vindicated by quantum theory?) or Darwin's
theory of pangenesis, as well as such disputed theories as that of extra-
sensory perception, on the evidence for which the philosophy of science,
if it is serious at all, ought to be prepared to pronounce some judgment.
In this case, however, the more advanced topics, such as the detailed
analysis of the concept of explanation, the development of logical calculi,
and explications of probability will require supplementary material of a
quite different nature, drawn from the literature of the philosophy of
science. Here the earlier classic works of Boole, Duhem, Herschel, Jevons,
Mill, Pearson, Peirce, Poincaré, Whewell, and others are extremely valuable, as well as the more recent contributions of Braithwaite, Carnap,
Hempel, Keynes, Kneale, Nagel, Popper, Reichenbach, and von Wright.
There should be no need to point out, in this connection, that some of the
greatest works in the philosophy of science are also central to the history
of philosophy itself—Aristotle's *Posterior Analytics*, Hume's *Enquiry*,
Kant's first *Critique*—the philosophy of science being, as was remarked
at the beginning of Chapter 1, an integral part of the discipline of philosophy.

INDEX OF NAMES

INDEX OF SUBJECTS